# PRENTICE HALL
# LITERATURE

PENGUIN  EDITION

# Reading Kit

World Masterpieces

PEARSON
Prentice
Hall

Upper Saddle River, New Jersey
Boston, Massachusetts

**This work is protected by United States copyright laws and is provided *solely for the use of teachers and administrators* in teaching courses and assessing student learning in their classes and schools. Dissemination or sale of any part of this work (including on the World Wide Web) will destroy the integrity of the work and is not permitted.**

Copyright © by Pearson Education, Inc., publishing as Pearson Prentice Hall, Boston, Massachusetts 02116. All rights reserved. Printed in the United States of America. This publication is protected by copyright, and permission should be obtained from the publisher prior to any prohibited reproduction, storage in a retrieval system, or transmission in any form or by any means, electronic, mechanical, photocopying, recording, or likewise. The publisher hereby grants permission to reproduce these pages, in part or in whole, for classroom use only, the number not to exceed the number of students in each class. Notice of copyright must appear on all copies. For information regarding permission(s), write to: Rights and Permissions Department, One Lake Street, Upper Saddle River, NJ 07458.

ISBN 0-13-165330-X

2 3 4 5 6 7 8 9 10    10 09

# Contents

## PART 1: PRACTICE AND ASSESS
### LITERARY ANALYSIS AND READING SKILLS

|  | Practice | Assess |
|---|---|---|

© Pearson Education, Inc., publishing as Pearson Prentice Hall.

## VOCABULARY SKILLS

## GRAMMAR SKILLS

© Pearson Education, Inc., publishing as Pearson Prentice Hall.

## WRITING

## PART 2: EVERYDAY READING STRATEGIES

© Pearson Education, Inc., publishing as Pearson Prentice Hall.

# PART 3: CLASSROOM MANAGEMENT FOR DIFFERENTIATED INSTRUCTION

### ■ Teacher-Mediated Classroom Reading Strategies

### ▼ Vocabulary and Concept Development

### ● Structuring Academic Discussion and Writing

# PART 4: PROFESSIONAL ARTICLES

© Pearson Education, Inc., publishing as Pearson Prentice Hall.

The *Reading Kit* has four parts, each designed to help you address the needs of students with varying ability levels.

- Use Part 1 to reteach and reassess unmastered skills
- Use Part 2 to develop independent application of active reading strategies
- Use Part 3 to ensure that students of all ability levels actively participate in learning activities and class discussions.
- Use Part 4 to devise strategies for addressing the special needs of diverse learners.

## Part 1 Practice and Assess

Part 1 is organized around the skills taught in the student edition and is organized in the order in which the skills are taught and assessed. These *Practice* pages are designed to reteach skills targeted by the benchmark, but you can use them at any time that you feel reteaching is needed. All *Practice* and *Assess* pages are also available electronically on Success Tracker.

- After administering a benchmark test, use the Interpretation Chart that accompanies the tests to determine which *Practice* pages should be assigned to students.
- After students complete the *Practice* assignments, use the *Assess* pages to check mastery of the specific skills that have been retaught.

## Part 2 Everyday Reading Strategies

Part 2 provides teacher and student pages for teaching reading strategies that develop active, thoughtful reading practices in *all* students. In addition, by giving direct instruction in these strategies, you will provide struggling readers with the tools they need to improve their comprehension and interpretation. These strategies can be used with any literature selection.

- Introduce the strategy, using the strategy plan and the graphic organizer.
- Once students are familiar with the strategy, encourage them to use the strategy independently with other selections.

## Part 3 Classroom Management for Differentiated Instruction

Part 3 describes practical, effective strategies for engaging students of all ability levels in learning activities and class discussions. These research-based, classroom-tested techniques allow you to support your struggling students and challenge your advanced students in the same discussion or activity. These frameworks can be used with any literature selection or discussion topic.

## Part 4 Language Arts Instruction—Professional Articles

Part 4 gives an overview of the diverse classroom. It also provides an analysis of the reading process, identifying the four aspects that need to be addressed to fully support diverse learners. Sections dedicated to specific characteristics of and challenges posed by three groups follow, along with discussion of strategies and resources for each: English language learners, less proficient learners, and special needs students.

© Pearson Education, Inc., publishing as Pearson Prentice Hall.

# Practice and Assess

# Adjusting Reading Rate

## Practice

When you need to locate specific information in a text that you have already read, you need to **adjust your reading rate.** Instead of rereading every word, skim and scan the text to help you locate information quickly and efficiently. Skimming is glancing through a written work to get a general idea of what it is about. Scanning is reading quickly while looking for key words or ideas. Textbooks are easy to scan through: their pictures, captions, charts, photos, and headings always show key words and ideas.

■ Decide if the following statements are true or false. Circle *T* or *F.* If the statement is false, give a correct version of the statement on the line provided.

**1.** T / F  I would read every word of the table of contents in a textbook to find the chapter I needed.

_____

**2.** T / F  I would not skim headings to see what topics were covered in a chapter.

_____

**3.** T / F  Captions of photos and labels of graphs are not worth scanning.

_____

**4.** T / F  I would scan paragraphs for key words and phrases related to the question I am trying to answer.

_____

**5.** T / F  I might skim a glossary if I was looking for a particular vocabulary word.

_____

**6.** T / F  If I was looking for a key idea in a textbook, I would look only at chapter titles, not at headings within the chapter.

_____

**7.** T / F  Maps and pictures are always important to the text; they can quickly give main facts and ideas to a reader who is skimming and scanning.

_____

© Pearson Education, Inc., publishing as Pearson Prentice Hall.

Name _____  Date _____

# Adjusting Reading Rate

Assess

**A** Read the following paragraph. Then, on the lines provided, explain how you would use skimming and scanning to find the answers. Include details about how you could use headings, maps, picture captions, and key phrases.

Mr. Danson gave his history class an open-book quiz on Chapter Three of their American History textbook. The class was allowed to use their textbooks to respond to the following prompts:

**1.** Explain what "taxation without representation" means.

_____

_____

**2.** List the thirteen colonies.

_____

_____

**3.** Define what a lobsterback is.

_____

_____

**B** Imagine that you are looking at a brochure for a local museum you plan on visiting. Then, read the following questions, and circle the letter of the best answer.

**1.** Under which heading would you find information about admission into the museum?

**A.** Museum Directions          **C.** Treasure of Ancient Egypt
**B.** Additional Services          **D.** Tickets and Reservations

**2.** Under which heading would you find the best route to the museum from your house?

**A.** Museum Directions          **C.** Treasure of Ancient Egypt
**B.** Additional Services          **D.** Tickets and Reservations

**3.** Under which heading could you find out whether the museum has a cafeteria?

**A.** Museum Directions          **C.** Treasure of Ancient Egypt
**B.** Additional Services          **D.** Tickets and Reservations

© Pearson Education, Inc., publishing as Pearson Prentice Hall.

Reading Kit **3**

# Allegory

## Practice

An **allegory** is a story in which all characters, settings, and events are symbols. A **symbol** is a person, an object, or an event that stands for an idea. For example, in the story of the tortoise and the hare, a turtle wins a race against an impatient rabbit by continuing his efforts, even though he is slower than the rabbit. The turtle is a symbol of patience.

---

**A** Each of the following items can be a symbol. For each item, name one thing it might stand for.

1. _____ a heart

2. _____ a rocking chair

3. _____ an open treasure chest filled with gold pieces

4. _____ a rainbow

---

**B** For each question, circle the letter of the best answer.

1. In a story about two tennis teammates, Sarah and Amah practice each day by taking turns serving the ball and returning it. They are both working on improving their serves. What might their tennis games symbolize?

   **A.** happiness          **C.** anger
   **B.** cooperation          **D.** sadness

2. In Jan's story, there is an event that is a symbol, but all of the characters and places are realistic. In Yuko's story, all of the events, characters, and places are symbols. Which of the following is true?

   **A.** Both stories are allegories.          **C.** Yuko's story is an allegory, but Jan's story is not.
   **B.** Neither story is an allegory.          **D.** Jan's story is an allegory, but Yuko's story is not.

3. In a story, Ricardo goes away from home for the first time. Before he leaves, his mother gives him a gold coin. When Ricardo gets nervous, he reaches into his pocket to touch the gold coin. What does the gold coin symbolize?

   **A.** great wealth          **C.** his clothing
   **B.** reassurance and safety          **D.** a new job opportunity

          © Pearson Education, Inc., publishing as Pearson Prentice Hall.

# Allegory

Assess

**A** Each of the following items can be a symbol. For each item, name one thing it might stand for.

1. _____ a snowman

2. _____ a shining sun

3. _____ a baby bird with its mouth held open

4. _____ a red-and-gold colored leaf

**B** For each question, circle the letter of the best answer.

1. Mr. Anderson writes a poem comparing life to a flower. The flower starts as a seed that grows and blooms, producing a beautiful pink blossom that is enjoyed by all. Then, at the end of the growing season, it withers and dies. What does the flower symbolize?

   **A.** the cycle of life          **C.** the poet's love
   **B.** the seed of a flower       **D.** the death of a flower

2. You are reading a story. How do you know that it is an allegory?

   **A.** None of the characters in the story is a symbol.
   **B.** Each character in the story is realistic.
   **C.** There are many symbols in the story.
   **D.** All of the characters in the story are symbols.

3. In a story, a child is worried about going to kindergarten for the first time. On the way to school, he sees a young bird perched on the edge of a nest. After a few minutes, the bird leaves the nest and flies successfully into the sky. What might the bird's flight symbolize?

   **A.** the sky                    **C.** the nest
   **B.** the school and education    **D.** the need to grow and change

© Pearson Education, Inc., publishing as Pearson Prentice Hall.

# Analogy

An **analogy** is a comparison of two things showing how they are similar. Analogies are usually used to explain something unfamiliar by showing how it is like something familiar.

> A computer virus is well named, since it behaves like a biological virus in many ways, and it can do great damage to the thing it attacks.

In each of the following items, underline the two things being linked in the analogy. Then, on the lines provided, explain how one term is similar to the other.

1. The old house was a great deal like the old woman who lived in it. Both came into existence in the year 1908, both were a bit fragile, yet both had carefully preserved memories of those long-ago days.

   _____

   _____

2. The scene between the two actors became a tennis match, with each pounding words back at the other. Nothing seemed out of bounds, and very few volleys were missed.

   _____

   _____

3. The 20-year-old street map was a snapshot of their early days in the town, with important spots (their now-adult son's elementary school, the now-closed grocery) marked with X's, and long-forgotten addresses scribbled in the margin.

   _____

   _____

4. The car should have been put out to pasture like an old horse, but it still worked—only slowly and with a lot of coaxing.

   _____

   _____

   © Pearson Education, Inc., publishing as Pearson Prentice Hall.

# Analogy

**A**  In each of the following items, underline the two things being linked in the analogy. Then, on the lines provided, explain how one term is similar to the other and what the analogy emphasizes.

1. His bits of advice were as valuable as diamonds—and just as rare and brilliant.

   _____

   _____

2. Think of the game of chess as a battle: each has two sides with objectives, strategies, and hierarchies of soldiers.

   _____

   _____

3. Being weightless in space is a little like being a cork in a bowl of water— except, of course, you are a cork with a sense of direction.

   _____

   _____

**B**  Write a few sentences in which you develop an analogy between two items of your own choosing. At the end of your paragraph, write a separate sentence explaining the main point you wanted to make by creating the analogy.

   _____

   _____

   _____

   _____

   _____

   _____

   _____

   _____

© Pearson Education, Inc., publishing as Pearson Prentice Hall.

# Analyzing Text Features

## Practice

**Analyzing text features** will help you meet the goal of better understanding textbook materials. Here are some tips to help you analyze text features:

- Find and preview the major headings, charts, diagrams, and pictures.
- Read the introductory and summary paragraphs.
- Study any review questions.
- Note any text that is printed in bold or italics. Such text may be a key term or a statement of an important idea.

Read the following text feature, and then answer the questions that follow it.

### Literary Analysis:
### Stream of Consciousness

People's thoughts do not flow in neat patterns; they proceed in streams of insight, memory, and reflection. During the early 1900s, some writers began using a literary device called **stream of consciousness,** in which they tried to capture the natural flow of thought. These narratives usually

- present sequences of thought as if they came directly from a character's mind.
- connect details only through a character's associations.

As you read this story, note the way some characters' thoughts wander among memories, dreamlike images, and accurate perceptions of the present.

1. Based on the main title, which item does the feature best help explain?

   **A.** an advertisement       **C.** a work of fiction
   **B.** a newspaper editorial       **D.** a consumer guide

2. Once you know the *general* topic, which item best identifies the *specific* topic of this text feature?

   **A.** the main title    **B.** the subtitle    **C.** the bulleted list    **D.** the entire feature

3. Which item provides the best summary of key points on this topic?

   **A.** the title       **C.** the last paragraph
   **B.** the subtitle       **D.** the bulleted list

4. Boldfacing of a term usually indicates which of the following?

   **A.** The term is important.       **C.** It is not an English word.
   **B.** The term is a proper noun.       **D.** It is a definition of a word.

© Pearson Education, Inc., publishing as Pearson Prentice Hall.

# Analyzing Text Features

Assess

Read the following text feature, and then answer the questions that follow it.

Literary Analysis:
Meter

Many of Robert Frost's poems do not contain rhyme, but their lines have a regular pattern of stressed and unstressed syllables, or **meter**.

- The basic unit of meter is a foot—usually one stressed syllable and one or more unstressed syllables.
- The most common foot is the iamb—one unstressed syllable followed by a stressed syllable.
- A line containing five iambs is written in *iambic pentameter.*
- Verse consisting of unrhymed lines of iambic pentameter is called *blank verse.*

As you read Frost's poems, identify those that have been written in blank verse and those that are in rhyming iambic pentameter.

1. Based on the introductory sentence, this passage deals with an aspect of which of the following?

    **A.** chemistry          **C.** poetry
    **B.** social studies      **D.** painting

2. What do the italic and boldface words in this passage have in common?

    **A.** They are not in English.   **C.** They rhyme.
    **B.** They are key terms.        **D.** They are unimportant terms.

3. Which is likely to be the most important word in the passage?

    **A.** the one boldfaced word    **C.** the first word
    **B.** one of the italicized words  **D.** the last word

4. What is the purpose of the bulleted list?

    **A.** It lists Web sites on the topic.   **C.** It highlights key points.
    **B.** It lists key page numbers.         **D.** It introduces the topic.

5. In one or two sentences, summarize the key points covered in this passage.

    _____

    _____

    _____

# Analyzing the Usefulness and Credibility of Web Sites

**Practice**

A **Web site** is a specific location on the Internet. A useful site is easy to understand and easy to navigate, with interesting and easy-to-follow graphics or links to other pages within the site. A credible site provides trustworthy, current information. Once you have located a Web site, you must analyze the usefulness and credibility of the source before using it for your research. Knowing who sponsors and maintains a Web site can help you determine its credibility. The URL ending typically indicates the source of a site

| URL Ending | Description | Usual Intent and Credibility |
|---|---|---|
| **.edu** *or* **.gov** | Site is maintained by an educational institution or government agency. | to provide reliable information; very credible |
| **.org** | Site is probably maintained by a nonprofit organization. | to provide information about an issue or cause; may be credible, but may be biased |
| **.com** | Site is maintained commercially or personally. | to sell or promote something; credibility varies |
| **.net** | Site is maintained by a network. | intent and credibility vary |

Circle the letter of the best answer choice.

**1.** Which of the following would make a Web site easy to use?

   **A.** a date that shows when the site was last updated
   **B.** colorful icons in the margins that link to other informative pages
   **C.** a list of content reviewers
   **D.** a large background image of a panda bear

**2.** If you were looking for the most rugged hiking trails in Pennsylvania, which Web site would provide the most credible information?

   **A.** a government Web site with information about state park trails
   **B.** the personal Web site of a hiker who lives in Pennsylvania
   **C.** a commercial Web site for the newest mountain bike
   **D.** a nonprofit Web site for a local environmental organization

© Pearson Education, Inc., publishing as Pearson Prentice Hall.

Name _____ Date _____

# Analyzing the Usefulness and Credibility of Web Sites

## Assess

Write the letter of the best answer for each of the following questions.

1. _____ Which URL endings probably include the greatest number of credible Web sites?

   **A.** .org and .com   **B.** .net and .com   **C.** .gov and .edu   **D.** .edu and .com

2. _____ If a site is maintained commercially, what is its probable purpose?

   **A.** to provide information about a cause
   **B.** to sell or promote something
   **C.** to provide information about an issue
   **D.** to provide reliable information

3. _____ If you were doing a research paper on the poet Sylvia Plath, which of the following would be a useful feature on a Sylvia Plath Web site?

   **A.** the Web site copyright information
   **B.** a list of famous Sylvia Plath scholars
   **C.** a link to another informative Sylvia Plath Web site
   **D.** the date that the Web site was last updated

4. _____ If you were creating your own Web site, which of the following features might you add to increase its usability?

   **A.** sound effects
   **B.** a large, eye-catching background photo
   **C.** phone numbers of all the friends who helped you put the Web site together
   **D.** a navigational bar, colorful icons, and links

# Annals

**Annals** are histories that present a year-by-year account of events. The word *annus*, in fact, is Latin for "year." Historians writing annals may include narratives of events or incidents, vivid descriptions, and/or explanations of causes and effects. Here is an example of a cause-and-effect explanation:

| The Roman annalist Tacitus explains that Nero's plan to dig a canal from a lake to the Tiber River failed. |
|---|
| **Cause 1:** There is not enough water in the area for a canal. → **Effect 1:** Work on the canal was abandoned. **Cause 2:** The work was too hard. **Effect 2:** You can still see the places where they started digging. |

**A**  Read these events from the life of Thomas Jefferson. Then, circle the number of the item that lists the events in the order they would be discussed in an annal.

(a) Completes Louisiana Purchase (1803)

(b) Serves as minister to France (1785)

(c) Drafts Declaration of Independence (1776)

(d) Elected president (1800)

(e) Sponsors Lewis and Clark Expedition (1804)

(f) Becomes Secretary of State (1789)

**1.** b, f, c, e, a, d          **2.** c, b, f, d, a, e          **3.** f, a, e, c, d, b

**B**  Write *C-E* if an item explains a cause-and-effect relationship. If not, leave the space blank.

**1.** _____ In the year 903, a Viking force went looting through the land of Mercia, in England. In 904, there was an eclipse of the moon.

**2.** _____ In the year 903, the Anglo-Saxon leader Aethelwald wanted more power in England. He stirred up the Vikings, persuading them to break their treaty and loot in the land of Mercia.

**3.** _____ In the year 64, a great fire swept through Rome. As a result, only four of Rome's fourteen districts remained intact. Much of the city had to be rebuilt.

© Pearson Education, Inc., publishing as Pearson Prentice Hall.

# Annals

Assess

**A**  In the blank, write **T** if the statement is true or **F** if it is false.

1. _____ Annals do not normally include vivid descriptions.

2. _____ Annals are works of history.

3. _____ In annals, the material is arranged chronologically.

4. _____ A person reading annals might expect to find narratives of events or incidents.

5. _____ The word *annals* comes from the Latin word for "truth."

6. _____ A writer of annals may include cause-and-effect explanations.

7. _____ Vivid descriptions may not appear in annals.

**B**  Read this list of events from the life of Benjamin Franklin. Then, in the space provided, list the letters of the events in the order they would appear in a work of annals.

(a) Born in Boston (1706)

(b) Serves as delegate to Constitutional Convention (1787)

(c) Founds University of Pennsylvania (1751)

(d) Publishes first edition of *Poor Richard's Almanack* (1732)

(e) Concludes alliance with France (1778)

(f) Invents lightning rod (1752)

_____

**C**  Write **C-E** if an item explains a cause-and-effect relationship. If not, leave the space blank.

1. _____ In 64, a great fire burned through Rome. Also during Nero's reign, gladiators revolted in the town of Praeneste in central Italy.

2. _____ After the great fire in Rome, many suspected that the fire had been set on purpose. To fight these rumors, the emperor Nero blamed various groups, including Christians, whom he persecuted.

© Pearson Education, Inc., publishing as Pearson Prentice Hall.

# Anticipating Events

## Practice

When you **anticipate events** in a story or other narrative, you look forward to what happens next. Anticipating events can help you connect with characters as you watch their lives unfold. For instance, you might read in an epic of a hero fighting a battle. When an enemy suddenly attacks, you can better appreciate the hero's courage and his fear if you think about whether the hero will win. If a goddess suddenly appears, you will appreciate the excitement more by anticipating that her help will lead to victory.

You can anticipate events by following these steps:

1. As you read, look for clues to later events. For example, in the epic the *Aeneid*, the Greeks leave a giant wooden horse outside of Troy, the city they are attacking. Many Trojans say they suspect a trick. With this clue in mind, you can anticipate that the Trojans will be attacked when they bring the horse into their city.

2. As you read, ask yourself what your past experiences and reading suggest about the story. For instance, you know from other stories that the hero typically wins in his battle with a monster. This knowledge can help you anticipate the hero's victory.

This passage is from the epic *Beowulf.* Beowulf is a heroic warrior. He is sleeping along with other warriors in a king's hall when the monster Grendel arrives. Grendel kills one sleeping man and then tries to kill Beowulf. Read the passage. Then, answer the questions.

Then [Grendel] stepped to another
Still body, clutched at Beowulf with his claws,
Grasped at a strong-hearted wakeful sleeper[1]—   1 a strong-hearted wakeful
And was instantly seized himself, claws                    sleeper Beowulf, the hero.
Bent back as Beowulf leaned up on one arm.
   That shepherd of evil, guardian of crime,[2]   2 That shepherd of evil, guardian
Knew at once that nowhere on earth                          of crime Grendel, the
Had he met a man whose hands were harder;                  monster.
His mind was flooded with fear. . . .

1. Underline a clue to the fight's outcome. Who do you think will win?

_____

_____

2. If *Beowulf* is similar to other stories you know about battles between heroes and monsters, what will happen next in *Beowulf*? Explain.

_____

   © Pearson Education, Inc., publishing as Pearson Prentice Hall.

## Anticipating Events

**Read each selection from "To Build a Fire." Then, answer the questions.**

. . . Fifty degrees below zero meant eighty-odd degrees of frost. Such facts impressed him as being cold and uncomfortable, and that was all. It did not lead him to meditate upon his frailty as a creature of temperature, and about man's frailty in general, able only to live within certain narrow limits of heat and cold. . . .

**1.** Underline a clue to what will happen in the story. Given this clue, what problem do you anticipate the man will face?

_____

**2.** Think of another story that takes place in extreme conditions. If "To Build a Fire" is similar to this story, what will happen next?

_____

_____

At a place where there were no signs, where the soft, unbroken snow seemed to advertise solidity beneath, the man broke through. It was not deep. He wet himself halfway to the knees before he floundered out to the firm crust.

He was angry, and cursed his luck aloud. He had hoped to get into camp with the boys at six o'clock, and this would delay him an hour, for he would have to build a fire and dry out his footgear. . . .

**3.** Circle a clue to what will happen next. What do you think the man will do?

_____

But he was safe. Toes and nose and cheeks would be only touched by the frost, for the fire was beginning to burn with strength. . . . The fire was a success. . . .

High up in the tree one bough capsized its load of snow. This fell on the boughs beneath, capsizing them. This process continued, spreading out and involving the whole tree. It grew like an avalanche, and it descended without warning upon the man and the fire, and the fire was blotted out!

**4.** Circle a clue to what will happen next. What do you think the man will do?

_____

© Pearson Education, Inc., publishing as Pearson Prentice Hall.

# Aphorisms

## Practice

**Aphorisms,** sometimes called maxims or proverbs, are short statements that express general truths or principles. Aphorisms may use rhyme, balance, contrast, or other devices to make a statement punchy and memorable. Here are two famous aphorisms:

A friend in need is a friend indeed. (Meaning: A friend who helps you when you are in trouble is a true friend.)

A fool and his money are soon parted. (Meaning: People will quickly take advantage of a foolish person, selling the person things or even swindling the person. A wise person is careful about spending money.)

**A**   In the blank, write *T* if the statement is true or *F* if it is false.

1. _____ Another word for *aphorism* is *proverb*.

2. _____ Aphorisms never include rhyme.

3. _____ An aphorism typically expresses a general truth or principle.

4. _____ Two devices that may appear in aphorisms are balance and contrast.

5. _____ An important characteristic of aphorisms is that they are memorable.

**B**   In the space provided, write *A* if you think the statement is an aphorism. If the statement is not an aphorism, leave the space blank.

1. _____ There are twenty-one counties in the state of New Jersey.

2. _____ All's fair in love and war.

3. _____ A stitch in time saves nine.

4. _____ Sunrise tomorrow will occur at 5:48 A.M.

5. _____ Don't put the cart before the horse.

© Pearson Education, Inc., publishing as Pearson Prentice Hall.

# Aphorisms

Assess

**A** In the space provided, write **A** if you think the statement is an aphorism. If the statement is not an aphorism, leave the space blank.

1. _____ Winning isn't everything; it's the only thing.

2. _____ To err is human; to forgive, divine.

3. _____ Many words in English come from Greek and Latin.

4. _____ Beggars can't be choosers.

5. _____ The early bird catches the worm.

6. _____ Lacrosse is a demanding sport.

7. _____ Many animal, bird, and insect species are migratory.

8. _____ Haste makes waste.

9. _____ Do your best on next week's test.

10. _____ Necessity is the mother of invention.

**B** For each aphorism, write your own interpretation of its meaning.

1. If wishes were horses, then beggars would ride.

_____

_____

2. No persons are more frequently wrong than those who will not admit they are wrong. (François de La Rochefoucauld, seventeenth-century French writer)

_____

_____

3. He governs best who governs least. (Lao Tzu, sixth-century B.C. Chinese philosopher)

_____

_____

© Pearson Education, Inc., publishing as Pearson Prentice Hall.

# Applying Background Information

**Background information** helps you understand what you are reading and appreciate it more. For example, background about the life of an author tells you what sort of person created the work you are reading. Background information can also answer questions you may have about unfamiliar material, such as historical or cultural references. You can gather background information from book jackets, interviews, author biographies, footnotes, even your own experiences. When you read background information, notice the questions that it answers. Think about the background information's facts, for they often give you insight into the work you are reading and help you interpret it more fully.

> Read this background information, found on a book jacket. Then, answer the questions.

William Shakespeare Barnett was born in 1970 in Philadelphia to a pair of English teachers (hence his name). He grew up all over the place, attending schools in such far-flung places as Alaska, Texas, Montana, and Virginia. His interest in science fiction began very early. At the age of eight, after reading many comic books, he became obsessed with the possibility of time travel, and he hasn't let go of the subject since, publishing over thirty stories about going back, forward, and all around time. This novel, his first, involves time travel, of course, and is set in his favorite historical period, the Age of the Pharaohs. It takes its inspiration from a story that he wrote while still in college. He lives in upstate New York with his wife, two sons, and "more cats than I care to think about."

**1.** How many novels has Barnett written? _____

**2.** When and how did he become interested in the subject for his book?

_____

_____

**3.** What facts from this brief biography seem most relevant to this novel?

_____

_____

**4.** What impression does this brief biography create? Explain.

_____

_____

_____

© Pearson Education, Inc., publishing as Pearson Prentice Hall.

## Applying Background Information

### Assess

**Read the following excerpt from an interview. Then, answer the questions and complete the activities that follow.**

**Q.** I'm talking to Paige Webster about her latest book, *Railroaded*. Ms. Webster—
**A.** Please! Call me Paige.
**Q.** OK. Paige, you've written eleven travel books, and now you've published your twelfth one, *Railroaded*. It's about your train travel all over the U.S., coast to coast, Alaska to Florida. What led you to write about this?
**A.** Well, I've always *loved* traveling on trains. Always. I even liked riding on the subway in New York when I was a kid! So, after riding on planes and trains, camels and donkeys and such to get wherever I needed to go for my other books, this time I just wanted to see what the pure train experience would be like, without worrying particularly about a destination.
**Q.** You've said you spent about two years writing your previous book. Did this one take more or less time to write?
**A.** Well, I kept journals about all my train trips when I was writing my earlier books. So, on and off, I've been writing this book for 15 years.
**Q.** Wow! How many miles did you travel in working on this book?
**A.** I figured two hundred thousand. Amazing, isn't it?

**1.** Where did the writer get the inspiration for her latest book? _____

_____

**2.** How long did it take her to research and write it? _____

**3.** From reading this interview, what personal qualities did you find in the author? What comments in the interview led you to this impression?

_____

_____

_____

**4.** Write two more interview questions, based on what you would still like to know about this author.

_____

_____

_____

_____

# Applying the Author's Biography

### Practice

**Applying an author's biography**—making connections from his or her life—can shed light on the meaning of a literary work. For example, the fact that a writer had studied painting helps explain why she has written a number of stories about artists and sculptors. Look for connections between the details of an author's life and details in that author's work. Keep in mind, though, that while authors draw on their own experiences and feelings in writing, they transform them into new, imaginary stories and characters.

Read the following short passage from a story. Then, answer the questions that follow.

The girl sat watching the birds build their nest. She knew she needed to be as still as possible, so as not to frighten them away. The birds were flying against the wind, which made it difficult for them to hold onto the various twigs and pieces of fluff that they were using in the nest. The girl worried about them, but she sensed that they would be all right. The two birds worked together, taking turns delivering material to the nest. They knew, somehow, exactly what each one needed to do to build their home. The girl wondered at so much care being given to something that would last such a short time.

**1.** _____ Each answer choice gives a detail from the author's biography. Which detail is reflected most significantly in this passage?

**A.** her study of medicine          **C.** her love of nature
**B.** her athletic ability            **D.** her childhood poverty

**2.** Which elements in the passage suggest the connection in question 1?

_____

_____

**3.** _____ Each answer choice is a detail from the author's biography. Which detail might be reflected in this passage?

**A.** her happy marriage             **C.** her knowledge of sailing
**B.** her resistance to political     **D.** her expertise in cooking
      repression

**4.** Which part of the passage suggests the connection in question 3?

_____

_____

          © Pearson Education, Inc., publishing as Pearson Prentice Hall.

# Applying the Author's Biography

Assess

**A** | Read the following short passage from a story. Then, answer the questions that follow.

The runner hunched over, glancing at the men on either side of him. He knew that the start would be the most critical part of the sprint, so he focused his attention on the sensation of his feet pushing against the starting blocks. He thought about his competitors. Only one worried him, the man immediately to his right. He wanted very much to beat this man. But thinking about his competitor would distract him from what he needed to do to run his best. He shook his head and fixed his eyes on the finish line, not so far away.

1. _____ Each answer choice gives a detail from the author's biography. Which detail is reflected most significantly in this passage?

   **A.** his study of art       **C.** his wartime service
   **B.** his childhood illnesses      **D.** his athletic ability

2. Which part of the passage creates the connection in question 1?

   _____

   _____

3. _____ Each answer choice gives a detail from the author's biography. Which detail might be suggested in this passage?

   **A.** his competition with his brother      **C.** his childhood poverty
   **B.** his love of sailing      **D.** his extensive travels

4. Which part of the passage creates the connection in question 3?

   _____

   _____

   _____

**B** | Write a short letter to the author, asking about what led him to write this passage and telling about your response to it.

   _____

   _____

   _____

   _____

© Pearson Education, Inc., publishing as Pearson Prentice Hall.

# Archetypes

**Archetypes** are plot patterns, character types, themes, or images that appear in the literature of many different cultures and time periods. Here are some archetypes arranged by category:

- **Plot patterns:** the birth of the hero, the hero's quest or search, disguised identity, ill-fated love
- **Character types:** the hero, the wise advisor, the evil stepmother, the outcast
- **Themes:** the victory of good over evil, the power of love
- **Images:** water representing life, a rose representing love

Archetypes often have a symbolic meaning. A **symbol** is a person, a place, an animal, an object, or an event that stands for a larger meaning. Some common symbols include the flag for the nation, fire for power, and a dove for peace.

**Circle the letter of the best answer to each question.**

1. Which character best qualifies as an archetype?

   **A.** a wise advisor      **B.** a mischievous child      **C.** a talented pianist

2. As an archetypal image, a dove might represent which element?

   **A.** swiftness      **B.** flight      **C.** peace

3. Which statement about archetypes is true?

   **A.** They appear only in Western literature.
   **B.** They rarely involve symbolism.
   **C.** They include plot patterns, character types, and themes.

4. In an archetypal plot pattern, which element of a hero's life might be included?

   **A.** marriage      **B.** quest      **C.** failure

5. Which theme would you identify as archetypal?

   **A.** the role of technology in modern life
   **B.** the triumph of good over evil
   **C.** the experience of loneliness in adolescence

© Pearson Education, Inc., publishing as Pearson Prentice Hall.

# Archetypes

**A**   Circle the letter of the best answer to each question.

1. Which phrase describes where archetypes can be found?

    **A.** only in poetry
    **B.** only in autobiographies
    **C.** in the literature of many different cultures and time periods

2. Which of the following could best be described as an archetypal character?

    **A.** an emperor      **B.** an architect      **C.** an outcast

3. Which statement about archetypes is true?

    **A.** They have symbolic meaning.
    **B.** They use proverbs.
    **C.** They have only a single character.

4. Which of the following correctly defines *symbol*?

    **A.** an exaggerated statement
    **B.** something that has its own meaning but also stands for a larger meaning
    **C.** a striking comparison that uses the words *like* or *as*

**B**   Write *A* if an item can be identified as an archetype. If not, leave the space blank.

1. _____ a skillful baseball player

2. _____ a wise counselor

3. _____ a hero on a quest

4. _____ a beautiful but mysterious rose

5. _____ a spring of water discovered in a desert

6. _____ a talented violinist

7. _____ a prize-winning historian

8. _____ the founder of a nation

© Pearson Education, Inc., publishing as Pearson Prentice Hall.

# Atmosphere

In literature, **atmosphere**—or mood—refers to the emotional quality of the world the writer creates. Atmosphere comes from descriptive details, particularly details of setting. For instance, a description of a den lit by a warm fire and filled with the smell of roasting chestnuts would probably have a cozy, pleasant atmosphere. Atmosphere can also be affected by the plot and often mirrors the feelings of the characters. For example, if someone in that cozy den heard a shriek somewhere in the house, the pleasant atmosphere would change instantly to one of terror. As you read, look for descriptive details that reflect characters' emotions and create atmosphere.

On the lines provided, describe the atmosphere in each item. Identify the details and other elements that create this atmosphere.

1. It was almost time for dinner. The old-fashioned kitchen was filled with the savory smell of chicken curry as the young parents cooked together, laughing as they put spice after spice into the bubbling pot. Their baby played in his high chair, stacking pieces of fruit and crowing happily.

_____

_____

2. Ron and his sisters edged carefully into the deserted old house. Each step made the floor creak. The place smelled dusty and musty, and the high ceilings were lost in dark shadows. They came to the bottom of a tall staircase and looked at each other. Who would go first? Would anyone?

_____

_____

3. Meredith turned in her test paper and then sat back down, losing herself in watching the snow falling outside the classroom. Every black tree branch was lined with a few inches of snow, and the school grounds were unbelievably quiet. Everything seemed wrapped up in a soft white blanket. The bell rang.

_____

_____

© Pearson Education, Inc., publishing as Pearson Prentice Hall.

# Atmosphere

Assess

**A** Read each of the following items. Then, on the lines provided, add another sentence either continuing *or* changing the atmosphere created in the rest of the passage. Finally, identify the original atmosphere, and indicate whether you continued it or changed it.

1. The 100-meter freestyle race was about to begin. Each swimmer huddled tensely over her lane, flexing shoulders, stretching. The piercing smell of chlorine prickled in everyone's noses, and the spectators' shouts mingled and echoed in the huge room. _____

_____

_____

2. Greg and his brother sat in the boat, each intent on his fishing line. The water was very still, a mirror to the early morning sky. A few gulls called overhead. _____

_____

_____

3. The speaker's words were drowned out by the shouts of 10,000 excited supporters and the blare of horns. Red, white, and blue balloons poured down on the crowd. The room shook as people yelled, "Run, Mike, run!"

_____

_____

_____

**B** Write a few sentences describing a scene. Aim to create a definite atmosphere. At the end of your passage, identify the atmosphere you have created.

_____

_____

_____

_____

_____

© Pearson Education, Inc., publishing as Pearson Prentice Hall.

# Author's Purpose

## Practice

An **author's purpose** is his or her main reason for writing. The most common purposes for writing are to inform, to persuade, and to entertain. To determine an author's purpose, notice the types of details included in the work. Writers may use facts and statistics to inform or persuade. They may use stories about personal experiences to inform or entertain. Often, authors will have more than one purpose—to inform while entertaining, for example.

**A** Read each paragraph. Then, answer the questions.

When you buy a bicycle helmet, make sure it fits you well. The foam pads should touch your head all around, and the helmet should sit level. Tighten the straps so that they are snug but comfortable. You must not be able to pull off the helmet, no matter how hard you try.

**1.** Is the author's <u>main</u> purpose to entertain, to inform, or to persuade?

_____

**2.** List two details from the paragraph to support your answer.

_____

_____

Wherever and whenever you ride your bicycle, you should wear a helmet. You may not know it, but statistics show that a bike rider can expect to crash at least once for every 4,500 miles of riding. Every year, more than 600 people die in bicycle crashes, mostly from head injuries. Your bicycle helmet can protect you. Don't go biking without it!

**3.** Is the author's <u>main</u> purpose to entertain, to inform, or to persuade?

_____

**4.** List two details from the paragraph to support your answer.

_____

_____

© Pearson Education, Inc., publishing as Pearson Prentice Hall.

Name _____ Date _____

# Author's Purpose

Assess

**A** Circle the letter of the choice that best answers the question. Then, explain your choice.

1. In an article about a new movie, a writer briefly describes the story, names the main actors, and tells the movie's rating. What is the writer's purpose?

   **A.** to persuade    **B.** to entertain    **C.** to inform    **D.** all three

   Explain: _____

2. In an article about the same movie, another writer tells the story in detail. He describes a confusing, slow-moving plot, actors who are not right for their roles, and dull background music. He ends with the line, "If you need to catch up on your sleep, this is the movie for you." What is the writer's purpose?

   **A.** to persuade    **B.** to inform    **C.** to entertain    **D.** all three

   Explain: _____

3. Another writer describes the movie in glowing terms—exciting story, great acting, terrific special effects. He ends his article with the line, "Don't miss it!" What is this writer's purpose?

   **A.** to persuade    **B.** to inform    **C.** to entertain    **D.** all three

   Explain: _____

**B** Read the following position statement. Then, answer the questions.

   For the past five years, Tall Pines students have won first- or second-place awards at the Regional Science Fair. The strong science department at Tall Pines deserves credit for the students' successes. The Parent Association proposes extending a special honor to the science faculty this year, including a plaque that will list all science fair winners and advisors.

1. Is the author's <u>main</u> purpose to entertain, to inform, or to persuade?

   _____

2. List two details from the paragraph to support your answer.

   _____

   _____

# Autobiography

In an **autobiography,** a person tells his or her own story. Usually written in the first person, autobiographies present life events as the writer sees them. Because an autobiography is written from memory by the individual who experienced these events, it is more personal and emotional than a biography. Autobiographies also provide a view of history that is more personal than accounts in history books.

**Read the following selection. Then, answer the questions that follow.**

I was born during the Dust Bowl years of our country back in 1931 in a small town down in Oklahoma. My earliest memories all seem to be steeped in shades of beige and dull brown. Whether this is because snapshots from the era were in sepia or because everything was covered in dust I'll never know. All I know is that I spent the first eight years of my life traveling from one small town to another. Crops were drying up, the heat from the sun was intense, with no rain in sight, and the enormous dust storms seemed to get worse and worse as the days went by. We were very poor, and my mother and father tried desperately to keep my brother and me from going hungry. It was throughout our travels that my brother became very ill from bacteria he had contracted from the unsanitary conditions we found wherever we traveled. It was during that time that it seemed my mother was wailing constantly. I also remember the terrible feeling of helplessness that I had at such an early age; it was a terrible time. Eventually, though, my brother did get better, and my family finally reached the west coast of California.

1. What features of an autobiography does this selection have?

_____

_____

2. List any details from this selection that provide support for your answer.

_____

_____

3. What personal details do you learn about the author's experience of living through the Dust bowl that you could not find in a history book?

_____

_____

© Pearson Education, Inc., publishing as Pearson Prentice Hall.

# Autobiography

Assess

**A** Circle the letter of the correct answer.

1. An autobiography is usually written from which point of view?

   **A.** third person
   **B.** third-person omniscient
   **C.** first person
   **D.** second person

2. What is the most important way in which autobiographical accounts differ from historical accounts in history books?

   **A.** They are more objective.
   **B.** They are more personal.
   **C.** They are more entertaining.
   **D.** They are more logical.

**B** Read the following selection. Then, answer the questions and complete the activity.

I began to work alongside my father in his carpentry shop when I was twelve. My schooling had consisted of several years of lessons in a one-room log cabin for which my parents had "subscribed" me for a couple of sessions. School wasn't free and open to all back when I was growing up, but paid for by the parents of the students. I learned enough to be able to read furniture plans and do simple sums. What I didn't learn in school, I then was able to learn as an apprentice to my father.

1. What makes this selection an autobiography?

   _____

   _____

2. List any details from this selection that provide support for your answer.

   _____

   _____

   _____

   _____

   _____

© Pearson Education, Inc., publishing as Pearson Prentice Hall.

# Breaking Down Long Sentences

## Practice

You can analyze confusing sentences by **breaking down long sentences.** Consider one section at a time. Look at complex sentences, and then separate the *who* from the *what.* Here are some tips:

- Begin by identifying subjects and verbs. A **subject** is a word in a sentence that tells who performs an action or who is being described. A **verb** is a word that tells what action the subject does or that links a subject to a description.

- If a sentence has more than one subject or more than one verb, write separate sentences that each have one subject and one verb.

- If a sentence has colons, semicolons, or dashes, write separate sentences by replacing those punctuation marks with periods.

In this example, the subjects are underlined once and verbs are underlined twice:

> **Lines from Poem:** The <u>moon</u> <u>was shining</u> sulkily, / Because <u>she</u> <u>thought</u> the sun / had got no business to be there / After the day was done—
> —from "The Walrus and the Carpenter" by Lewis Carroll

> **Broken Down:** The moon was shining sulkily. She thought the sun had got no business to be there after the day was done.

---

**Read these lines from "Adventures of Isabel" by Ogden Nash. Then, respond to each item.**

> Isabel met an enormous bear,
> Isabel, Isabel didn't care;
> The bear was hungry, the bear was ravenous,
> The bear's big mouth was cruel and cavernous.

**1.** What are the two verbs in the first two lines of the poem?

_____

**2.** Rewrite the first two lines of the poem as two separate sentences.

_____

**3.** What is the subject that is repeated in the third line?

_____

**4.** Rewrite the third line as two separate sentences.

_____

© Pearson Education, Inc., publishing as Pearson Prentice Hall.

## Breaking Down Long Sentences

Assess

**A** Read these lines from "Wilbur Wright and Orville Wright" by Rosemary and Steven Vincent Benét. Then, answer the questions that follow.

> And so they built a glider, first,
> And then they built another.
> —There never were two brothers more
> Devoted to each other.
> 5  They ran a dusty little shop
> For bicycle-repairing,
> And bought each other soda-pop,
> And praised each other's daring.

**1.** What are the two subjects and the two verbs repeated in lines 1 and 2?

**Subject 1:** _____ **Subject 2:** _____

**Verb 1:** _____ **Verb 2:** _____

**2.** Rewrite the first two lines of the poem as two separate sentences.

_____

**3.** What is the verb in line 5? _____

**4.** What is the verb in line 7? _____

**5.** What is the verb in line 8? _____

**6.** Rewrite lines 5 through 8 as three separate sentences.

_____

_____

_____

_____

**B** Now, write what the lines mean in your own words.

_____

_____

_____

_____

© Pearson Education, Inc., publishing as Pearson Prentice Hall.

# Cause and Effect

Practice

A **cause** is an event, an action, or a feeling that produces a result. That result is called an **effect.** You will understand the characters in a story better if you identify cause-and-effect relationships among them. If you do not see the cause-and-effect relationship in a passage, reread to look for connections among the words and sentences. Some words that identify causes and effects are *because, so, since,* and *as a result.*

**A** The first column lists causes, and the second column lists effects. Put the letter of the effect in the blank next to its cause.

1. ____ The rain poured last night.      **A.** Paula couldn't get into the house.

2. ____ The storm caused power outages.   **B.** The streets were wet this morning.

3. ____ The front door was locked.       **C.** Schools were closed for the day.

**B** In the following sentences, underline the causes once and the effects twice.

1. Jack missed the school bus because he overslept.

2. Traffic was terrible, so we were two hours late getting home.

3. Rachel felt unhappy because she was unable to find a summer job.

4. Ice covered the road, so traffic moved slowly.

5. Kathy couldn't ride her bike because it had a flat tire.

**C** Read the paragraph. Then, list two causes and their effects on the lines.

I told my brother that it was foolish to drive over the speed limit. He did it anyway because he liked to show off. But I think he learned his lesson last Saturday. First, he hit a pothole too fast and damaged his car. Then, he got a speeding ticket. Mom said he had to pay the fine and couldn't drive the car for a month. I don't think he'll be speeding again.

**Causes**                                    **Effects**

_____                    _____

_____                    _____

© Pearson Education, Inc., publishing as Pearson Prentice Hall.

# Cause and Effect

Assess

**A**    In the following sentences, underline the causes once and the effects twice.

1. Because of the rain, our basement flooded.

2. Jake broke his leg; therefore, he couldn't play in the game.

3. As a result of last night's power outage, we ate a cold dinner by candlelight.

4. Jane forgot to put the top on the grasshopper's box; consequently, the insect escaped.

5. Since it has not rained in several days and because it has been cold, the new seedlings have died.

6. Joe's dad left his car's headlights on last night, so now the car won't start.

7. The farmland meant everything to the Hutchinsons because it had been in the family for generations.

8. Rosemary overslept this morning, so she didn't have time to eat breakfast.

**B**    Fill in the blanks to complete each statement.

1. Our air conditioner is broken; as a result, _____

_____

2. If transportation were cheaper, _____

_____

3. _____; consequently, I couldn't complete my homework.

4. I fell and twisted my ankle because of _____

_____

5. _____; therefore, I'm not going to the party.

6. The snow slid down the mountain, and as a result, _____

_____

7. _____, which is why I have no money left.

© Pearson Education, Inc., publishing as Pearson Prentice Hall.

# Challenging the Text

## Practice

When a writer makes an important statement, you should challenge that statement. To **challenge the text,** follow these steps:

- Identify the writer's key point and the writer's evidence for the point.
- Ask yourself whether the point is logical and whether evidence supports or proves it.
- Ask yourself whether your own experience supports the writer's arguments.

Here is an example of how you might challenge a text:

**Writer's Point:** It is more important to be an individual than to be rich.
**Writer's Evidence:** A friend of mine is wealthy but unhappy.

**Challenge the Logic:** Why is his friend unhappy? Is it because the friend is not an individual? Could there be some other reason?

**Check Your Experience:** I know people who are real individuals but who are not happy.

---

Read the passage. Then, answer the questions that follow.

People find their greatest moments of happiness when they are alone. It is only when they are alone that they are truly free. When I am with my boss, I cannot be myself. I must act as a worker. Even when I am with my best friend, I feel the pressure of my friend's enthusiasm or boredom, hope or disappointment.

**1.** Underline the writer's key point.

**2.** What two examples does the writer give to support the point? _____

_____

**3.** Do you agree that you cannot be free when you are with others? Explain.

_____

_____

**4.** Explain what your own experiences show about the writer's point. _____

_____

  © Pearson Education, Inc., publishing as Pearson Prentice Hall.

# Challenging the Text

**A**    Read the passage, and then answer the questions that follow.

The best way to live is to follow your own beliefs. You can listen all you want to other people's ideas. In the end, though, you are the one who will be unhappy if those ideas are bad ones. Your own ideas may be good or bad. If you follow them, though, you can always be happy knowing you tried your best.

My friend George once followed some bad advice from a man he trusted. For years, George complained that this man had betrayed him. I said, "George, if you had come up with that idea all by yourself, would you have spent years blaming yourself? Or would you have gotten over it and moved on?" George was stumped.

**1.** What is the writer's key point?

   **A.** You can listen all you want to other people's ideas.

   **B.** Other people's ideas are bad.

   **C.** The best way to live is to follow your own ideas.

   **D.** People want to be happy.

**2.** What evidence does the writer give for this point?

   **A.** an expert's opinions

   **B.** a story about a friend

   **C.** a strong quotation

   **D.** a specific example of bad advice

**3.** To challenge the writer's logic, which question might you ask?

   **A.** Shouldn't you listen to other people's ideas if they are better than your own?

   **B.** What does George do for a living?

   **C.** Shouldn't people ignore bad advice?

   **D.** What does George's friend do for a living?

**4.** Which experience might a reader use to challenge the text?

   **A.** the experience of following bad advice and being unhappy

   **B.** the experience of following good advice and being happy

   **C.** the experience of giving good advice and not being listened to

   **D.** the experience of giving bad advice and making someone unhappy

**B**    On a separate sheet of paper, write a few sentences challenging the passage above. First, tell what the writer's point is. Then, explain whether your own experiences support this point. Finally, tell whether or not you agree with the writer.

© Pearson Education, Inc., publishing as Pearson Prentice Hall.

Name _____  Date _____

**Characterization** is the art of creating and developing characters. There are two types of characterization:

- **Direct characterization:** The writer tells you exactly what the character is like. For example, the writer might say that the character is "young" or "giving."

- **Indirect characterization:** The writer reveals what a character is like by describing his or her appearance, words, and actions and by noting what other characters say about him or her. For example, instead of saying that a character is athletic, a writer may reveal this through indirect characterization, as in this description:

    Elizabeth was a member of the school's tennis club. In addition, she often played basketball with her friends on the weekends.

---

**A** Write *Direct* for each item that uses mainly direct characterization. Write *Indirect* for each item that uses mainly indirect characterization.

1. _____ Keira is so friendly and trustworthy that it is clear why she has so many friends.

2. _____ As he pulled his car in front of the building, Derek noticed the fire zone markings and illegal parking signs. He parked his car anyway.

3. _____ Simon is energetic and happy-go-lucky.

4. _____ Theresa's best friend no longer speaks to her. She says that Theresa has become too full of herself.

---

**B** In this example of indirect characterization, underline two clues that show what the character is like. Then, use the clues to describe the character directly.

**Olivia:** "Attention, everyone, I have arrived," said Olivia energetically, stepping into the room. She handed her varsity cheerleading jacket to Alice, the freshman who followed her everywhere. Olivia was donning a designer shirt and expensive sneakers. She spun around so that others could admire her.

**What Olivia is like:** _____

_____

© Pearson Education, Inc., publishing as Pearson Prentice Hall.

# Characterization

**A**  Write *Direct* for each item that uses mainly direct characterization. Write *Indirect* for each item that uses mainly indirect characterization.

1. _____ Martin is a hard worker and always does a great job.

2. _____ My sister, Clarice, has long brown hair, is 5' 6", and has several freckles decorating the bridge of her nose.

3. _____ Joanna nervously glanced at her watch. Then, taking a deep breath, she glanced ahead to see how many test questions still remained to be answered.

4. _____ Although he had never performed in front of an audience before, Ethan quickly mastered the art of stand-up comedy and soon had the audience rolling on the floor with laughter.

5. _____ Since Robert has low self-esteem and is very sensitive to criticism, he refuses to submit any of his poems to the literary digest.

**B**  In each example of indirect characterization, underline two clues that show what the character is like. Then, use the clues to describe the character directly.

**Rachel:** Rachel's friend John was having trouble in math, and there was a big test coming up. Rachel knew John did not want to ask for help. She knew a way around that problem, though. She would tell him she was worried about the test, too, and ask him to help her study. To get ready, Rachel reached over to a standing file of clearly labeled folders and quickly found the one in which she had filed her old math tests.

**What Rachel is like:** _____

_____

**George:** When the coach said George had not made the varsity team, George did not say anything. When he heard that his friend Phil had made the team, he congratulated him. After school, some friends asked George if he wanted to go fishing with them. George said no—he had too much homework. Later, though, his friends saw him walking down the side of the road, kicking stones.

**What George is like:** _____

_____

© Pearson Education, Inc., publishing as Pearson Prentice Hall.

# Characterization in Drama

Practice

**Characterization** is the means by which a writer reveals a character's personality. Playwrights, like writers of fiction, use a number of different techniques to show the personality traits of the characters in a drama. These methods include the following:

- a character's **dialogue,** or what the character says to other characters. For example, a greedy character might boast about his money to others.

- speeches, called **soliloquies,** in which a character speaks his or her thoughts aloud while alone. For example, a sad character might explain her troubles in a soliloquy.

- **comments about a character** made by other characters. For example, if other characters complain about how boring Fred is, you can conclude that Fred is boring.

- **stage directions,** which might describe what a character does, what gestures he or she makes, what tone of voice he or she uses, and so on. For example, stage directions might describe a sneaky character going through someone's desk.

**A** Circle the letter of the answer that best completes each statement.

**1.** The purpose of characterization is to

    **A.** mock or satirize a character.     **B.** reveal a character's personality.

**2.** Stage directions are important to characterization because they

    **A.** tell the character's name.     **B.** tell about the character's actions.

**B** For each item, describe the character whose name is in italics. Base your description on the statement by or about the character or on the stage directions.

**1.** *HENRY:* I never go to rock concerts. I think they're silly!

_____

**2.** ELSIE: Some day *Irene* will discover that life is not always about "My way or the highway!"

_____

**3.** *JOHN:* [always eager to please] I'll lend you the money for the tickets, Paul.

_____

© Pearson Education, Inc., publishing as Pearson Prentice Hall.

# Characterization in Drama

Assess

**A**  Write *T* if the statement is true or *F* if it is false.

1. _____ Characterization only applies to the major figures in a drama.

2. _____ Playwrights may use stage directions to reveal the personality traits of their characters.

3. _____ A character in drama may be characterized through his or her own words.

4. _____ Characterization in drama is completely different from characterization in fiction.

5. _____ When you are considering a character's personality in drama, you may safely ignore what other characters have to say about him or her.

**B**  Use the statement by or about the character in italics to make an inference about his or her personality.

1. GRETCHEN: *Warren* told me that the song's romantic words reminded him of Judy, and he thought of her eyes.

_____

2. PAULA: *Brian* is envious of the Otis brothers because they've created such a successful business empire.

_____

3. [Enter *TIM*, slowly dragging his feet, with his head down.]

_____

4. ZACH: Will you turn that music down, *Barb*? Don't you know I'm trying to concentrate?

_____

5. [*WILL* cradles the baby in his arms and smiles broadly.]

_____

© Pearson Education, Inc., publishing as Pearson Prentice Hall.

# Characters: Dynamic and Static

A **character** is a person or an animal who takes part in the action of a literary work. Characters can be divided into types:

- A **static character** is one whose attitudes and behavior remain essentially stable throughout a literary work.

- A **dynamic character** experiences a change in attitude or behavior during the course of a work.

Identify each character as *static* or *dynamic*. Write your answer in the blank.

**1. Bob** _____

***Beginning of the story:*** Bob feels it is important to be an informed voter.

***End of the story:*** Bob does research into the voting records of the presidential candidates.

**2. Linda** _____

***Beginning of the story:*** Linda works hard and loves playing soccer.

***End of the story:*** Linda gives up some of her hours at work so she can play soccer. Linda still works hard and still loves playing soccer.

**3. Superguy** _____

***Beginning of the story:*** Superguy believes he can solve most problems using his special powers.

***End of the story:*** Superguy is unable to save his friend from an illness. Superguy realizes he cannot solve every problem.

**4. Max** _____

**Beginning of story:** Max lets his friends talk him into skateboarding where it is not allowed.

***End of story:*** Max's friends see someone coming. They run away without telling Max and let him get caught. Max realizes he should not have let his friends persuade him to break the rules—especially because they did not save him from trouble.

© Pearson Education, Inc., publishing as Pearson Prentice Hall.

# Characters: Dynamic and Static

Assess

**A**  Identify each character as *static* or *dynamic*. Write your answer in the blank.

**1. Samantha** _____

*Beginning of the story:* At school, Samantha is shy and reserved.

*End of the story:* Samantha makes new friends at school. She speaks up more in class.

**2. Joe** _____

*Beginning of the story:* Joe enjoys learning about the ocean and the scientific world.

*End of the story:* Joe majors in biology at college and, after graduation, gets a job as an oceanographer.

**3. Lateesha** _____

*Beginning of the story:* Lateesha keeps busy with activities in her city. She daydreams about living in the country.

*Ending of the story:* Lateesha watches a video she has rented about a boy who lives on a farm. After watching the video, she wonders about what she would have to do to become a farmer.

**B**  Read the beginnings of these stories. Then, write brief endings to the stories that demonstrate a change in the characters.

**1. Dr. Bad**

*Beginning of the story:* Dr. Bad plans to take over the world. He does wrong whenever he can.

*End of the story:* _____

_____

**2. Eliana**

*Beginning of the story:* Eliana has always been afraid of public speaking. During class presentations, her voice trembles and her hands shake.

*End of the story:* _____

_____

© Pearson Education, Inc., publishing as Pearson Prentice Hall.

# Characters' Motives

Practice

A **character's motives** are the reasons for his or her actions. Motives are usually related to what a character wants, needs, or feels. For example, jealousy might motivate a character to speak badly about another character.

**A**  Several powerful motives include *anger, hope,* and *fear.* For each item, write the word that best describes each character's motives.

1. _____ Mrs. Harris walked to the bus station for the third morning in a row. All day, she waited and watched travelers coming and going. Her son promised he would be coming home soon. She wanted to be there to greet him.

2. _____ Ella left without saying good-bye. Later, when her phone rang, she ignored it and turned up her music to drown out the ringing.

3. _____ Thinking he had heard a noise, Alex cautiously parted the curtains. He peered into the darkness. Then, he turned the deadbolt on the front door.

**B**  Circle the letter of the best answer. Then, explain your choice.

1. As Vicki passed the bulletin board in the front hallway, a small sign caught her attention. It said "Volunteers Needed" and showed a picture of a sad-looking dog at a local animal shelter. Teary-eyed, Vicki scribbled her name and phone number on one of the sign-up lines below the picture. What motivates Vicki to help at the shelter?

   **A.** jealousy       **B.** compassion       **C.** hope       **D.** fear

   Explain: _____

2. Members of the science club have been working for months to design a bridge for an upcoming competition. Every time they think they have it figured out, something goes wrong. Still, they refuse to give up. What motivates the science club members?

   **A.** frustration       **B.** fear       **C.** determination       **D.** kindness

   Explain: _____

© Pearson Education, Inc., publishing as Pearson Prentice Hall.

## Characters' Motives

Assess

Read the passage. Then, circle the letter of the answer that best completes each statement.

All season Tyra had fought hard to maintain her place as the seventh member of the varsity team. It had not been easy. A sophomore runner, she had experienced fierce competition from Danielle, a senior. They always started out strong, but Tyra usually overtook Danielle just before the end of the race. She knew her place on varsity was secure.

In addition to being the final meet, it was also Senior Day. It was the last time seniors would run in a home meet as part of the team. Two hundred feet before the finish line, Tyra was on Danielle's heels. Tyra could hear her breathing hard. She knew Danielle had worked just as hard as she had this season. It would mean a lot to her to finish seventh today. Tyra crossed the finish line a fraction behind Danielle.

1. A character's motives can best be defined as

   **A.** his or her personality.

   **B.** the main theme of the story.

   **C.** the reasons for his or her actions.

   **D.** the problems that he or she faces.

2. Tyra has been running hard all season because

   **A.** she does not like Danielle.

   **B.** she wants to stay on the varsity team.

   **C.** she wants to be the best runner.

   **D.** she will graduate this year.

3. Tyra slows down her pace in the end because

   **A.** she wants Danielle to finish before her.

   **B.** she is not very competitive.

   **C.** she feels tired.

   **D.** she wants Caley to catch up.

4. The word that best describes Tyra's motivation for doing so is

   **A.** kindness.

   **B.** fatigue.

   **C.** desperation.

   **D.** guilt.

© Pearson Education, Inc., publishing as Pearson Prentice Hall.

Name _____ Date _____

# Chinese Poetic Forms

Chinese literature has its own poetic forms—some of them different from European and American forms of poetry. **Chinese poetic forms** include the following:

- *Shih* **poems**—poems that, in the original Chinese, have an even number of lines, each with the same number of words. Old-style *shih* poems can be of any length, but the new-style version used in the 700s has strict rules about length and form.

- **Songs**—poems that were originally set to music and have strong, regular rhythms. Songs may also include **refrains**—words or phrases repeated at regular intervals. If one or two words within a refrain are varied from one stanza to the next, this technique is called **incremental variation.** Here is an example of a refrain with incremental variation:

   Thick grow the rush leaves; / Their white dew turns to frost. /. . . / Close grow the rush leaves, / Their white dew not yet dry. ("Thick Grow the Rush Leaves," from *The Book of Songs*, translated by Arthur Waley)

- **Ballads**—songs that tell stories.

Write *T* if the statement is true or *F* if it is false.

1. _____ *Shih* poems have an even number of lines.

2. _____ Each line in a *shih* poem can have a different number of words.

3. _____ New-style *shih* poetry has fewer restrictions than old-style *shih* poetry.

4. _____ A refrain repeats words or phrases at regular intervals in a poem.

5. _____ Chinese songs typically have irregular, unpredictable rhythms.

6. _____ Refrains appear only rarely in Chinese songs.

7. _____ Chinese songs were not set to music but were sung by an unaccompanied voice.

8. _____ Chinese ballads, like English and American ones, typically tell a story.

© Pearson Education, Inc., publishing as Pearson Prentice Hall.

# Chinese Poetic Forms

## Assess

Circle the letter of the item that best answers each question or completes each statement.

**1.** A Chinese *shih* poem always has

   **A.** an even number of lines.       **B.** an odd number of lines.

**2.** In a *shih* poem, each line has the same number of

   **A.** syllables.       **B.** words.

**3.** Tighter restrictions on length and form are found in which of the following?

   **A.** old-style *shih* poems       **B.** new-style *shih* poems

**4.** If you wanted to tell a story, which might you compose?

   **A.** sonnet       **B.** ballad

**5.** Refrains in poetry involve

   **A.** metaphor.       **B.** repetition.

**6.** In which poetic form was Chinese verse set to musical accompaniment?

   **A.** song       **B.** *shih* poem

**7.** The following lines are from "I Beg of You, Chung Tzu," translated by Arthur Waley, from *The Book of Songs*. Circle the letter of the example of incremental variation.

   **A.** "Do not break the willows we have planted. / Not that I mind about the willows, / But I am afraid of my mother and father."

   **B.** "I beg of you, Chung Tzu, / Do not climb over our wall, / Do not break the mulberry trees we have planted. / . . . / I beg of you, Chung Tzu, / Do not climb into our garden, / Do not break the hardwood we have planted. . . ."

   **C.** "Chung Tzu I dearly love; / But of all that people will say / Indeed I am afraid."

© Pearson Education, Inc., publishing as Pearson Prentice Hall.

# Chronological Order

Sometimes, authors write stories that jump about in time. They may tell events in the present first and then tell events in the past. To keep track of events in such stories, identify **chronological order,** the order in which events happen in time. Look for signals that suggest the actual order of the events. Such signals may include the following:

- the tense of the verbs. Usually, stories are written in the past tense: *She went to the store.* Look for shifts to the past perfect tense: *She had gone to the store.* The past perfect tense tells of events from before the present time in a story.

- the age of the characters and other details that help indicate time

- transitional words and phrases like *first, later, on the next day,* or *after that*

    **Example:** Pete calmly watched the cattle herd move through the pasture. He remembered the mistakes he had made on his first day on the ranch, and how nervous he had been. Now, four years later, he was one of the more experienced workers.
    **Event that came first in time:** The mistakes Pete made on his first day on the ranch.
    **Signals:** He remembered; had made; had been; Now; four years later

---

**Read the passage. Then, respond to each item.**

As she drove south along the coastline to her vacation home on the shore, Anne passed miles of empty beaches. How different this trip was from the one family trip to the seashore she had taken during her childhood. Then, Anne's father had driven the whole family to a beach two hours away. Unlike this one, that trip had been noisy and crowded. All five children had squeezed into the back seat of their father's car. Also, it seemed to take forever because Anne's father had missed the turnoff for the beach three times in a row. While the beaches had not changed much since that trip in her childhood, the trip sure had. Anne turned the car into the driveway of her house, parked it, and walked inside.

1. Underline the sentence describing the earliest event. Explain your answer.

_____

2. Underline the words and phrases taking place in the present time of the

    story. Explain your answer. _____

_____

   © Pearson Education, Inc., publishing as Pearson Prentice Hall.

## Chronological Order

**A**  Read the passage. Then, respond to each item.

As the train pulled out of the station, John ran as fast as he could. He had to catch it. It was the last train out that night. Coming home tomorrow would be too late. John's heart raced. Sweat ran down his face. He waved his hands frantically to get the conductor's attention. It was all for nothing. Just as he reached the platform, the train pulled away.

John could now laugh about this terrible moment. As it turned out, his sister's surprise party had not been scheduled for the next day. Instead, it had been scheduled for the following week! These days, John carefully recorded his appointments on a calendar.

1. Which event in the passage came first?

    **A.** John laughed.                     **C.** John tried to catch the train.
    **B.** John missed the train.            **D.** John missed his sister's party.

2. Underline an action in the present time of the story. Explain your answer.

    _____

3. How does the writer indicate that John's efforts to catch the train occurred

    in the past? _____

**B**  Underline the words and phrases that help you clarify the order of events. Then, list the events of the story in the order in which they occurred.

Sarah watched her children playing in the yard from her kitchen window. They were involved in a game of hide-and-seek, and they did not notice her watching. Sarah cast her mind back to the day she had brought her twin daughters home from the hospital. She had felt tired and overwhelmed, and she didn't know how she would survive a week without the help of the hospital nurses. However, in time, she had learned to manage the challenge of caring for two active little girls. Today, as she watched them running happily about the yard, she could not imagine her life without them.

_____

_____

_____

_____

© Pearson Education, Inc., publishing as Pearson Prentice Hall.

# Comparing and Contrasting Characters

### Practice

When you **compare and contrast characters,** you look for similarities and differences between them. Categories in which characters may be similar or different include appearance, actions, and motives. Characters may also be compared in terms of their background, or social position and past experiences, and their fate, or what happens to them in the story.

■ Read the passage. Then, fill in the chart.

O'Malley, the president of the company, dressed like an executive. He enjoyed looking good, for he had gotten his job the hard way by starting at the lowest level of the company and working his way up. O'Malley had never gone to school beyond high school, but his experience at the company helped him fill in the gaps in his education. Because he had done just about every job there, he was truly familiar with every part of the company. He often stopped to chat with employees who held jobs he once had filled.

Now, however, O'Malley found his job being threatened. McSwain, the owner of the company, had always promised the president's job to his son. It was almost time for Junior to take over. Junior had a fine education, but he had only worked in the high-paying jobs in the company. He knew no one in the mailroom or the factory. In fact, he never even visited there. Junior liked to dress as "one of the guys," usually wearing casual work shirts and blue jeans.

| | O'Malley | Junior |
|---|---|---|
| 1. How the character looks | | |
| 2. What the character does | | |
| 3. Character traits of each character (name at least two) | | |

© Pearson Education, Inc., publishing as Pearson Prentice Hall.

## Comparing and Contrasting Characters

Assess

**A** Explain what similarity or difference between Victoria and Kirsten is shown in each item. Then, circle the category of the similarity or difference you wrote about.

1. **Victoria:** grew up with Kirsten on a rural farm

   **Kirsten:** grew up with Victoria on the farm

   _____

   **appearance/personality  background  actions/feelings  motives  fate**

2. **Victoria:** wants to be popular at school

   **Kirsten:** wants to become valedictorian

   _____

   **appearance/personality  background  actions/feelings  motives  fate**

3. **Victoria:** is happy when she forms her own small group of friends and no longer worries about being popular

   **Kirsten:** is happy when she becomes valedictorian

   _____

   **appearance/personality  background  actions/feelings  motives  fate**

**B** Use these words to compare the characters in each pair of sentences below.

friendly     calm     lonely     restless

1. **A.** _____ "I took some cookies over to the new neighbors. They seem like nice people!"

   **B.** _____ "I wish I had more friends, but I don't know how to talk to people."

2. **A.** _____ "When I meditate, I imagine the sound of the wind in the trees."

   **B.** _____ "Each morning I can't get my shoes on and get out the door fast enough. Then I jog in place while I wait for my bus. Sometimes it's hard to sit through a whole class."

© Pearson Education, Inc., publishing as Pearson Prentice Hall.

# Comparing and Contrasting Critical Reviews

### Practice

A **critical review** is an analysis and evaluation of a work—a book, a play, a movie, a concert, a dance performance, an art exhibit, or a consumer product. A review presents opinions about the work, supporting them with evidence and reasons. A review's purpose is to persuade the reader to accept the reviewer's judgment of what is being evaluated.

You should **compare and contrast** different reviews of a work to see if the work appeals to you or meets your needs. Compare several reviews to see where the critics agree. Then, contrast the reviews to see where they disagree, and why. Finally, decide what *you* think.

> **Read the following passages from two reviews of a book. Then, answer the questions.**

> *Review #1:* This novel begins with a charming encounter between its two main characters—and then goes downhill from there. This yawnful (628 pages!) Civil War love story brings together a Confederate officer and the sister of a Union colonel—a slightly new turn on an old cliché. Because the characters are paper-thin, we don't care if their love triumphs or not.

> *Review #2:* This subtle, powerful novel opens engagingly. Two people from different sides in the Civil War (he is a Confederate officer, her brother is a Union colonel) meet. They fall in love and then struggle as that love tears their lives apart. At 628 pages, the book is a bit long, but its story is so gripping and its characters are so winning, you hardly notice.

**1.** What facts about the book did you learn from these reviews?

_____

_____

**2.** On what points do the reviewers agree? _____

_____

_____

**3.** On what points do they disagree? _____

_____

_____

_____

© Pearson Education, Inc., publishing as Pearson Prentice Hall.

Name _____ Date _____

## Comparing and Contrasting Critical Reviews

■ Read the following passages from two reviews of a concert. Then, answer the questions.

*Review #1:* The new rock band Wet Paint Drying raised the roof at the Asher Auditorium last night. The band hit its stride in the very first number, "Slapping It On," with a rousing solo by lead guitarist Ron G and weirdly wonderful vocal harmonies by Michael Sorin and Steve Randall. And the concert just got better and better.

*Review #2:* Last night's concert by Wet Paint Drying at the Asher Auditorium was uneven but promising. The first number, "Slapping It On," featured a stunning guitar solo by Ron G, but the vocals by Michael Sorin and Steve Randall were muddy and lacked energy. However, subsequent numbers showed that Wet Paint Drying may well be a group to watch.

1. What facts about the concert did you learn from these reviews?

_____

_____

2. On what points do the reviewers agree? _____

_____

_____

3. On what points do they disagree? _____

_____

_____

4. Based on these reviews, would this concert appeal to you? Explain.

_____

_____

_____

_____

_____

_____

# Conflict

## Practice

**Conflict** is a struggle between opposing forces. While there are many different types of literary conflict, they can be divided into two general categories:

- In an **external conflict,** a character struggles with an outside force, such as another character, a group of characters, or a force of nature, such as weather.

- In an **internal conflict,** the character struggles with his or her own beliefs, desires, or values. For example, a woman trying to save money might feel torn between her desire to save and her desire to buy a new mountain bike.

Write *External* before each sentence that describes an external conflict. Write *Internal* before each sentence that describes an internal conflict.

1. _____ A group of picnickers struggle to survive in a big rainstorm.

2. _____ Drew is afraid Bridget will say no if he asks her out. He works up his courage and calls her.

3. _____ Michael tried to protect his home from being affected by the hurricane that was on its way. But the wind caused a tree to crash into one of the bedrooms.

4. _____ Andrea is angry when she learns that a worker who was just hired has been promoted and will be making a lot more money than she does.

5. _____ The FBI arrested a man accused of robbing a number of banks in the area.

6. _____ A flood threatens the town where Rebecca lives.

7. _____ Sue listened to the conversation between her mother and father and realized they knew that she had failed the science test. She was concerned about what her punishment would be.

© Pearson Education, Inc., publishing as Pearson Prentice Hall.

# Conflict

Assess

**A** Write *External* before each sentence that describes an external conflict. Write *Internal* before each sentence that describes an internal conflict.

1. _____ Claudia wanted to go on a camping trip with her friends over the weekend, but she was disappointed when she heard she had to stay at home and baby-sit her younger sister.

2. _____ Jake has been picking on Tommy every day at lunch just because Tommy is a new student.

3. _____ Roger is trying to decide what to do. He wants to go to the movies with his friends, but he promised his father he would help him paint the den.

4. _____ Lisa must decide what college she wants to attend. She is not sure if she wants to go to a school where she can live at home or go to a school far away where she can live on campus.

5. _____ When the Nelsons return home from a day in the city, they realize their house has been vandalized.

6. _____ Phil's doctor tells him he should not play football for a week because of his sprained ankle. Phil wants to follow his doctor's advice, but he does not want to miss playing in the game on Saturday.

7. _____ Aaron goes in search of underwater treasure. His one-person submarine gets stuck in a cave.

8. _____ In the dark of night, Terri and his fellow freedom fighters stage a raid against the enemy.

**B** Give your own examples of external and internal conflict.

**External:** _____

_____

**Internal:** _____

_____

© Pearson Education, Inc., publishing as Pearson Prentice Hall.

# Cultural and Historical Context

**Practice**

The **cultural and historical context** of a story, poem, or other work of literature is the specific time and place in which it was written. To understand the work, you may need to understand its context:

> **Example:** In a story written in the nineteenth century, Fred moves west. He worries about his family in Kentucky. He waits for months for a letter from them.
>
> **What Context Explains:** Why didn't Fred just call his family?
>
> **Context:** In the nineteenth century, there were no telephones or e-mail providers. There were no airplanes or cars. The only way to communicate across a long distance was through the mail, which could take a long time.

The context of a work includes beliefs and customs as well as specific events.

> **Example:** In a letter written in the sixteenth century, a woman writes that her husband went walking at night and so fell sick.
>
> **Context:** In the sixteenth century, people believed that the air at night was filled with unhealthy vapors or clouds.

---

For each question, circle the letter of the best answer.

**1.** Imagine that this diary entry was written by a woman in colonial America.

> My brother John is going to a fine school, Harvard College. How I wish I could go there and study all those wonderful books! I am a young woman, though. Everyone knows that women do not study at college. It is not proper.

Judging from the diary entry, what did people of the writer's time believe about women?

**A.** Women should study hard.

**B.** Women were not meant to be educated.

**C.** Women were equal to men.

**D.** Women should go to the same schools as men.

**2.** Which best describes the historical context of the letter?

**A.** In colonial times, people believed in the value of education.

**B.** In modern times, people believe in the value of education.

**C.** In colonial times, people did not believe in equality for women.

**D.** In modern times, people believe in equality for women.

© Pearson Education, Inc., publishing as Pearson Prentice Hall.

# Cultural and Historical Context

Assess

**A**   Circle the likeliest description of the cultural and historical context of each work.

1. The Blackfoot Indians tell the myth of a boy who brought the first horses to people. The boy went on a quest. With the help of one spirit, he was able to get the horses from the spirit who owned them.

   **A.** The Blackfeet believe that important parts of their lives, such as horses, come from spirits.
   **B.** The Blackfeet do not know very much about breeding or riding horses.

2. In 1950, Ray Bradbury published a short story called "There Will Come Soft Rains." The story tells of a time in the future when atomic bombs have wiped out entire cities.

   **A.** The United States had used the first atomic bombs against Japan in 1945. People of the day were frightened that such powerful atomic weapons might destroy humanity.
   **B.** Another country, the Soviet Union, had tested its own atomic bomb in 1949. As a result, people knew that they were safe from atomic bombs.

3. In a Hindu story from India, King Sibi wounds himself to protect the life of a dove and to keep a promise. The god Indra praises the king's goodness and heals him.

   **A.** Hindus believe that doves were sent by the gods to punish people.
   **B.** Hindus believe that all life is sacred.

**B**   Write a brief description of the cultural and historical context of this passage. Then, explain what the context helps you understand.

In a story about King Arthur and his knights, a giant green knight comes to Arthur's castle. He challenges the knights to fight him. No one speaks up at first. Gawain is very concerned. He thinks that if no one fights the knight, then the world will think King Arthur's knights are cowards. He tells the giant knight he will fight him, with the king's permission.

**Context:** _____

**What the context helps me understand:** _____

_____

© Pearson Education, Inc., publishing as Pearson Prentice Hall.

# Cultural Attitudes, Beliefs, and Values

## Practice

**Culture** includes the attitudes, beliefs, goals, and values of a group of people. For example, in modern American culture, earning money is a common goal, and a comfortable lifestyle is highly valued.

A story or other work of literature reflects the values of the writer's culture. To understand a work, **make inferences** about the writer's culture, forming a logical picture based on details in the text. To help you make inferences, ask and answer questions about details.

> **Example:** In the Greek poet Homer's epic the *Iliad*, King Agamemnon takes back from the warrior Achilles a woman they have captured in battle. Achilles feels his honor is at stake. He refuses to fight for Agamemnon.
> **Questions:** How could a king "give" one person to another? Why doesn't Achilles just ask the king for something else he wants?
> **Answer/Inference About Culture:** The ancient Greeks of Homer's day must have looked at captives as part of the loot of war. Honor must have been a main value among these warriors, more important than loyalty.

The epic *The Nibelungenlied* describes the hero Siegfried and reflects the values of a feudal society. Read the passage. Then, make inferences about feudal culture.

His hunting suit was all of otter-skin, varied throughout its length with furs of other kinds from whose shining hair clasps of gold gleamed out on either side of this daring lord of the hunt. The handsome sword he wore was Balmung, a weapon so keen and with such excellent edges that it never failed to bite when swung against a helmet. . . .

1. **Detail:** The epic describes Siegfried's hunting outfit at length.

   **Questions:** Why does the poet describe Siegfried's clothes in such detail? What does this show about the culture's view of clothing?

   **Answer/Inference:** _____

   _____

2. **Detail:** Siegfried's sword has a name, Balmung, just like a person.

   **Question:** Why would a warrior's sword have a name?

   **Answer/Inference:** _____

   _____

© Pearson Education, Inc., publishing as Pearson Prentice Hall.

# Cultural Attitudes, Beliefs, and Values

Assess

**A** Circle the letter of the best inference about the cultural attitudes, beliefs, and values reflected in each passage.

1. In a fable by the thirteenth-century Persian Sa'di, a king takes more and more from his people. An advisor tells him that the rule of a king depends on the people. The king grows angry and punishes the advisor. Soon, two of his nephews lead a rebellion against him. The people of the kingdom gather in support of the rebels, and the king loses power.

   **A.** Persians felt that kings had divine authority to rule absolutely.
   **B.** Persians felt that kings owed their power to the people.

2. In the Renaissance novel *Don Quixote*, Miguel de Cervantes pokes fun at a poor nobleman who loses his mind and believes that he is a heroic knight. He sets out on a quest to slay giants and rescue fair maidens.

   **A.** Europeans like Cervantes continued to follow the values of the Middle Ages, when knights were courageous and courtly.
   **B.** Europeans like Cervantes felt that they lived in a world in which the old values seemed foolish and unreal.

**B** The medieval English poem *The Canterbury Tales* by Geoffrey Chaucer describes a pardoner, or seller of religious wares. Read the passage. Then, make inferences about feudal culture.

> How well he read a lesson or told a story!
> But best of all he sang an Offertory,*
> For well he knew that when that song was sung
> He'd have to preach and tune his honey-tongue
> And (well he could) win silver from the crowd.
> That's why he sang so merrily and loud.

\* **Offertory** song that is sung during the collection of offerings at a church service.

1. **Detail:** A man like the pardoner could make a living preaching.
   **Question:** Why would a crowd give so much money to a traveling preacher?

   **Answer/Inference:** _____

2. **Detail:** The poet implies that the pardoner is mainly interested in money.
   **Question:** Why doesn't the poet show more trust in a man who preaches?

   **Answer/Inference:** _____

© Pearson Education, Inc., publishing as Pearson Prentice Hall.

# Descriptive Details

## Practice

**Descriptive details** appeal to the five senses—sight, sound, smell, taste, and touch. A writer will use descriptive details to create a vivid impression of a person, a place, or an object. Description can be found in all types of writing.

**A**   Circle the sense or senses to which each description appeals.

**1.** The freezing wind stung my face and made my eyes water.

   sight                smell                taste                touch

**2.** Clouds of white steam poured out of the whistling teakettle.

   sight/smell        smell/taste        sight/sound        taste/touch

**3.** This lemonade is the perfect chilly combination of sour and sweet.

   sound/smell        touch/smell        touch/taste        smell/taste

**B**   Read the example. Then, respond to each item below.

> I remember being startled when I first saw my grandmother rocking away on her porch. All my life I had heard that she was a great beauty and no one had ever remarked that they meant a half century before. The woman that I met was as wrinkled as a prune and could hardly hear and barely see and always seemed to be thinking of other times. But she could still rock and talk and even make wonderful cupcakes which were like cornbread, only sweet.
> —from "On Summer" by Lorraine Hansberry

**1.** List three words or phrases the author uses to describe her grandmother.

_____

_____

_____

**2.** List two words or phrases the author uses to describe the cupcakes.

_____

**3.** Choose one description in the paragraph, and tell the sense or senses to

which it appeals. _____

_____

          © Pearson Education, Inc., publishing as Pearson Prentice Hall.

# Descriptive Details

Assess

**A**  Read each description. Then, write the word that best completes each sentence.

Jan yawned loudly as she stared at the page with heavy-lidded eyes.

**1.** Jan is feeling _____.

excited                      tired                      frightened

In the lush green garden, birds sang cheerfully, and the perfume of lilacs sweetened the air.

**2.** The season the writer describes is _____.

autumn                      winter                      spring

**B**  Read the example. Then, complete the activity.

We lived on Waverly Place, in a warm, clean, two-bedroom flat that sat above a small Chinese bakery specializing in steamed pastries and dim sum. In the early morning, when the alley was still quiet, I could smell fragrant red beans as they were cooked down to a pasty sweetness. By daybreak, our flat was heavy with the odor of fried sesame balls and sweet curried chicken crescents. From my bed, I would listen as my father got ready for work, then locked the door behind him, one-two-three clicks.

—from *The Joy Luck Club* by Amy Tan

Write a word or phrase from the paragraph that appeals to each sense.

Sight: _____

Sound: _____

Smell: _____

Taste: _____

Touch: _____

© Pearson Education, Inc., publishing as Pearson Prentice Hall.

# Didactic Literature

**Didactic literature** teaches lessons on ethics, or ideas about right and wrong and rules about how to act. This type of literature often reflects the values of the society that produces it. Didactic literature usually presents specific situations or details from which a more general lesson, or **moral,** may be drawn. For example, one didactic tale tells of a lazy grasshopper and a hard-working cricket. The cricket survives the winter, while the grasshopper perishes. The moral of this fable is that hard work is rewarded.

In order to teach its lessons, didactic literature uses these literary techniques:

- **Aphorisms**—short, pointed statements expressing a general truth or rule, such as *He who turns and runs away, lives to fight again another day.*

- **Personification**—a technique that gives human qualities to nonhuman things, such as attributing laziness to a grasshopper.

- **Metaphor**—a figure of speech in which one thing is spoken of as if it were something else, such as *My love is a rose.*

---

**A**  Circle the letter of the answer that best completes each statement.

**1.** Didactic literature is written primarily to

   **A.** entertain.          **B.** teach.          **C.** persuade.

**2.** The lesson in didactic literature is called a

   **A.** simile.          **B.** flashback.          **C.** moral.

**3.** Metaphor, which commonly appears in didactic literature, is based on

   **A.** a comparison.          **B.** repetition.          **C.** realism.

---

**B**  Mark an item with *D* if it seems related to didactic literature. If the item cannot be classified as didactic, leave the space blank.

**1.** _____ a newspaper article about an increase in property taxes

**2.** _____ a fable about a cunning fox and a crow who likes flattery

**3.** _____ a ballad telling the story of an ill-fated romance

**4.** _____ a newspaper editorial endorsing a candidate for public office

**5.** _____ a collection of proverbs praising hard work and thriftiness

© Pearson Education, Inc., publishing as Pearson Prentice Hall.

# Didactic Literature

### Assess

**A**  Circle the letter of the best answer to each question.

**1.** Which of the following is the best definition of ethics?

    **A.** principles of economics
    **B.** surveys of the history of literature
    **C.** rules of right and wrong conduct

**2.** Which of the following would most likely be a didactic writer?

    **A.** a writer of love sonnets
    **B.** a thoughtful philosopher
    **C.** a composer of musical comedies

**3.** In didactic literature, which of the following might you expect?

    **A.** hyperbole, or strong exaggeration for effect
    **B.** personification, or attributing human qualities to nonhuman things
    **C.** avoidance of any kind of moral or lesson

**4.** Which of the following correctly defines *aphorism*?

    **A.** brief, pointed statement
    **B.** dedication on the title page of a book
    **C.** ironic understatement

**B**  Mark an item with *D* if it can be related to didactic literature. If the item is not related to didactic literature, leave the space blank.

**1.** _____ a fable about a town mouse and a country mouse

**2.** _____ a folk ballad about a miner who won a contest

**3.** _____ a tale about a hero founding a great city

**4.** _____ a play about a nutty professor

**5.** _____ an essay explaining the strengths and weaknesses of democracy

© Pearson Education, Inc., publishing as Pearson Prentice Hall.

# Drawing Conclusions

Practice

When you **draw conclusions,** you use your reasoning to reach logical decisions on the basis of evidence. When reading, you draw conclusions by applying your knowledge and experiences to details from the work.

**A** Read the following stanza from "The Village Blacksmith" by Henry Wadsworth Longfellow. Then, answer the questions.

Under a spreading chestnut tree
   The village smithy stands;
The smith, a mighty man is he,
   With large and sinewy hands;
And the muscles of his brawny arms
   Are as strong as iron bands.

1. What details does the poet include and emphasize?

_____

_____

2. How are the details related?

_____

3. From the details, what conclusion can you draw about the blacksmith?

_____

**B** Read the following haiku by Buson. Then, answer the questions.

Deep in a windless
wood, not one leaf dares to move . . .
Something is afraid.

1. Circle the important details. What do the details suggest?

_____

2. What conclusion can you draw about the details and the poet's meaning?

_____

      © Pearson Education, Inc., publishing as Pearson Prentice Hall.

# Drawing Conclusions

**Assess**

Read the following selection. Then, write the letter of the best answer to each question.

In the harbor between New York and New Jersey lies Ellis Island. Operating between 1892 and 1954, Ellis Island welcomed approximately 12 million steerage and third-class passengers arriving by ship to America. These passengers had often endured two weeks or more of seasickness in cramped, crowded conditions. Most had little in their home countries and came to America in hopes of an opportunity for a better life.

Upon arrival, passengers had to pass a medical examination before being allowed into America. Immigrants were required to walk up a long flight of stairs as doctors watched for signs of lameness and breathing problems. Immigrants also had their eyes, ears, noses, and throats checked for difficulties or sickness. Those who were sick were required to stay on Ellis Island until they were well. Those who failed to recover were sent back to their home countries.

1. ____ Which conclusion can you make about one of the primary functions of Ellis Island?

   **A.** It was a place to dock the many ships arriving with immigrants.
   **B.** It provided a location to screen immigrants for medical problems.
   **C.** It was a location to provide much-needed food and rest for the immigrants.
   **D.** It provided a place where sick immigrants could recover.

2. ____ What can you conclude about the passengers arriving at Ellis Island?

   **A.** All were wealthy and could afford to travel.
   **B.** All were healthy, having had adequate food and space on the voyage.
   **C.** Most were poor and often sick upon arrival.
   **D.** Many went back to their home countries.

3. ____ What can you conclude about the doctors at Ellis Island?

   **A.** Doctors determined whether or not immigrants were allowed into the country.
   **B.** Doctors had well-equipped offices and very expensive equipment.
   **C.** Doctors were well educated.
   **D.** All doctors were immigrants.

© Pearson Education, Inc., publishing as Pearson Prentice Hall.

# Drawing Inferences

Practice

**Drawing inferences** means making educated guesses based on specific details the author provides.

- Read between the lines to look for any implied meaning.
- Explore passages for clues about characters, setting, plot, and mood.

**A** Read the paragraph. Then, answer the questions.

As Ann turned away from the window, she was frowning deeply. She walked quickly across the room toward the door to the kitchen and to the back stairs. Then she stopped and turned back into the living room. A loud knock sounded at the front door. Hearing it, Ann jumped slightly and grabbed the back of a chair. The knock came again. Biting her knuckle, Ann glanced toward the kitchen door and then back toward the front door. A third knock sounded. Ann could hear her mother calling her name. But still she stood, nervously holding the back of the chair.

**1.** How do you think Ann feels? _____

**2.** Underline the words and phrases that suggest Ann's feelings.

**3.** What do you think Ann would like to do?

_____

_____

**B** Read each passage. Then, answer each question.

You ask your cousin how she did on her job interview. She replies by slamming her briefcase down and snapping, "I don't want to talk about it."

**1.** What would you guess happened?

_____

On Monday morning, the back tire of your car suddenly goes flat. A friend, who says she knows tires, patches the leak and says that your tire is as good as new. The next morning, on the way to school, you feel a thumping from the back tire.

**2.** What can you infer about your tire and your friend?

_____

     © Pearson Education, Inc., publishing as Pearson Prentice Hall.

# Drawing Inferences

Read each passage. Then, circle the letter of the best answer to each question, or respond to each item.

As Sam walked through the doorway, he fiddled with the zipper on his jacket. The room was filled with kids who all looked like they had known each other forever. Sam found an empty desk at the back of the room. He sat down and glued his eyes to the desk.

**1.** Who is Sam?

    **A.** a new student in the class        **B.** a substitute teacher

**2.** Underline the words in the paragraph that support your answer.

**3.** How does Sam feel?

    **A.** nervous        **B.** bored

**4.** Circle the words in the paragraph that support your answer.

Above all, Pam loved the color of the glass. There were sheets of the deepest red. Some sheets were pale green and other light colors. Many of the clear pieces had bumps or ridges to give them texture. With so much to pick from, Pam thought, I can certainly create my masterpiece.

Just then, Mrs. Laurenti came into the shop. She looked around in a bored way. "Still picking up scraps of useless glass, eh, Pam?" she remarked. Then, she strolled out the door.

**1.** What is Pam's plan?

    **A.** to pick pieces of glass to put on sale        **B.** to make a beautiful window

**2.** What words in the passage support your answer?

_____

**3.** How does Mrs. Laurenti feel about Pam's work?

    **A.** She does not appreciate Pam's work.        **B.** She wants to give Pam better glass.

**4.** What words in the passage support your answer?

_____

# Epic

## Practice

An **epic** is a long poem that tells a story of the adventures of heroes and gods. The stories in an epic help the people who told the epic understand themselves, as in these examples:

- **Indian epics** such as the *Mahabharata* and the *Ramayana* tell the adventures of Indian heroes. These heroes are models of Indian values. For instance, the hero Rama of the *Ramayana* shows virtues such as spirituality and devotion to his duties. These virtues are central to Hindu culture in India.

- A **national epic** tells the story of the beginning of a nation or culture. The Roman national epic, the *Aeneid,* tells how a hero of ancient Greek epics, aided by the gods, founded Rome. In this way, the poem shows Romans that they are connected to the ancient Greeks, whom the Romans admired. It also tells Romans that they are favored by the gods.

- In **medieval epics,** such as the *Song of Roland* and *The Nibelungenlied,* knights do great deeds in their thirst for honor or out of love or loyalty. These epics provide models of **feudal values** such as honor, loyalty, courage, and devotion in love and religion. A medieval epic may reflect the worldview and values of Christianity.

A **conflict** is a struggle between two opposing forces. In an **epic conflict,** the hero typically struggles against a series of obstacles. These obstacles may include powerful enemies or difficult voyages. For instance, the *Aeneid* tells how the hero Aeneas sails through storms, fights deadly enemies, and faces the despair of his crew. In the end, Aeneas triumphs over these obstacles.

For each question, circle the letter of the best answer.

1. Which is the best description of an epic?

   **A.** a poem about Indian heroes, gods, and goddesses
   **B.** a tale of knights
   **C.** the story of the founding of a nation
   **D.** a long poem telling stories of the heroes of a nation or culture

2. The hero of a medieval epic often has characteristics that were admired by feudal society. Which is likeliest to be true of the hero of a medieval epic?

   **A.** He shares Indian values.
   **B.** He is brave in battle, and he is devoted in love or religion.
   **C.** He is religious, and so he avoids fighting in battle.
   **D.** He is brave but disloyal.

© Pearson Education, Inc., publishing as Pearson Prentice Hall.

# Epic

**A** Circle the letter of the best answer to each question.

1. Which of the following accurately describes an epic?

   **A.** a brief poem praising the gods
   **B.** a long poem telling of gods and heroes
   **C.** a historical account of how a nation was founded
   **D.** a long poem telling of ordinary life

2. Which statement is true of a medieval epic?

   **A.** It tells of the founding of Rome.
   **B.** It expresses feudal values such as ambition and the pursuit of wealth.
   **C.** It expresses feudal values such as honor and devotion in love or religion.
   **D.** It celebrates Indian values.

3. Which item most clearly shows the characteristics of an epic conflict?

   **A.** The hero struggles with his own feelings of guilt.
   **B.** The hero battles first one monster, then another, and finally another.
   **C.** The hero fights and wins just one battle, and the story is over.
   **D.** The hero must battle his brother to determine who will rule.

**B** On the first line, identify each item as an *Indian,* a *national,* or a *medieval* epic. Then, explain your choice.

1. _____ A hero goes in quest of the Holy Grail, the cup that Christ was said to have used at his last supper with his disciples.

   _____

2. _____ A hero, troubled when his spiritual guide asks him to fight a female monster, believes that he has a duty not to harm women. The guide explains that his duty is to rid the world of the monster.

   _____

3. _____ A hero visits the home of the gods and is granted a vision of the long line of kings who will rule the nation that he will soon found.

   _____

© Pearson Education, Inc., publishing as Pearson Prentice Hall.

# Epiphany

In a traditional short story, the plot moves toward resolution, a point at which the conflict is untangled and the outcome of the action becomes clear. However, many twentieth-century writers turned away from such traditional plot structures. These writers constructed plots that move toward an **epiphany,** a moment when a character has a flash of insight that may alter the nature of the conflict without resolving it.

**Read the passage. Then, answer the questions.**

Jackson reached to answer the ringing telephone, but he stopped when he saw Sid's name on the caller ID. He had been avoiding Sid for weeks now. Sid was caught up in the latest diet fad and always prattled on about it. Jackson had his own ideas about nutrition, but Sid never wanted to hear them. Of course, Jackson never wanted to hear about Sid's new diet either. He always tuned him out when he talked about it. It suddenly occurred to Jackson that if he and Sid ever listened to each other, they might learn something.

1. What is an epiphany in a literary work?

   **A.** a resolution            **C.** a conflict

   **B.** a flash of insight      **D.** a traditional plot structure

2. Which character above experiences an epiphany? _____

3. What epiphany does this character have?

   **A.** He realizes that he should answer his telephone.
   **B.** He realizes that his friend is not a good listener.
   **C.** He realizes he and his friend might learn from each other.
   **D.** He realizes he needs to change his eating habits.

4. What is most likely to occur next in the story as a result of this epiphany?

   **A.** Sid will listen to Jackson's ideas about nutrition.
   **B.** Jackson will give Sid's new diet a try.
   **C.** Sid will tune Jackson out when he talks about nutrition.
   **D.** Jackson will answer the phone and talk to Sid.

5. Will this epiphany resolve the conflict between the characters? Explain.

   _____

   _____

© Pearson Education, Inc., publishing as Pearson Prentice Hall.

# Epiphany

**Read the selection. Then, complete the chart below.**

Before Liz and Alex decided to run for senior class president, they had been close friends. Now, it seemed, they were archenemies. Alex used every opportunity to criticize Liz's leadership abilities, and Liz was always looking for ways to outshine Alex. They were both so absorbed in campaigning against each other that they had ignored Danielle, the other candidate in the race. Danielle was quiet and unassuming, so they did not consider her a threat. When it came time to give their campaign speeches, Danielle went first. She gave a moving and intelligent speech that earned a standing ovation from her classmates. Both Liz and Alex were stunned. They quickly realized that Danielle had a very good chance of winning the election.

| | |
|---|---|
| 1. Epiphany | |
| 2. Characters Who Experience the Epiphany | |
| 3. Event Likely to Occur Next as a Result of the Epiphany | |
| 4. How the Epiphany Might Affect the Outlook of the Characters Who Experience It | |

© Pearson Education, Inc., publishing as Pearson Prentice Hall.

# Evaluating a Writer's Message or Philosophy

### Practice

When you are reading, **evaluate** the writer's ideas using logic and your own imagination to discover whether the writer's ideas make sense and whether the ideas fit your own experiences. First, identify the writer's message or philosophy (view of life). Then, ask and answer these questions:

- Does the message always hold true, or are there exceptions?
- Do the writer's arguments and other evidence support the message?

Here is a sample evaluation of a writer's message:

**Writer's Philosophy:** You should always tell the truth, no matter what.
  **Question 1 Are there exceptions?** Sometimes people lie so they will not hurt other people's feelings. They think that it is all right to tell these lies.
  **Question 2 Does the message fit my experience?** Yes, because I believe it is wrong to lie. I don't like it when people lie to me.
**Writer's Argument:** If people lied whenever they felt like it, then no one would ever believe anyone else.
  **Question 3 Does this argument support the message?** No; the argument does not seem true. Some people lie, but people still believe one another.

---

Read the message, and then respond to each item.

Reading opens people's minds and helps them understand others.

**1.** Circle the letter of the argument that best supports this message.

  **A.** A survey shows that 85% of people in high-paying jobs are good readers.
  **B.** Readers get insights into characters that help them understand people.
  **C.** Some books spread false ideas about groups of people and create prejudice.

**2.** Give an example that either proves this idea or shows that there are exceptions to it. Explain the support your example provides.

_____

_____

**3.** What does your own experience show about this message? _____

_____

**4.** Do you agree with the message? Explain. _____

_____

© Pearson Education, Inc., publishing as Pearson Prentice Hall.

# Evaluating a Writer's Message or Philosophy

Assess

**A** Read the passage, and then circle the letter of the best answer to each question.

When I was young, I hated weeding the garden with my brother Sam. "Aw, do we have to?" was his response when our mother reminded us of the chore. Every time Sam bent over to pull out a dandelion, he grumbled. With Sam, twenty minutes of weeding seemed like three hours.

I loved to weed with my brother Jim, though. Before we went off to the garden, he saluted our mother as if he were a soldier on a mission. He spent the entire time pretending we were agents hunting down spies. Every time he pulled out a weed, he would say something like, "A-ha! Mr. Crabgrass! Just passing through? A likely story." The time flew by.

I learned a lesson weeding with my brothers. There is no work that is so dull that it cannot be made fun with the power of imagination.

1. What is the message in this passage?

   **A.** Work can be fun or boring, depending on what you make of it.
   **B.** Gardening is not for everyone.
   **C.** People should do their chores when they are supposed to.
   **D.** Crabgrass is a deadly enemy.

2. What support does the writer give for this point?

   **A.** the example of Sam's poor attitude
   **B.** the example of Jim's good attitude
   **C.** the fact that he weeded as a boy
   **D.** the story of the difference made by Jim's approach to work

**B** Respond to each item below.

1. Give an example of an exception to the message above.

   _____

2. To support this message, the writer gives an example from childhood. Do you think that this example is too limited to apply to adult life? Explain.

   _____

   _____

3. Do you agree with the writer's message? Explain. _____

   _____

© Pearson Education, Inc., publishing as Pearson Prentice Hall.

# Evaluating Author's Support

### Practice

Feature articles often present a writer's opinion or evaluation of a topic. Writers prove or support their opinions with evidence, as in this example:

> Opinion: The new mall is a disaster!
> Support: Ever since they built the mall, traffic is backed up in town.

To determine whether you agree with the writer's opinions, **evaluate the support** and decide whether or not the evidence is persuasive and valid. Evidence may take these forms:

- **statements of fact,** or claims that can be proved true: *Sugar can cause cavities.*

- **statistics,** or information from analyzing numbers: *Ninety percent of accidents at the intersection occurred during rush hour.*

- **observations,** or personal experience with the subject: *I noticed that many of the shoppers walked right past the new display.*

- **examples,** or specific stories that make a general point: *Mr. Jones is one man who has continued working well past retirement age.*

---

**Read the following selection, and then answer the questions.**

1     Some argue that dress codes in schools create a better sense of discipline and
2 purpose—a more serious and studious atmosphere. But learning isn't mainly about
3 routines and discipline. The most important element of learning is creativity, and one
4 recent study concluded that dress codes foster a spirit of conformity that can stifle
5 students' creative spirit. Also, a recent national poll found that 66 percent of students
6 are opposed to dress codes.
7     Free expression is the first step in gaining a deeper understanding of the world,
8 whether expressed in schoolwork or clothing. In my years as an educator, I have seen
9 that if you clamp down on the variety and liveliness of the clothing, the students'
10 schoolwork will become duller as well.

**1.** In which lines does the author first give his or her own opinion?

    **A.** 1–3          **B.** 3–5          **C.** 7–8          **D.** 8–10

**2.** In lines 5–6, what support can be found for the author's opinions?

    **A.** a study          **B.** a statistic          **C.** observation          **D.** no support

**3.** In lines 8–10, what support can be found for the author's opinions?

    **A.** a statistic          **B.** a study          **C.** observation          **D.** no support

© Pearson Education, Inc., publishing as Pearson Prentice Hall.

# Evaluating Author's Support

Assess

Read the following selection, and then answer the questions that follow.

1    Even if some believe that genetically modified (GMO) foods are not harmful,
2 they should be labeled so that consumers can make a free, informed
3 choice about what kinds of things they are putting in their bodies. Many European
4 countries already require such labeling, in fact. Some might argue that such
5 labeling would be like a skull-and-crossbones that would needlessly
6 damage the sales of foods containing GMO ingredients. However, there is much
7 research that remains to be done about the potential risks of GMO foods, to both
8 humans and the entire ecosystem. A recent survey of biologists found that only
9 38 percent were fully convinced of the long-term safety of GMO foods. So, it is
10 all the more strange that, on a recent trip to the supermarket, I could find no
11 labeling of the GMO ingredients that now are part of most of our packaged
12 food supply. Consumers ought to have the ability to reject GMO foods until all
13 scientists—not just some—are satisfied that they are completely safe.

**1.** In which lines does the author first give an opinion?

   **A.** 1–3       **B.** 3–4       **C.** 4–6       **D.** 11–13

**2.** The sentence that begins "Many European countries . . ." in lines 3–4
contains which kind of support for the author's opinions?

   **A.** a fact       **B.** an observation    **C.** a quotation    **D.** the results of
                                                                        a study

**3.** In lines 8–9, what kind of support can be found for the author's opinions?

   **A.** a fact       **B.** an observation    **C.** a quotation    **D.** statistic

**4.** In lines 10–12, what kind of support can be found for the author's opinions?

   **A.** a fact       **B.** an observation    **C.** a quotation    **D.** a statistic

**5.** Which kind of support for the author's opinions used in this passage did
you find most effective? Why?

_____

_____

© Pearson Education, Inc., publishing as Pearson Prentice Hall.

# Evaluating Characters' Decisions

**Evaluating characters' decisions** means judging the choices a character makes and the effects of those choices. A **character's motives** are the reasons for his or her actions. Part of evaluating characters' decisions is questioning characters' motives, or thinking about why characters do what they do. Follow these steps to evaluate:

- Think about whether the character benefits from the decision in the way he or she imagined.
- Analyze the effect each decision has on other characters.
- Judge whether the decision has good or bad results.

> Read this summary of "A Devoted Son," a short story by Anita Desai. Then, answer the questions that follow.

Rakesh's family save and sacrifice to send him to college and then to medical school. He is the first in the family to be educated. They are ecstatic when he excels. Rakesh studies and works for a while in America, but he returns to India. Indian tradition tells sons to be respectful of their fathers, and Rakesh is a model son. Yet Rakesh brings new ideas from America. When his father grows elderly and ill, Rakesh carefully monitors his diet. Rakesh will not let him eat too much. He forbids his father to eat the treats that he loves. Rakesh makes him take various medicines. The old man comes to hate his life under Rakesh's care.

1. How do Rakesh's decisions about his father's diet affect his father?

_____

2. Do you think Rakesh made a good or a bad decision? Explain your answer.

_____

_____

3. In the end, does Rakesh's father benefit from his decision to send his son to school?

_____

_____

4. Do you think Rakesh's father made a good or a bad decision? Explain.

_____

_____

     © Pearson Education, Inc., publishing as Pearson Prentice Hall.

# Evaluating Characters' Decisions

Assess

Read the passage, and then answer the questions that follow.

In the O. Henry short story "The Gift of the Magi," a young married couple struggle with decisions about buying each other Christmas gifts. They do not have any money to spare. They have two possessions that they value a great deal. Della has long, beautiful hair, which falls below her knees. Jim loves her hair. Jim has a gold pocket watch that had been his father's and his grandfather's. Della decides to cut her hair off and sell it. She uses the money to buy Jim a watch chain for the pocket watch. In the meantime, Jim has already sold the pocket watch so that he can buy Della jeweled combs for her hair.

1. What is the best definition of a character's motive?

   **A.** his or her personality          **C.** the reason for his or her actions
   **B.** the main theme of the story     **D.** the problem he or she face

2. Which of the following is the likeliest motive for the decisions made by Della and Jim?

   **A.** greed                           **C.** fear of appearing stingy
   **B.** love for each other             **D.** pity

3. Does Della's decision to sell her hair affect anyone except herself? Explain.

   _____

   _____

4. In what ways do Jim and Della benefit from their decisions to sell their most prized possessions?

   _____

   _____

   _____

5. On a separate sheet of paper, write a paragraph in which you give your judgment about whether Jim and Della made good or bad decisions.

# Existentialism

**Existentialism** is a mid-twentieth-century philosophy that teaches the importance of freedom. Existentialists agree on these basic points:

- The universe is indifferent to human action and suffering and can provide no answers.

- Our lives matter because of our own actions, not because we are part of a greater plan.

- The individual has total freedom to choose and total responsibility for his or her life.

- Individuals choose the values that they live by and must take responsibility for them. People are hiding from this responsibility when they try to justify their acts according to other people's standards or rules.

- Freedom is the most important, and most frightening, part of life.

Many late-twentieth-century works reflect these ideas by portraying individuals who feel isolated and who struggle over difficult decisions with complex consequences.

Read the summary of "Comrades," a story by Nadine Gordimer that is set in South Africa during the period when blacks and whites were required to live in separate places. Then, answer the question.

Mrs. Hattie Telford, a white woman, is driving through a university campus in South Africa when a group of young black men politely ask her for a ride to the bus station. She agrees. From their awkward conversation, she learns that they have been attending a youth conference and that they are hungry. On an impulse, she offers them lunch at her home. They accept. The young men seem intimidated by her comfortable house. Watching them eat hungrily, Mrs. Telford is shaken by the idea that one day, these young men will carry weapons and plant land mines to overthrow the white government that oppresses them. "She can see that they have been terribly harmed but cannot believe they could harm."

Why might Mrs. Telford's decisions to give the young men a ride and to serve them lunch be viewed as Existential actions? _____

_____

_____

_____

© Pearson Education, Inc., publishing as Pearson Prentice Hall.

## Existentialism

Assess

**A** Read the following passage. Then, answer the questions.

Henry got off the bus and crossed the busy street. He had chosen this destination simply: this was as far as he felt like going that day. Tomorrow, he would probably get on the same bus and go farther. He doubted he knew anyone in this place, even though it was far from deserted. People walked by him, looking in store windows. Right then, all that Henry cared about was dinner. He figured that he would find restaurants all along such a busy street. The sun was setting, and the darkening air smelled of winter, which he liked, but which also made him realize he needed to find somewhere to sleep. Far ahead, lights in a hotel sign blinked on, and he walked toward it. The hotel was quite large and warm inside. A small shop just off the lobby sold books, among other items, and Henry found two that he wanted to read. He could smell food—the hotel probably had a restaurant. He decided that he might stay more than one night in this place.

**1.** Why could Henry's situation at the beginning be described as Existential?

_____

_____

**2.** Why might Henry's various decisions be viewed as Existential actions?

_____

_____

**B** Write a paragraph explaining how the story would be different if Henry had based his decisions on a standard code of behavior or beliefs rather than an Existential one. Use an additional sheet of paper if necessary.

_____

_____

_____

_____

_____

_____

_____

© Pearson Education, Inc., publishing as Pearson Prentice Hall.

# Fables

## Practice

**Fables** are brief stories that teach a simple lesson. This lesson, or **moral,** may be directly stated at the beginning or end of the tale. Often, fables point out a particular human fault or weakness. The characters in fables are often animals that speak and act as if they were human. Fables can be told in verse as well as in prose.

One very well-known fable is the story about the race between the tortoise and the hare. Certain he will beat the slow tortoise, the fast hare wastes his time rather than concentrating on running. At the same time, the slow tortoise keeps plodding along. Despite the hare's greater speed, the tortoise's steady, hard work pays off, and he ultimately wins. The fable criticizes overconfidence and values hard work. Its moral is "Slow and steady wins the race."

Read this summary of a fable. Then, respond to the items that follow.

The grasshopper made fun of the ant for working hard all summer. The grasshopper would dance and sing and call out "Enjoy yourself" to the ant. But the ant was too busy to hear, since she was constantly running around, gathering food and storing it away in the shelter she had built. Summer ended, and finally winter came. The grasshopper had not built a shelter, and he had not saved any food. He was cold and hungry. He knocked at the ant's door and asked for a crumb of the food the ant had stored away. The ant felt sorry for the grasshopper and gave him a crumb to eat. The grasshopper realized that he had been foolish.

1. Identify the main characters in this fable, and point out the human

   qualities they show. _____

   _____

   _____

2. What character fault does the fable make fun of, and how? _____

   _____

   _____

3. State the moral that you would expect to see at the end of this fable. _____

   _____

© Pearson Education, Inc., publishing as Pearson Prentice Hall.

# Fables

**A**   Read the fable below. Then, respond to the items that follow.

It was a cloudy day, and the old sun was resting. The young wind grew proud. He boasted that he was much stronger than the sun. The sun didn't like to argue, but he was getting tired of the youngster's noise. Finally the wind said: "Let's have a contest to see who is stronger!" The sun accepted the challenge, knowing the ways of the world better than the young wind did.

Just then they spied a man walking along, wearing a coat. "Aha!" shouted the wind. "Whoever can rip that coat from that man's back will win." The wind was confident, for he had been able to rip large branches off huge trees. Tearing a coat from a little man's back would be easy. The wind went to work. He blew as hard as he could. But the harder the wind blew, the more tightly the man gripped his coat. Finally the wind grew tired and gave up. It was the sun's turn. The sun didn't want to work hard, but he didn't have to, since the wind had already blown all the clouds away. All the sun had to do was shine right down onto the man. The man grew warmer and warmer, as the sun knew he would. The man stopped clutching his coat, and after a while, he took it off. The young wind grumbled, but he had to admit that the old sun had won, fair and square.

**Moral:** Strength isn't everything; it helps to know a few things too.

**1.** Identify the main characters in this fable, and point out the human

qualities they show. _____

_____

_____

**2.** What character fault does the fable make fun of, and how? _____

_____

_____

**3.** Restate the moral of this fable in your own words. _____

_____

**B**   On a separate sheet of paper, write a few sentences describing a real human situation that this fable would apply to.

© Pearson Education, Inc., publishing as Pearson Prentice Hall.

# Folk Tales

**Folk tales** are part of the oral tradition, which is the body of stories, poems, and songs that are passed down by word of mouth from generation to generation. Most folk tales include the following characteristics:

- a lesson about life
- magical or supernatural elements
- characters who possess one or two main traits
- a clear separation between good and evil

Read the following summary of a folk tale. Then, write the letter of the best answer to each question.

A king had three sons, all born on the same day but each with a very different personality. One was strong and handsome; one was clever and mean; one was gentle and thoughtful. When it came time to decide who should inherit the throne, the king asked each prince a question: "What do you want most in life?" The strong prince said, "Great wealth, for then I can buy anything I want." The handsome prince said, "Great power, because I will be able to make others do what I want." The gentle prince said, "I want others to be as happy as I am." The king decided to make the gentle prince his heir, for he would be the best king.

1. _____ Which statement describes why the king chose the third prince?

   **A.** The first two princes thought only of themselves, but the third thought of others.
   **B.** A happy person is likely to be a good leader.
   **C.** It didn't matter which prince he selected, so he chose the one who spoke last.
   **D.** The strong prince and the handsome prince didn't seem to want to be king.

2. _____ What lesson about leadership does this folk tale teach?

   **A.** Being royal does not guarantee that someone is a good leader.
   **B.** The best leader puts the happiness of others above his or her own.
   **C.** Money and power are useful for getting other people to do things for you.
   **D.** Gentle people are always better leaders than beautiful or strong people are.

3. _____ Which of these qualities does the folk tale show as the highest good?

   **A.** strength          **B.** obedience          **C.** wisdom          **D.** selflessness

          © Pearson Education, Inc., publishing as Pearson Prentice Hall.

# Folk Tales

**Read the following summaries of folk tales. Then, answer the questions.**

A farmer's daughter had milked the cows. As she returned home, the milkmaid began daydreaming. "I can get cream from the milk in my pail. I will make butter from the cream and sell it. I will buy eggs, which will hatch into chickens. Soon, I will sell the chickens and use the money to buy a new gown. I will be so pretty that the handsome prince will marry me. I will live in the castle forever."

The farmer's daughter was too busy daydreaming to watch where she was going. She tripped on a rock and dropped her pail in the dirt. Her milk and her dreams spilled out onto the road.

Once a boy was walking through the forest. He spied a fox through the trees. The fox was fast asleep. The boy got very excited.

"I could trap the fox and sell it in the market," he thought. "I will use the money to buy seeds to grow a great garden. People will see my garden and be very jealous. They will want to steal my vegetables. If they do, I will shout at them, 'Get out of my garden!'"

The boy shouted so loudly that the fox woke up and ran into the forest. The boy lost his fox and his great garden.

1. What lesson is contained in these stories?

   **A.** It is better to work slowly and not make mistakes.
   **B.** Dreams almost never come true.
   **C.** Old dogs can learn new tricks.
   **D.** It is better to have loved and lost than never to have loved at all.

2. How are the two characters alike?

   **A.** They have plans that help other people.
   **B.** They lost what they had because of other people.
   **C.** They made a mistake that ruined their plans.
   **D.** They ended up with more than they started.

3. What character trait do the two characters share?

   **A.** They work hard.
   **B.** They are daydreamers.
   **C.** They are evil.
   **D.** They plan well.

© Pearson Education, Inc., publishing as Pearson Prentice Hall.

## Following Directions

Practice

Your ability to **follow directions** is an important life skill. Here are some helpful tips for following directions:

- Read the directions thoroughly before beginning the task.
- As you work through the task, do not skip any steps.
- Study diagrams or illustrations.
- Consider whether your finished product is what you expected it to be.
- If there are problems with your finished product, review the directions and diagrams to determine where you went wrong.

Read the directions below, and then answer the questions that follow.

### Desk Lamp Diagram and Parts

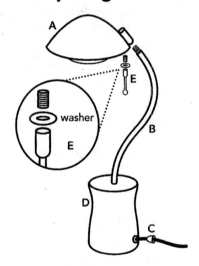

### Desk Lamp Assembly Instructions

1. Screw the lamp shade (A) onto lamp pole (B) by turning lamp pole clockwise.
2. Push the power cord clip (C) into the hole in the base (D).
3. Screw the handle (E) to the lamp shade (A), using the washer as shown.

1. _____ Under which heading in bold print will you learn what parts come with the lamp?

2. _____ Under which heading in bold will you find a picture that shows exactly where the washer will be used?

3. _____ To fasten the shade in place, in which direction should you turn the lamp pole?

© Pearson Education, Inc., publishing as Pearson Prentice Hall.

Name _____ Date _____

Read the directions below, and then answer the questions that follow.

## Cordless Telephone Diagram and Parts

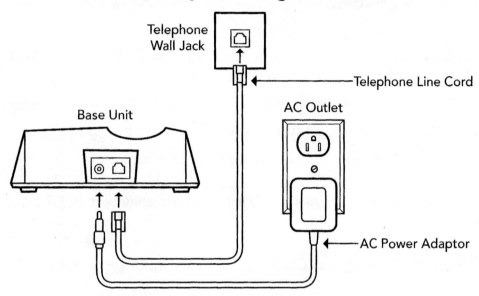

## Cordless Telephone Installation Instructions

1. On the back of the handset, slide off the battery cover.
2. Place the battery pack into the compartment. Replace the battery cover.
3. Plug one end of the Telephone Cord into the Base Unit as shown. Plug the other end of the telephone cord into the Telephone Jack as shown.
4. Plug the small end of the Power Adaptor into the base of the telephone as shown. Plug the large end into an electrical outlet as shown. You are now ready to use your telephone.

**1.** Under which heading do you first learn that there is a Power Adaptor?

_____

**2.** Under which heading do you learn when the telephone is ready for use?

_____

**3.** What conclusion can you draw about why the writer of the instructions has written "as shown" as part of instructions 3 and 4?

_____

© Pearson Education, Inc., publishing as Pearson Prentice Hall.

# Hyperbole and Understatement

Practice

People who write satire, or humor used to expose and ridicule human foolishness, use tools such as the following:

**Hyperbole or exaggeration:** a deliberate exaggeration or overstatement

It was so funny, I nearly died laughing.

**Understatement:** a figure of speech in which the stated meaning is purposely less than (or under) what is really meant

It was 105 degrees in the shade, and my mother said, "It's a little warm today."

**Faulty logic:** an assumption made about something that is not true

Noses were made to wear glasses, so we wear glasses.

For each item, write *H* if it is hyperbole, *U* if it is an understatement, or *F* if it is an example of faulty logic.

1. _____ More people have cats than dogs, so cats must be easier to take care of.

2. _____ "It does seem a bit damp in here," said Matt as the water soaked through his shoes.

3. _____ I'm so hungry, I could eat a horse.

4. _____ Asked how he felt, an army officer who had just received a bullet wound said, "It stings a bit."

5. _____ I had to wait an eternity for the file to download.

6. _____ If I wear the same kind of shoes that Michael Jordan wears, I will be able to jump just as high.

© Pearson Education, Inc., publishing as Pearson Prentice Hall.

# Hyperbole and Understatement

**A**  For each item, write **H** if it is hyperbole, **U** if it is an understatement, or **F** if it is an example of faulty logic.

**1.** _____ That man is as big as a house.

**2.** _____ The two boys are with Mrs. Rodriguez; therefore, they are her sons.

**3.** _____ The Sears Tower in Chicago is a little taller than some buildings.

**4.** _____ The telephone rang immediately after the thunder sounded, so the thunder must have caused the telephone to ring.

**5.** _____ After watching a tornado carry away two picnic tables, my uncle remarked, "The weather is not ideal."

**6.** _____ I found my missing sock in the dryer. It was a joyous reunion.

**B**  Rewrite each sentence as hyperbole, an understatement, or an example of faulty logic according to the word in parentheses.

**1.** Joanne is unfriendly. (hyperbole) _____

_____

**2.** It is cold in here. (understatement) _____

_____

**3.** My father's car got stuck in the snow. (faulty logic) _____

_____

**4.** I am sick. (understatement) _____

_____

**5.** Randy is funny. (hyperbole) _____

_____

**6.** The last time I wore this shirt, I got an A. (faulty logic) _____

_____

© Pearson Education, Inc., publishing as Pearson Prentice Hall.

# Hypothesizing

Practice

To **hypothesize** means to make informed guesses or to propose ideas based on clues in the text. Your informed guess is also known as a **hypothesis.** To see if your hypothesis is true, you should look for additional details in the text.

For example, Colette's story "The Bracelet" begins with a woman, rather bored, counting 29 perfect small diamonds. You can hypothesize from this detail that the woman has seen so many diamonds in her life that 29 perfect diamonds mean little to her. Reading further will show you that your informed guess about the woman is true, for she is the wife of a successful merchant.

Read the following passage from *Rosa Parks: My Story.* Then, answer the questions.

When I got off work that evening of December 1, I went to Court Square as usual to catch the Cleveland Avenue bus home. I didn't look to see who was driving when I got on, and by the time I recognized him, I had already paid my fare. It was the same driver who had put me off the bus back in 1943, twelve years earlier. He was still tall and heavy, with red, rough-looking skin. And he was still mean-looking. I didn't know if he had been on that route before—they switched the drivers around sometimes. I do know that most of the time if I saw him on a bus, I wouldn't get on it.

1. What can you hypothesize from the phrase *that evening of December 1?*

_____

_____

2. What can you hypothesize from the fact that Parks recognized the driver from something that had happened twelve years before?

_____

_____

3. What can you hypothesize from the fact that Parks would refuse to get on a bus if she saw that this man was the driver?

_____

_____

© Pearson Education, Inc., publishing as Pearson Prentice Hall.

# Hypothesizing

Read the following passage from Voltaire's novel *Candide*. Then, answer the questions.

[Candide's teacher] Pangloss taught metaphysico-theologo-cosmolonigology. He proved admirably that there is no effect without a cause and that in this best of all possible worlds, My Lord the Baron's castle was the best of castles and his wife the best of all Baronesses.

"'Tis demonstrated," said he, "that things cannot be otherwise; for, since everything is made for an end, everything is necessarily for the best end. Observe that noses were made to wear spectacles; and so we have spectacles."

1. What can you hypothesize from the fact that Pangloss teaches a subject with a long and silly name?

_____

_____

_____

2. What can you hypothesize about Pangloss from the statement that he "admirably proved" that his master's castle is "the best of castles" and his master's wife is "the best of all Baronesses"?

_____

_____

_____

3. What can you hypothesize about Pangloss from his statement that everything is necessarily made for the best possible outcome?

_____

_____

_____

4. What can you hypothesize about Pangloss from his statement about noses and spectacles?

_____

_____

_____

© Pearson Education, Inc., publishing as Pearson Prentice Hall.

# Identifying With a Character

To **identify with a character,** put yourself in his or her place. Ask yourself, *How would I react in his or her situation?* Even if the character lives in a time and place far from your own, you can compare the character's basic situation to your own experiences or to those of people you know.

**Example:** On his first day as captain, Pritchard was nervous. He worried that the men would not obey him. He worried that he would not command well if pirates attacked.

**Basic situation:** A person with new responsibility wonders whether he will be respected and whether he will do a good job.

**My own experience:** When I was a new counselor at summer camp, I worried that the campers would not listen to me.

**How I would react in Pritchard's situation:** I would be nervous.

---

Explain how you might identify with each of the following characters.

1. Sam frowned as soon as Big Bill walked into the cowboy's camp. For some reason, Big Bill had been trying for years to beat Sam. Once, Big Bill rode all night just so he could get his cattle to the train ahead of Sam. Sam used to be sweet on Little Lil, but then Big Bill stole her away from him.

**Basic situation:** _____

**My own experience:** _____

**How I would react:** _____

2. The year of the big dust storm, our neighbors Joe and Sara decided to leave town. Times were hard, and people no longer bought as many shoes from Joe as they once did. I watched sadly as they loaded up their car to go to California. With Sara gone, I didn't know who I'd borrow sugar from or trade canning recipes with anymore. I didn't know who I would talk with about the latest gossip, or about my own silly ideas.

**Basic situation:** _____

**My own experience:** _____

**How I would react:** _____

© Pearson Education, Inc., publishing as Pearson Prentice Hall.

# Identifying With a Character

Assess

**A**  Describe the basic situation in each of these selections. To identify the basic situation, leave out details that are specific to the time and place of the story.

The tent flap opened. In walked a young soldier, the latest to join Washington's forces. He looked around nervously at the weary veterans resting there. One waved him in. "Don't be shy, son," he said. "The cold is likelier to kill you than we are."

**1. Basic situation:** _____

Mistress Molly's young sister Sally had wandered off while they were picking berries, and Molly could not find her. The colonists quickly organized search parties. Soon, the group led by Molly let out a whoop of joy. Little Sally, her mouth smeared with red berries, had just come wandering out of the big hollow tree where she had fallen asleep.

**2. Basic situation:** _____

Bernard looked at his business partner, Marvin, in disbelief. "Marvin, I told you the market wasn't right for those fancy watches. I told you. Now you are telling me you bought a case of them?"
"Oh, I'm sorry, we're partners, but only you get to make the decisions, right?"

**3. Basic situation:** _____

**B**  For each situation in Exercise A, give a related experience of your own or of someone you know. Explain how you would react in the character's situation.

**1.** new soldier in Washington's camp

**My own experience:** _____

**How I would react:** _____

**2.** Mistress Molly

**My own experience:** _____

**How I would react:** _____

**3.** Bernard

**My own experience:** _____

**How I would react:** _____

© Pearson Education, Inc., publishing as Pearson Prentice Hall.

# Imagery

**Imagery** refers to language that uses **images**, words and phrases that appeal to one or more of the senses of sight, hearing, touch, taste, or smell. For example, these lines from the Chinese poem "Thick Grow the Rush Leaves" contain images that appeal to the senses of sight and touch: "Thick grow the rush leaves; / Their white dew turns to frost." The poet tells you how something looks: "rush leaves" growing close together. The poet also tells you how something feels: the coldness that makes dew turn "to frost."

As you read works of literature, **picture the imagery** by identifying the senses to which it appeals. Then, imagine the sensory experiences it describes. Here is an example:

| Images from Poem | Picturing the Imagery |
|---|---|
| "The stream swirls. The wind moans in / The pines. Gray rats scurry over / Broken tiles. . . ." <br>—from "Jade Flower Palace" by Tu Fu | I **see** water in the stream going round and round, the pines blown by the wind, and a gray rat running across cracked tiles. I **hear** the sad sound of the wind. |

**A** Circle the letter of the sense or senses to which the imagery mainly appeals.

1. "On the cypress mountain, / Autumn evening." (from tanka by Priest Jakuren)

   **A.** sight      **B.** hearing      **C.** touch      **D.** taste      **E.** smell

2. "Spring rain: / Soaking on the roof / A child's rag ball." (haiku by Yosa Buson)

   **A.** sight/touch      **B.** hearing/touch      **C.** touch/taste
   **D.** sight/taste      **E.** smell/sight

**B** For the following passage, write a brief description picturing the imagery.

   . . . the seaweed / whips around / the sea pushes through and rolls back— / the rocks seem motionless.

   —from "Pride" by Dahlia Ravikovitch

_____

_____

_____

© Pearson Education, Inc., publishing as Pearson Prentice Hall.

# Imagery

**A**  For each image, circle the letter of the sense to which it mainly appeals.

1. "While my hair was still cut straight across my forehead" (from "The River-Merchant's Wife" by Li Po, translated by Ezra Pound)

   **A.** touch        **B.** hearing        **C.** sight        **D.** taste        **E.** smell

2. "The river blew so cold" (from tanka by Ki Tsurayuki)

   **A.** sight        **B.** hearing        **C.** touch        **D.** taste        **E.** smell

3. "The cuckoo— / Its call stretching / Over the water" (from haiku by Matsuo Bashō)

   **A.** sight        **B.** hearing        **C.** touch        **D.** taste        **E.** smell

**B**  For each passage, write a brief description in which you picture the imagery.

1. "A youthful soldier, mouth agape, head bare, / . . . / Sleeps stretched in grass . . ."
   (from "The Sleeper in the Valley" by Arthur Rimbaud)

   _____

   _____

   _____

2. "Violins complain / Of autumn again, / They sob and moan." (from "Autumn Song" by Paul Verlaine)

   _____

   _____

   _____

3. "Vegetable peddlers shout in the street / And a yellow-sailed boat comes nearer the island . . ." (from "A Song on the End of the World" by Czeslaw Miłosz)

   _____

   _____

   _____

© Pearson Education, Inc., publishing as Pearson Prentice Hall.

# Indian Fable

A **fable** is a brief, simple tale that teaches a lesson. An **Indian fable** teaches a lesson about proper conduct in Indian culture. Fables often feature animal characters who behave like humans. Events in the fable point to a lesson called a **moral.** The moral may be stated directly or merely implied. If it is implied, you must use details from the fable to make an inference, or an informed guess, about the fable's message.

The characters in a fable often represent common human personality traits. For example, in fables from around the world, a smaller animal, such as a rabbit or a spider, uses quick wits to overcome larger, stronger animals. This type of character is known as a **trickster** figure.

**A**  In the blank, write *T* if the statement is true or *F* if it is false.

1. _____ A fable teaches lessons about proper conduct within a certain culture.

2. _____ The imagery that the writer of a fable uses is called the story's moral.

3. _____ A fable's lesson is always directly stated.

4. _____ Trickster figures never appear in fables.

**B**  Circle the letter of the item that best completes the statement or answers the question.

1. The hero in a fable

   **A.** is always a human being.       **B.** might well be an animal character.

2. Animal characters in fables.

   **A.** remain unrelated to the moral.       **B.** may illustrate the moral through their behavior.

3. The point of telling a fable is usually to

   **A.** teach.       **B.** inform.

4. From what you know about fables, which of the following might you expect in this type of story?

   **A.** tragedy       **B.** humor

© Pearson Education, Inc., publishing as Pearson Prentice Hall.

# Indian Fable

## Assess

**A**   In the blank, write *T* if the statement is true or *F* if it is false.

**1.** _____ A fable always contains a direct statement of the story's lesson.

**2.** _____ The most effective fables are those that remain independent of the values of the culture that produces them.

**3.** _____ You can usually expect that a fable will contain a moral or lesson.

**4.** _____ Animals characters may appear in fables, but they are usually not given human personality characteristics.

**5.** _____ In most fables from around the world, trickster figures are doomed to failure.

**B**   On the lines below, briefly tell why you think each situation would or would not be a good basis for a fable.

Two friends meet at the library. They share their reactions to a movie that they have both seen recently.

**1.** _____

_____

A lion meets a leopard and roars out a challenge. The smaller cat slyly flatters the lion for his impressive mane, then distracts him and steals his prey, bounding up a tree with it.

**2.** _____

_____

A young man is invited to attend a wedding. Although he knows that his hosts are very traditional, he dresses for the occasion as if he were going to a rock concert. When all the guests stare at him, he leaves the party in embarrassment.

**3.** _____

_____

© Pearson Education, Inc., publishing as Pearson Prentice Hall.

# Interpreting Imagery

Practice

Imagery is the use of language that appeals to one or more of the five senses and creates mental pictures for the reader. To **interpret an image,**

- identify which of the five senses it involves.
- classify the physical experience the image creates by the sight, sound, taste, smell, or sense of touch it evokes.
- define the emotion or idea the image conveys.

**A** For each image, circle the letter of the sense to which it mainly appeals.

**1.** gooey caramels stuck to the plush car seat

   **A.** sight      **B.** hearing      **C.** touch      **D.** taste      **E.** smell

**2.** trumpets blaring defiance to the enemy

   **A.** sight      **B.** hearing      **C.** touch      **D.** taste      **E.** smell

**3.** a shirt the color of flames

   **A.** sight      **B.** hearing      **C.** touch      **D.** taste      **E.** smell

**B** Identify an idea or emotion that each image evokes.

**1.** walking alone down a long, dark, silent street

_____

**2.** warm breeze, twittering birds, sunshine

_____

**3.** dark, damp, musty basement

_____

**4.** the taste of sweet, smooth, creamy chocolate

_____

**5.** being awakened in the middle of the night by the screaming of a siren

_____

© Pearson Education, Inc., publishing as Pearson Prentice Hall.

# Interpreting Imagery

Assess

**A** For each image, circle the letter of the sense to which it mainly appeals.

**1.** the sweet scent of freshly cut hay

    **A.** sight        **B.** hearing        **C.** touch        **D.** taste        **E.** smell

**2.** the rich, smoky sweetness of a chocolate-covered cherry

    **A.** sight        **B.** hearing        **C.** touch        **D.** taste        **E.** smell

**3.** scratchy wool pants brushing my legs like sandpaper

    **A.** sight        **B.** hearing        **C.** touch        **D.** taste        **E.** smell

**4.** a meadow of wildflowers waving gently in the summer breeze

    **A.** sight        **B.** hearing        **C.** touch        **D.** taste        **E.** smell

**5.** fingernails being raked down a chalkboard

    **A.** sight        **B.** hearing        **C.** touch        **D.** taste        **E.** smell

**B** On the line provided, list some words that describe the mood or general idea that each image creates.

**1.** Like a small, shy deer, the child peered out from behind its mother's skirts.

_____

**2.** At the signal, twenty silver warplanes ignited their engines, thundering the news of battle to the heavens.

_____

**3.** On a dark, moonless night, a tree branch taps against the windowpane.

_____

**4.** A man walks west down a dusty road, a silhouette against the setting sun.

_____

**5.** Sitting on the warm sand, I smiled as each new wave gently caressed my feet.

_____

© Pearson Education, Inc., publishing as Pearson Prentice Hall.

# Irony

**Irony** is the difference between what someone believes to be true and what actually is true. It can also be the difference between what someone expects and what actually happens. There are three main types of irony in literature:

- **Verbal irony** is the use of words to suggest the opposite of their usual meaning. *Example:* Friends call a bald man "Curly."

- **Situational irony** occurs when something happens that directly contradicts expectations. *Example:* Someone buys an expensive outfit for a party where the main activity turns out to be playing soccer in the mud.

- **Dramatic irony** occurs when the reader or the audience is aware of something that a character is not. *Example:* Fans watch as a confused player spikes the ball and starts a victory dance one foot short of the goal line while opposing linebackers close in.

---

Write *Verbal, Situational,* or *Dramatic* in the blank before each item that describes that type of irony. If an item does not contain irony, write *No irony.*

1. _____ In the second chapter of a book, a character named Gary leaves his house to take the bus, expecting to get to work on time. The reader has learned in the first chapter that the bus is not running that day.

2. _____ A construction worker who stands six feet, five inches tall and weighs 280 pounds is nicknamed Tiny.

3. _____ A woman adopts a dog small enough to fit in her purse and names him Tiny.

4. _____ In a play, Jose complains that his wife Josephine has forgotten the couple's anniversary. In Act I, however, Josephine showed her friend Inez the beautiful anniversary gift she bought to surprise Jose.

5. _____ A woman spends over an hour in the blazing sun watering the plants in her yard. As soon as she comes inside, it begins to rain.

6. _____ On a television show, a slightly crazy rich man gets ready to go out to eat. Meanwhile, at a restaurant, the waiters are talking about the health inspector who is due to arrive. When the rich man arrives at the restaurant, he starts talking to the waiter about germs. The waiter believes that he is the health inspector. He tells the other waiters. They all put on surgical masks to show the rich man that their restaurant is germ-free.

© Pearson Education, Inc., publishing as Pearson Prentice Hall.

# Irony

**A**  Write *Verbal*, *Situational*, or *Dramatic* in the blank before each item that describes that type of irony. If an item does not contain irony, write *No irony*.

**1.** _____ In the first chapter of a novel, the reader finds out that a man named Terence will lose everything he owns when he travels out west to find gold. In the second chapter, the reader meets Terence, who happily prepares to head west to seek his fortune.

**2.** _____ A mother takes her two young children to play in the park. They see a little boy who lives on their block. The three children play happily all afternoon.

**3.** _____ During the night, the house across the street from the fire station burns to the ground.

**4.** _____ A young man invites his parents to visit his first apartment. It is a small room on the sixth floor of a run-down building with no elevator. When his parents arrive, he says "Welcome to my palace!"

**B**  For each example of dramatic irony below, fill in the blanks to show the difference between what the character thinks is true and what the audience knows to be true.

**1.** In a play, Gina and Simone tell Carly that she will get the international music scholarship. In a later scene, Amanda asks Gina who will get the scholarship. "A very deserving woman who plays the piano beautifully." says Gina. Amanda, who plays the piano, thinks Gina means her. Later, Amanda tells her boyfriend that she has won and that they must break up because the scholarship requires her to move to another country.

**What Amanda thinks:** _____

**What the audience knows:** _____

**2.** In a book, the reader learns in the first chapter that Marcus will be getting a new computer from his parents as a surprise graduation gift. In the second chapter, Marcus decides he needs a new computer badly and spends all his savings to buy one.

**What Marcus thinks:** _____

**What the reader knows:** _____

© Pearson Education, Inc., publishing as Pearson Prentice Hall.

# Japanese Poetic Forms

## Practice

Traditional **Japanese verse forms** include two important types of poem, each with strict formal requirements. (English translations of these poems may break some of these rules.)

- A **tanka** consists of five lines. The lines have five, seven, five, seven, and seven syllables. A tanka tells a brief story or expresses a single thought or insight, often about love or nature. Most tanka include at least one **caesura,** or pause, which is often indicated by punctuation in English translations.

- A **haiku** consists of three lines of five, seven, and five syllables in the original Japanese. Haiku usually focus on some aspect of nature and often include a *kigo,* or seasonal word like "snow" or "cherry blossom" to indicate the time of year being described. Most haiku present a comparison or contrast of two images, actions, or states of being.

Tanka and haiku poets convey a great deal of meaning in a small number of words by using vivid **imagery**, or language that appeals to the five senses: sight, hearing, smell, taste, and touch.

In the spaces provided, write *T* if the statement is true or *F* if it is false.

1. _____ The subject of a tanka is often love or nature.

2. _____ In the original Japanese, a tanka has a total of 31 syllables.

3. _____ A tanka is always shorter than a haiku.

4. _____ A haiku is composed of five lines.

5. _____ Sensory imagery is usually unimportant in tanka and haiku.

6. _____ Tanka and haiku are alike in that they often relate to some aspect of nature.

7. _____ Comparison and contrast are often features of haiku.

8. _____ A *kigo* is a seasonal word, indicating a setting at a particular time of year.

9. _____ Tanka never contain a caesura, or pause.

10. _____ The total number of syllables in a haiku is 17.

© Pearson Education, Inc., publishing as Pearson Prentice Hall.

# Japanese Poetic Forms

Assess

**A** For each item in Column A, write the letter of the item in Column B that makes the best match.

**Column A**

1. _____ tanka
2. _____ sensory imagery
3. _____ *kigo*
4. _____ caesura

**Column B**

**A.** sight, hearing, smell, taste, touch
**B.** 31 syllables
**C.** tanka
**D.** haiku

**B** Read the following poems, and complete the activities.

1. Write three reasons that the lines qualify as a haiku.

> Autumn clouds descend—
> Temple bells on the hillside—
> My heart awakens.

_____

_____

_____

2. Write two reasons that the following poem qualifies as a tanka. Then, explain one way in which this translation does not follow the rules for tanka.

> When I went to visit
> The girl I love so much,
> That winter night
> The river blew so cold
> That the plovers were crying
>            –Ki Tsurayuki, translated by Geoffrey Bownas

_____

_____

_____

_____

© Pearson Education, Inc., publishing as Pearson Prentice Hall.

# Journal

## Practice

A **journal** is a day-by-day account of the writer's thoughts and experiences. Reading a journal from the past can help readers understand the culture and the historical period in which the journal was written. A journal can also give clues about the writer's personality.

Journals are usually for personal use. However, many journals, such as those of early explorers, give accounts of events and provide valuable details that only a participant or an eyewitness can supply. When journals are written for a particular audience, the writer may color the details to give a particular impression.

**A**    Read the example, and then respond to the items that follow.

> **Nov. 3, 200_** It's the last day before the election. The mood at campaign headquarters is tense again. Joe is ahead in the polls, but workers are feeling the pressure and snapping at one another. Ken Barber tried to take over the operation, but I persuaded him to cooperate and go with the original plan.

**1.** What situation does the writer describe in this journal entry?

_____

**2.** List two details that describe the atmosphere. _____

_____

**3.** Do you think the writer might intend to publish this journal entry for others

to read? Why or why not? _____

_____

**B**    Write *T* if an item is true or *F* if an item is false.

**1.** _____ In a journal entry, the writer uses the pronoun *I*.

**2.** _____ A journal is a form of correspondence between two people.

**3.** _____ Journals contain details about day-to-day life.

**4.** _____ In journal entries, writers often describe their personal thoughts and experiences.

© Pearson Education, Inc., publishing as Pearson Prentice Hall.

## Journal

Assess

**A** Put a check mark next to the characteristics that describe a journal.

**1.** ____ includes details of day-to-day life

**2.** ____ is told from the point of view of a fictional character

**3.** ____ gives clues about the writer's personality

**4.** ____ can help readers understand a culture or time period

**5.** ____ never includes the writer's opinions or personal beliefs

**6.** ____ can create an impression of a time, a place, or an event

**B** Read the journal passages. Then, respond to the items that follow.

The melody of the birds was so exquisite that one was never willing to part from the spot. . . . A thousand different sorts of trees, with their fruit, were to be met with, and of a wonderfully delicious odor.
—from *Journal of the First Voyage to America* by Christopher Columbus

**1.** What is Columbus's attitude toward the scene he describes?

_____

**2.** List two words that reveal his attitude.

_____

At this time men were often drilled in company . . . long before they learned the manual of arms, because of the difficulty of obtaining muskets. . . . [W]e would willingly have resigned [the muskets] after carrying them a few hours. The musket, after an hour's drill, seemed heavier and less ornamental than it had looked to be.
—from "Recollections of a Private" by Warren Lee Goss

**3.** This journal entry was written by a Civil War soldier. What is one historical detail the journal reveals about the war?

_____

**4.** How does Goss feel about performing drills while carrying a musket?

_____

© Pearson Education, Inc., publishing as Pearson Prentice Hall.

Name _____ Date _____

# Locating Information Using Maps and Atlases

**Atlases** provide a variety of information. Some information is presented graphically. For example, towns with a population of over 100,000 people may be marked on a map with a special symbol. To locate the information you need, decide what category it falls under. For example, information about how many people live in a country falls under the category of "population." Then, scan for headings that concern that category. Also, study the legend, or key, to the map. The legend will explain the symbols used on the map and the kind of information found there.

> Read the following atlas entry. Then, answer the questions.

### EAST ASIA

China: Quick Fact
China is the world's third-largest country and a major industrial nation.

### Population
    Most of China's one billion people live in the eastern part of the country, where climate is most favorable. Urban areas there house more than 250 million people. Almost 75% of the population, though, live in villages and farm the land.

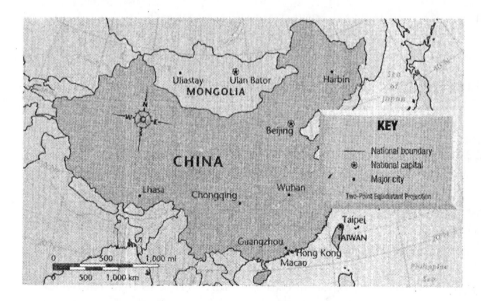

1. How do most people in China make a living? _____

2. Under what heading did you find the answer to question 1? _____

3. What symbol is used to indicate China's capital? _____

© Pearson Education, Inc., publishing as Pearson Prentice Hall.

Name _____ Date _____

# Locating Information Using Maps and Atlases

Assess

Read the following atlas entry. Then, answer the questions.

## NORTHERN AFRICA
### Geography
Bordering the northern coast of the African continent, Morocco, Algeria, and Tunisia are home to the high Atlas Mountains. To the east lie Libya and Egypt, also bordering the sea. Both countries are largely desert, though the Nile River in Egypt keeps the surrounding land fertile.

### Population
The main population centers of Morocco, Algeria, and Tunisia are located in large coastal cities and farming towns. Though large in size, Libya has a population of only 5.7 million compared to 77 million in Egypt, whose Nile River provides fertile ground for 98% of its population.

**1.** Why do more people live in Egypt than in Libya? _____

_____

**2.** Under what heading did you find the answer to question 1? _____

**3.** What symbol is used to indicate Libya's capital? _____

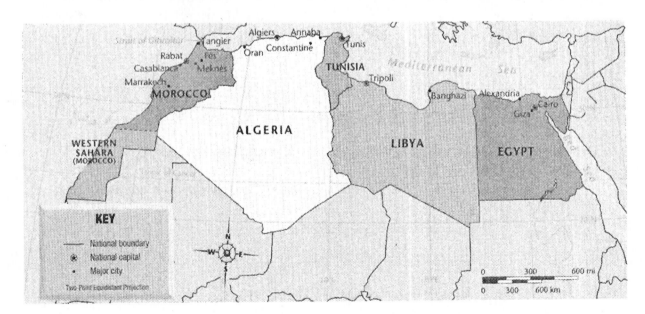

# Lyric Poetry

Every poem has a **speaker,** the character or voice that "says" its words. **Lyric poetry** is poetry in which a single speaker makes observations or expresses feelings and insights. Unlike narrative poetry, lyric poetry does not tell a complete story. Instead, it focuses on creating a main impression or a mood (a general feeling). A lyric poem may also build to a moment of insight called an **epiphany,** in which the speaker sees something clearly.

The following example is taken from the lyric poem "The Road Not Taken" by Robert Frost. The speaker comes to a fork in a path and realizes that he can take only one of the two roads.

> Two roads diverged in a wood, and I— / I took the one less traveled by, / And that has made all the difference.

In this example, the speaker has an epiphany about his life. He chose a path in life that was not "well traveled"—an uncommon choice. His whole life has been determined by that choice.

For each passage from a lyric poem, tell what main impression, feeling, or insight the poem conveys.

The sky is low. / The wind is gray. The radiator / Purrs all day.
            —from "January" by John Updike

**1.** _____

_____

_____

She spoke a tongue I knew no word of, / and I was sad I could not understand, / but I could hug her.
            —from "Grandma Ling" by Amy Ling

**2.** _____

_____

_____

© Pearson Education, Inc., publishing as Pearson Prentice Hall.

# Lyric Poetry

Assess

**A** In the blank, write *T* if the statement is true or *F* if it is false.

**1.** _____ A lyric poem tells a detailed, complete story.

**2.** _____ In a lyric poem, a single speaker presents his or her feelings or observations.

**3.** _____ An epiphany is a moment of insight or a realization.

**B** For each passage from a lyric poem, tell what main impression, feeling, or insight the poem conveys.

It won't all end in tears and blood. Today is heavy with tomorrow— / the future was planted yesterday. / Hope is a burden all of us shoulder / though we might stumble under the load.

—from "Also All" by Shu Ting

**1.** _____

_____

_____

My eyes grew dim, and I could no more gaze; / A wave of longing through my body swept, / And, hungry for the old familiar ways / I turned aside and bowed my head and wept.

—from "The Tropics in New York" by Claude McKay

**2.** _____

_____

_____

Ah, love, let us be true / To one another! For the world, which seems / To lie before us like a land of dreams, / So various, so beautiful, so new, / Hath really neither joy, nor love, nor light, / Nor certitude, nor peace, nor help for pain. . . .

—from "Dover Beach" by Matthew Arnold

**3.** _____

_____

_____

© Pearson Education, Inc., publishing as Pearson Prentice Hall.

# Magical Realism

**Magical realism** is writing that combines realistic events with fantasy, including elements of myth, magic, and marvels of nature. Magical realism arose in Latin American in the 1940s.

**A** Answer the following questions.

1. Based on the following titles, which story would you expect to contain elements of magical realism?

   **A.** In the Mountains on a Summer Day
   **B.** A Very Old Man With Enormous Wings
   **C.** The Return of the Wanderers

2. Which detail in the following passage transforms an otherwise realistic event—the dressing of a dead man—into something magical and strange?

   There had not been enough canvas, the poorly cut and worse sewn pants were too tight, and the hidden strength of his heart popped the buttons on his shirt.

   —"The Handsomest Drowned Man in the World" by
   Gabriel García Márquez

---

**B** Read the following passage from "The Handsomest Drowned Man in the World" by Gabriel García Márquez, a story about a drowned giant whose body washes ashore. Then, complete the chart by listing elements of fantasy and realism in the passage.

They wanted to tie the anchor from a cargo ship to [the giant's body] so that he would sink easily into the deepest waves, where fish are blind and divers die of nostalgia, and bad currents would not bring him back to shore, as had happened with other bodies.

| Fantasy | Reality |
|---|---|
|  |  |

© Pearson Education, Inc., publishing as Pearson Prentice Hall.

# Magical Realism

Assess

**A**  Choose the letter of the best answer to each question.

**1.** To what does magical realism refer?

    **A.** factual events so unbelievable as to seem magical

    **B.** the combination of realistic events with elements of fantasy

    **C.** a work of pure fantasy with no basis in fact

    **D.** realistic events in which magic almost never occurs

**2.** Where did magical realism originate?

    **A.** China in the 800s

    **B.** North America in the 1820s

    **C.** Latin America in the 1940s

    **D.** Europe in the 1990s

**B**  Read the following passage from "The Handsomest Drowned Man in the World" by Gabriel García Márquez, a story about a drowned giant whose body washes ashore. Then, follow the directions.

    They thought that if that magnificent man [the giant] had lived in the village, his house would have had the widest doors, the highest ceilings, and the strongest floor, his bedstead would have been made from a midship frame held together by iron bolts, and his wife would have been the happiest of women. They thought that he would have had so much authority that he could have drawn fish out of the sea simply by calling their names and that he would have put so much work into his land that springs would have burst forth from among the rocks so that he would have been able to plant flowers on the cliffs.

**1.** List two instances of magical ideas in the above passage.

_____

_____

**2.** List three details in the passage that are based in reality.

_____

_____

_____

© Pearson Education, Inc., publishing as Pearson Prentice Hall.

# Making Generalizations

A **generalization** is a broad statement that applies to many examples and is supported by details or evidence. The statement that "dogs make good pets" is a generalization. It applies to dogs in general. You can support it with details about dogs who have made good pets. You can **make generalizations** when reading by noticing clues to an author's beliefs or ideas. See, for example, how three details from Rumi's "The Guest House," translated by Coleman Barks, lead to a generalization:

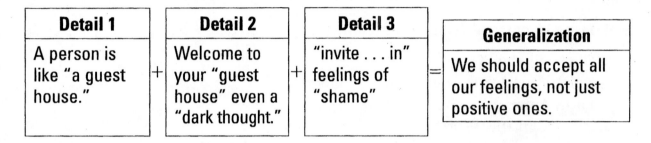

| Detail 1 | | Detail 2 | | Detail 3 | | Generalization |
|---|---|---|---|---|---|---|
| A person is like "a guest house." | + | Welcome to your "guest house" even a "dark thought." | + | "invite . . . in" feelings of "shame" | = | We should accept all our feelings, not just positive ones. |

■ Following are details from Rumi's poem "Elephant in the Dark," translated by Coleman Barks. Circle the number of the generalization that is best supported by these details. Then, explain your answer.

    **Details from poem:** An elephant is in a completely dark room. People who have never seen an elephant will try to figure out what it is. They go into the room one by one. Each touches a different part of the animal: trunk, ear, leg, or tusk. Each person's description of the elephant is based on the part he or she touches. The person who touched the trunk says the elephant is like a snake. The one who touches the tusk says the elephant is like a sword. The poet concludes by saying that if each "held a candle" and they "went in together," they would "see" the elephant.

1. Areas where people rely on candles rather than electricity are at a disadvantage.

2. The sense of sight is always much more reliable than the sense of touch.

3. To understand reality, people must cooperate and use the light of wisdom.

4. An elephant is a very mysterious beast because it is so large.

_____

_____

_____

© Pearson Education, Inc., publishing as Pearson Prentice Hall.

## Making Generalizations

Assess

**A** Circle the number of the statement that is a generalization about the poet Rumi. Then, on the lines below, explain how you know it is a generalization.

1. Rumi belonged to a spiritual community known as the "Whirling Dervishes."
2. Rumi lived from 1207 to 1273.
3. Rumi's poems often praise the value of solitude.

_____

_____

**B** Below is a generalization about the poet Rumi. Circle the number of the detail you would use to support this generalization. Then, explain your choice.

Generalization: Rumi valued spiritual experience more than book learning.

1. sales figures for his books, showing the popularity of his work
2. stories about him that demonstrate his powerful spiritual feelings
3. poems in which he says that spirituality is more valuable than book learning

_____

_____

_____

**C** Following are details from Rumi's poem "Two Kinds of Intelligence." Circle the number of the generalization that is best supported by these details. Then, explain your answer.

Details from poem: There are two kinds of intelligence. One is based on memorizing facts from books. This kind of intelligence helps you get ahead in the world. The second kind of intelligence is already inside you. It is like a fountain that is always fresh.

1. Study hard in school, and you will get ahead.
2. Learn to trust your own inner sense of the world.
3. There is no point at all in studying facts.

_____

_____

© Pearson Education, Inc., publishing as Pearson Prentice Hall.

# Metaphor

A **metaphor** is a figure of speech that compares two apparently unlike things without using the words *like* or *as*. **Direct metaphors** directly name the two things being compared. **Implied metaphors** only suggest the comparison. In an implied metaphor, the writer describes one thing using ideas and terms that usually describe something else.

Direct metaphor: John is a peacock.

Implied metaphor: John swelled and ruffled his feathers.

An **extended metaphor** compares several aspects of the two things, not just one.

Extended Metaphor: The waves charged the shore, snarling and snapping at the sand. As soon as they struck, though, their courage fled, and they went whimpering back out to the sea. *(The waves are compared to dogs.)*

Read each sentence. Then, write *D* if the metaphor is direct, *I* if the metaphor is implied, or *E* if the metaphor is extended.

1. _____ My teardrop was morning dew running down my cheek.

2. _____ Rachel is a lighthouse guiding her fellow workers.

3. _____ The student's daily tardiness made the teacher boiling mad.

4. _____ The wind blew tuneful melodies across the tall grasses, while the woodpeckers kept rhythm with the beat they drummed on the trees.

5. _____ The cat flew across the backyard.

6. _____ The snarling and hissing of the flames grew louder as it raced down the hallway.

© Pearson Education, Inc., publishing as Pearson Prentice Hall.

# Metaphor

**A**  Read the following statements. Write *T* if the statement is true or *F* if the statement is false.

**1.** ____ Metaphors use the words *like* and *as.*

**2.** ____ Most metaphors are long.

**3.** ____ Implied metaphors directly compare two unlike things.

**4.** ____ An extended metaphor compares several aspects of two things.

**B**  For each metaphor, write *D* if it is direct or *I* if is implied. If the metaphor is extended, add *E* to your answer.

**1.** _____ (*This metaphor compares a volcano to an old woman.*) "Around her machinery growls, / snarls and plows / great patches / of her skin. / She crouches / in the north, / her trembling / the source / of dawn. / Light appears / with the shudder / of her slopes, / the movement / of her arm." (from "Loo Wit" by Wendy Rose)

**2.** _____ "Life is but a toy that swings on a bright gold chain / Ticking for a little while / To amuse a fascinated infant, / Until the keeper, a very old man, / Becomes tired of the game / And lets the watch run down." ("Life" by Naomi Long Madgett)

**C**  Read the passage. Respond to the items that follow.

The fire's orange claws reached in and around the door. The snarling and hissing of the flames grew louder as it raced down the hallway. Suddenly, it burst through a window with its flaming mane, sending slivers of glass falling to the ground below.

**1.** Circle the words that suggest a comparison between the fire and an animal.

**2.** Which animal is most likely being compared to the fire?

    **A.** a hungry dog       **B.** a tired bear       **C.** an angry lion

© Pearson Education, Inc., publishing as Pearson Prentice Hall.

# Modern Realistic Drama

### Practice

**Modern realistic drama** refers to plays written from the nineteenth century on that have these characteristics:

- The playwright tries to capture how people actually talk. These plays are written in prose, not verse.

- The drama depicts characters and situations as they really are, not as we might imagine or wish them to be.

- The drama may address a controversial issue. For example, the plays of Henrik Ibsen addressed issues such as women's rights, a shocking subject in his day.

- The drama may challenge common values and assumptions of society.

- The leading characters typically experience both internal and external **conflicts,** or struggles between opposing forces.

Read the following ideas for a drama. Briefly explain whether each situation is or is not suitable for a modern realistic drama.

1. A hero of superhuman strength squares off against a villain who wants to rule the world. Their conflict will decide the future of the human race.

_____

_____

2. Nan prepares mentally for the championship race. She realizes that, in order to win, she will have to beat Ellie. She also realizes that she both admires and fears Ellie.

_____

_____

3. Kayla does not understand why all the stores in her neighborhood are owned by people who do not live there. The stores charge prices that she thinks are unfair, so she decides to organize a boycott. As the boycott is underway, she meets the son of the owner of one of the stores and falls in love with him.

_____

_____

© Pearson Education, Inc., publishing as Pearson Prentice Hall.

# Modern Realistic Drama

Assess

**A** Circle the letter of the item that best completes each statement.

**1.** Modern realistic drama is written in

    **A.** verse and prose.     **B.** verse.     **C.** ordinary language.

**2.** In modern realistic drama, you can expect to find an emphasis on

    **A.** conflict.     **B.** harmony.     **C.** personal opinions.

**3.** The issues in a modern realistic drama may best be described as

    **A.** technical.     **B.** controversial.     **C.** straightforward.

**4.** In modern realistic drama, you might expect to find as a character

    **A.** a superhero.     **B.** a giant.     **C.** an ordinary housewife.

**B** Read the following ideas for a drama. Briefly explain whether each situation is or is not suitable for a modern realistic drama.

**1.** A woman is offered a job as a college professor in a distant city. Her husband is a well-paid engineer, but he might find it hard to get such a good job if the couple moves.

_____

_____

**2.** A water purity expert finds that a small town's water supply has been severely contaminated. The mayor, however, is concerned about the town's reputation as a seaside resort. With the support of many of the influential townspeople, he urges the expert to remain silent.

_____

_____

**3.** A larger-than-life hero embarks on a quest for the legendary Fountain of Youth. Although she fails in the end, we are thrilled by her heroic quest.

_____

_____

© Pearson Education, Inc., publishing as Pearson Prentice Hall.

# Modernism

## Practice

In the late 1800s and early 1900s, many writers began turning away from the style, form, and content of the familiar literature of their time. Instead, they found new themes and startling new techniques in a movement known as Modernism. Most Modernist works share certain characteristics:

- They attempt to capture the realities of modern life.
- They express uncertainty and alienation, a feeling of not being at home in society.
- Rather than sending a straightforward message, they leave readers to draw their own conclusions.

**A**   Circle the best answer to each question below.

1. Which of the following accurately describes the attitude of early Modernists?

   **A.** They accepted the literature of their time, but they wanted to update it.
   **B.** They rejected the style, form, and content of the literature of their time.

2. Modernist literature is characterized by which of the following?

   **A.** uncertainty and alienation           **B.** amusing humor

3. What approach should one take when reading Modernist works?

   **A.** look for familiar themes           **B.** draw one's own conclusions

**B**   In the blank, write *T* if the statement is true or *F* if it is false.

1. _____ In general, Modernist writers may be expected to reflect the values of their society.

2. _____ Modernist writers typically conclude their works with an explicit statement of their theme, or overall message.

3. _____ In a Modernist novel or play, you might expect the characters to talk as they would in real life.

4. _____ The prevailing mood of a Modernist work might be predicted to be strongly optimistic and upbeat.

© Pearson Education, Inc., publishing as Pearson Prentice Hall.

# Modernism

**A**  In the blank, write **T** if the statement is true or **F** if it is false.

1. _____ Modernist fiction often presents sentimental, idealized plots that show the world as it might be, rather than as it really is.

2. _____ Modernism came into being as a result of a strong reaction against traditional styles and forms.

3. _____ A Modernist writer might be expected to express and agree with the values and standards of his or her society.

4. _____ Modernist writers generally leave readers to draw their own conclusions.

**B**  For the items below, circle the letter of the answer that correctly fills in the blank.

1. Modernist writers attempted to capture the _____ of modern life.

   **A.** realities                **B.** hopes and dreams

2. The attitude of most Modernists toward the past was one of

   _____.

   **A.** rejection               **B.** obedience

3. The period from _____ witnessed the rise and flowering of Modernism.

   **A.** 1500 to 1633            **B.** 1890 to 1930

4. A Modernist writer is likeliest to tell a story using _____.

   **A.** a traditional narrator   **B.** the confused flow of a character's thoughts

5. A Modernist poem is likeliest to present ideas in _____.

   **A.** a series of fragmented images   **B.** a clever, amusing argument

6. A Modernist painting is likeliest to present a scene _____.

   **A.** from a perspective that shows its tranquil beauty   **B.** by showing several different perspectives on the scene

© Pearson Education, Inc., publishing as Pearson Prentice Hall.

# Monologue

A **monologue** is a long and revealing speech by one character. As you read monologues, look for statements that reveal the character of the speaker.

**Read the passage, and then answer the questions that follow.**

There are a few people in our neighborhood whom some might call nosy, and I can see their point. Some prefer to keep their business to themselves and not have to answer to anyone. Others, however, find comfort in a friendly, inquisitive neighbor. They feel someone is paying attention, interested in their well-being, even looking out for them. Being gone most of the day, I certainly appreciate having neighbors who know when something out of the ordinary is happening. I know they will alert the authorities to suspicious activities, and that gives me peace of mind.

1. Which of the following could be used to describe the person who speaks in this monologue?

   **A.** suspicious and defensive
   **B.** mean and unfriendly
   **C.** open-minded and appreciative
   **D.** nosy and loud

2. Which statement backs up your answer to item 1?

   **A.** I know they will alert the authorities to suspicious activities.
   **B.** I certainly appreciate having neighbors who know when something out of the ordinary is happening.
   **C.** I can see their point.
   **D.** Some prefer to keep their business to themselves.

3. What can you learn by listening to a monologue?

   **A.** how old the speaker is
   **B.** something about the speaker's character
   **C.** something about the speaker's looks
   **D.** what part of the country the speaker is from

© Pearson Education, Inc., publishing as Pearson Prentice Hall.

# Monologue

Assess

**A** On the lines below, briefly tell why you think each situation would or would not be suitable for a monologue.

1. A high-school senior telephones the boy she likes, and they make a date for dinner and a movie the following weekend.

    _____

2. A brother feels his sister is making the wrong decision, so he practices what he will say to her to change her mind.

    _____

3. Two close friends chat with each other while they enjoy watching a hockey game on television.

    _____

**B** Read the passage, and then answer the questions that follow.

We've worked really hard this year to create a sense of team spirit in debate club. We've looked at the issues from all angles. We've helped one another fine-tune our arguments. We've prepared and practiced. I just know all our hard work will pay off.

1. Which of the following best describes the speaker of this monologue?

    **A.** unfriendly
    **B.** optimistic
    **C.** silly
    **D.** accusing

2. Which statement backs up your answer to item 1?

    **A.** We've worked really hard this year.
    **B.** We've looked at the issues from all angles.
    **C.** I just know all our hard work will pay off.
    **D.** We've prepared and practiced.

© Pearson Education, Inc., publishing as Pearson Prentice Hall.

# Myth

**Myths** are stories that belong to ancient oral traditions. Before being written, myths were told from one generation to the next. Myths attempt to explain natural phenomena and to reflect on life's challenges. There are different types of myths, some of which are listed below:

- **origin** myths, which explain how the world began
- myths involving characters with **superhuman** qualities, such as gods or heroes such as Hercules, the Greek hero with the strength of many men
- **quest** myths, which involve a journey in search of knowledge or for a higher, perhaps mystical, purpose
- **transgression** myths, which tell of the breaking of an important rule. Pandora, for example, is warned never to open a box. When she breaks the rule and opens the box, she releases evil into the world.

Myths naturally reflect the culture of the people who created them. For example, the Greeks valued strong male leaders, thus their ruling god was Zeus, a father figure.

**Answer these questions about myths.**

1. Which is the best definition of myths?

   **A.** fairy tales for children
   **B.** stories that explained life for ancient peoples
   **C.** legends made for entertainment
   **D.** logical explanations of natural phenomena

2. What does an origin myth attempt to do?

   **A.** explain how the world began
   **B.** warn against breaking the rules
   **C.** feature a superhuman character
   **D.** describe a journey

3. What is the best definition of a transgression myth?

   **A.** a tale that tells of humanity's beginning
   **B.** a tale that tells of overcoming obstacles
   **C.** a tale that tells of how mankind got fire
   **D.** a tale that tells of a rule being broken

4. If a culture were ruled by a queen and a council of wise old women, what would most likely be included in their myths?

   **A.** a beautiful young sea god
   **B.** a wise, strong goddess
   **C.** a fierce, warlike god
   **D.** a vain and foolish goddess

© Pearson Education, Inc., publishing as Pearson Prentice Hall.

# Myth

Assess

Read this summary of the Greek myth of Phaëthon. Then, answer the questions that follow.

Phaëthon is the son of the god Apollo and the mortal woman Clymene. He often brags about his father, who drives the sun's golden chariot across the sky each day. When another boy accuses him of making false claims, Phaëthon visits his father to ask for proof.

Apollo promises to give Phaëthon anything he wants. When Phaëthon asks to guide the sun's chariot across the sky, Apollo warns him that he does not have the skills to handle such a difficult task. However, Phaëthon proudly insists. Shortly after Phaëthon sets out, he loses control, and the chariot swerves too close to Earth. The heat of the sun scorches the earth until Zeus finally hurls a thunderbolt at Phaëthon, sending him crashing to the ground.

**1.** What sort of myth is this?

**A.** an origin myth

**B.** a transgression myth

**C.** a quest myth

**D.** a myth featuring a hero

**2.** What rule does Phaëthon break?

**A.** Respect the feelings of others.

**B.** Do not be prideful.

**C.** Do not lie.

**D.** Do not steal horses.

**3.** What natural event might this myth explain?

**A.** a lunar eclipse

**B.** thunder and lightning

**C.** sunrise and sunset

**D.** a rainbow

**4.** After reading this passage, what would you say is one thing Greek culture admired?

**A.** good horsemanship

**B.** boastful youths

**C.** obedient sons

**D.** strong sunshine

**5.** What might this passage reveal about ancient Greek culture's idea of fatherhood?

**A.** Fathers are stern and harsh.

**B.** Fathers are loving and indulgent.

**C.** Fathers are not interested.

**D.** Fathers are misunderstood.

© Pearson Education, Inc., publishing as Pearson Prentice Hall.

# Narrative Account

**Narrative accounts** are stories about real-life events. They are usually written in the first person by authors who either participated in or directly witnessed the events. Often, the events described have important historical, scientific, or cultural significance. The authors usually include details that offer glimpses into the personal aspects of such public matters. For this reason, narrative accounts are often useful to historians and other scholars. Like other types of storytelling, narrative accounts are shaped by each writer's personal **narrative style.** This style is defined, in part, by these key elements:

- *Diction and syntax:* word choice and word order
  For example, one writer may describe a "brick-red scarf," while the other describes "a scarf of deepest crimson."

- *Sentence structure:* the length and type of sentences the author favors

**A**    For each question, circle the letter of the best answer.

1. Which is the best definition of a narrative account?

   **A.** imaginative work about the past
   **B.** personal tale mixing fantasy and reality
   **C.** story of real-life events, usually told by someone who was there
   **D.** scholarly report about historical, scientific, or cultural topics

2. Which are the key elements of a personal narrative style?

   **A.** word choice and descriptions
   **B.** first-person narration and personal details
   **C.** sentence length and style
   **D.** diction, syntax, and sentence structure

**B**    Read the narrative account below. Then, answer the questions.

> I thought the home team would fall apart before we even got started. We had never been defeated, so I thought it could never happen. I was wrong. At the bottom of the third inning, they were down by five runs. Then, they sent a new hitter out. I threw the ball. I heard a *thwack,* and the ball sailed into the outfield. By the end of the inning, they were ahead by three runs. On that green field that afternoon, I learned a lesson in humility.

What personal insight about a public event does the author share? Explain.

_____

_____

© Pearson Education, Inc., publishing as Pearson Prentice Hall.

# Narrative Account

**A**  For each item, circle the letter of the best answer.

1. Which is the most accurate definition of a narrative account?

    **A.** a true story based on research
    **B.** an imaginary story about real people and places
    **C.** a novel-like story about a historic event
    **D.** a first-person tale of real-life events

2. Narrative accounts are of interest to historians because they

    **A.** show that literature is important.
    **B.** prove a variety of theories.
    **C.** offer insight into important events.
    **D.** are written in an interesting style.

**B**  Read the passage. Answer the questions that follow.

We did not realize that the odd birds flitting above our heads would be such an important discovery. The purpose of the expedition had been to study the tiny monkeys that lived in that part of the jungle. One day, while setting up camp, Alicia noticed the peculiar birds filling the treetops above our heads. Even though they were very fast, she managed to photograph a few. It was not until we enlarged the pictures and studied them that we realized what we had found. The purpose of the expedition changed that day.

1. How do you know that this is a first-person narrative account?

_____

2. What is the purpose of this account? Underline a sentence that supports your answer.

_____

3. Why might a historian or other scholar want to read this narrative account?

_____

4. What personal insight into a public event does the writer provide?

_____

# Narrative Poetry

**Narrative poetry** is poetry that tells a story. Like other narrative forms, narrative poetry features characters and tells of their thoughts and actions. It also has a plot, or tells a series of events. These events take place in a setting, or a definite time and place. One type of narrative poetry is **epic poetry.** Epic poems are long poems, usually celebrating the deeds of gods or heroes.

Some epic poems, such as Ovid's *Metamorphoses*, retell **myths.** Myths are tales of gods and heroes. Myths often explain the causes of natural features, the origins of the world or a people, the origins of place names, or the reasons for a people's values, customs, and beliefs.

---

**A**  For each question, circle the letter of the best answer.

**1.** Which is the best definition of narrative poetry?

**A.** verse that tells a story

**B.** verse that expresses the thoughts of a single speaker

**C.** verse that expresses the values of a culture

**D.** verse that is rhythmic and memorable

**2.** Which is the best definition of an epic?

**A.** a long poem with a specific meter

**B.** a long song-like poem

**C.** a long poem about gods or heroes

**D.** a long poem explaining the causes of natural features

---

**B**  In myth, Daedalus and his son Icarus escape from Crete on wings made of wax and feathers. Icarus flies too close to the sun, and his wings melt. Read this passage from the poet Ovid's retelling of the myth. Then, respond to each item below.

> . . . And Daedalus
> Father no more, called "Icarus, where are you!
> Where are you, Icarus? Tell me where to find you!"
> And saw the wings on the waves, and cursed his talents,
> Buried the body in a tomb, and the land
> Was named for Icarus.

**1.** Circle one detail in the passage that reflects the setting. Underline one detail that describes what Daedalus thinks and one that describes what he does.

**2.** Myths often explain the origins of natural features, beliefs, or place names. What origin does this myth explain?

---

© Pearson Education, Inc., publishing as Pearson Prentice Hall.

## Narrative Poetry

Assess

**A** For each item, circle the letter of the answer that best completes the definition.

**1.** Narrative poetry is verse that

  **A.** tells stories of gods or heroes.       **C.** has a setting, characters, and plot.
  **B.** expresses the beliefs of a culture.     **D.** is structured as a song.

**2.** An epic is a

  **A.** short poem about a hero.          **C.** long poem that expresses the
  **B.** short poem that explains              thoughts of a single speaker.
     the origins of a culture.          **D.** long poem about gods or heroes.

**3.** Epic poetry based on myth might tell about

  **A.** a culture's origins.             **C.** everyday life in ancient times.
  **B.** romantic and tragic love.         **D.** modern-day heroes.

**B** Read the passage from Ovid's poetic retelling of the myth Daedalus and Icarus. Then, respond to each item.

They were over Samos, Juno's sacred island.
Delos and Paros toward the left, Lebinthus
Visible to the right, and another island,
Calymne, rich in honey. And the boy
Thought *This is wonderful!* And left his father,
Soared higher, higher, drawn to the vast heaven,
Nearer the sun, and the wax that held the wings
Melted in that fierce heat, and the bare arms,
Beat up and down in air, and lacking oarage[1]
Took hold of nothing. *Father!* he cried, and *Father!*
Until the blue sea hushed him, the dark water
Men call the Icarian now.

1. oars; something to help him catch the air.

**1.** Circle details in the passage that describe the setting of this narrative poem.

**2.** Underline details that describe the thoughts, statements, and actions of characters.

**3.** What feature often found in myths is evident in the last line of the passage?

© Pearson Education, Inc., publishing as Pearson Prentice Hall.

# Novella

Practice

A **novella** is a short prose tale. First written as early as the fourteenth century, the novella influenced the later development of the novel and the modern short story. Like other short prose stories, these novellas share the following elements: a **setting,** or specific time and place where events happen; well-developed **characters;** a **theme,** or a message about life; a **conflict,** or struggle between opposing forces; a **plot,** or series of related events, including a **climax,** or turning point, and a **resolution,** or solution to the conflict

Read this paragraph from the *Decameron* by Giovanni Boccaccio. Then, answer the questions and follow the directions.

In this way, spending far more than he could afford and deriving no profit in return, Federigo lost his entire fortune (as can easily happen) and reduced himself to poverty, being left with nothing other than a tiny little farm, which produced an income just sufficient for him to live very frugally, and one falcon of the finest breed in the whole world. Since he was as deeply in love as ever, and felt unable to go on living the sort of life in Florence to which he aspired, he moved out to Campi, where his little farm happened to be situated. Having settled in the country, he went hunting as often as possible with his falcon, and, without seeking assistance from anyone, he patiently resigned himself to a life of poverty.

1. Circle the details in the paragraph that identify the setting.

2. Which passage hints at Federigo's noble character? _____

_____

3. Underline the words and phrases in the following passage that reflect the themes of generosity and ideal love.

Thenceforth, finding himself married to this great lady with whom he was so deeply in love, and very rich into the bargain, Federigo managed his affairs more prudently, and lived with her in happiness to the end of his days.

4. The above passage provides information about the novella's

    **A.** setting.          **B.** main conflict.       **C.** climax.          **D.** resolution.

© Pearson Education, Inc., publishing as Pearson Prentice Hall.

# Novella

**A**  Circle the letter of the best answer to each question.

**1.** What is the definition of a novella?

   **A.** a brief tale that focuses on a single event in a character's life
   **B.** a novel-length work whose resolution offers a surprising twist
   **C.** a short tale with well-developed characters and plot
   **D.** a collection of short stories that revolve around a single theme

**2.** Which of the following elements do all novellas share?

   **A.** setting, characters, and plot
   **B.** themes of good versus evil
   **C.** poetic language
   **D.** a frame, or fictional background, that introduces the story

**B**  Read the following story summaries. Then, answer the questions.

   **Story A:** Julia owns a thriving small town video store. She worked hard to build her business and is proud that her store provides needed jobs in the area. One day, a representative for a video chain store offers to buy Julia's store for a lot of money. Julia is tempted to sell, but she feels that it would be bad for the town.

   **Story B:** Alan, a fashion photographer, hosts a lavish party in his New York City loft to raise money for hurricane victims. He invites famous models, celebrities, magazine editors, and area business leaders. A huge success, the party raises over a million dollars for the cause.

**1.** Describe the main character in Story A. _____

_____

**2.** Which story introduces a clear conflict, and what is that conflict?

_____

_____

**3.** Which of the following themes is likeliest to be explored in Story B?

   **A.** spite          **B.** jealousy          **C.** generosity          **D.** isolation

© Pearson Education, Inc., publishing as Pearson Prentice Hall.

# Paradox

A **paradox** is a statement that expresses contradictory ideas yet reveals a truth. A situation described by such a statement is also called a paradox. Here are examples of paradoxes:

> Young people cannot wait until they are grown up. Adults wish they were young again.

> The harder you work, the more money you make—and the less time you have to enjoy it.

Zen Buddhism is a school of Japanese thought that uses paradoxes in its teachings. Many Zen paradoxes show how people can be frustrated or held back by the way they look at life. By studying paradoxes, students of Zen hope to achieve greater insight and freedom.

**A** Write *P* for each item that states a paradox. Write *NP* for each item that does not.

1. _____ It is cruel to be kind.

2. _____ Early to bed and early to rise, makes a man healthy, wealthy, and wise.

3. _____ The more time we are apart, the better I like you.

**B** Describe the two contradictory ideas demonstrated in the following paradox. Then, explain what truth or lesson the paradox suggests.

The teacher sends his student to draw a fish. The student studies the fish carefully and draws every detail. The master, though, says the drawing is not lifelike. The student goes back, studies the fish, and tries again. Again, the master rejects the drawing. The student tries again and again for days, but the master rejects each drawing. Finally, the student returns to find that the fish has completely rotted away. Only the skeleton is left. The student quickly draws the fish as he remembers it. The master looks at this drawing and says, "Perfect."

**Idea 1:** _____

**Idea 2:** _____

**Truth or Lesson:** _____

_____

© Pearson Education, Inc., publishing as Pearson Prentice Hall.

Name _____ Date _____

# Paradox

Assess

**A** Write *P* for each item that states a paradox. Write *NP* for each item that does not.

**1.** _____ The harder you work, the happier you will be.

**2.** _____ The harder you try to be happy, the less happy you will be.

**3.** _____ The more you get, the more you want.

**B** For each situation, write the letter of the paradox that best describes it.

**1.** _____ The man at the gas station gave such long, detailed directions that the driver was completely confused.

**2.** _____ For years, Al dreamed of owning a fancy car. He read car magazines and collected models. Finally, he bought a fancy car. He felt sad and empty.

**3.** _____ Sara studied writing with a famous writer and imitated his style. He complained about everything she wrote, though. In frustration, she wrote a book in her own style. Everyone loved it.

**A.** The best teacher teaches students to find their own way.

**B.** It is better to have a dream than to have a dream fulfilled.

**C.** Less is more.

**C** Describe the two contradictory ideas that are demonstrated in the following paradox. Then, explain what truth or lesson the paradox suggests.

A wise man visiting a school asked a group of students what the best way to live is. Each student in turn proudly recited his best ideas. Each quoted from difficult books to show his great learning. Each listened with envy as the other students spoke. Just then, a small boy ran into the room, laughing as he chased a ball. "Ah," said the wise man, "I see your teacher has arrived."

**Idea 1:** _____

**Idea 2:** _____

**Truth or Lesson:** _____

_____

# Parallelism

## Practice

**Parallelism** is the repetition of words, phrases, clauses, or sentences that have the same grammatical structure or the same meaning. Also known as parallel structure, it is a rhetorical device used in poetry, speeches, and other types of writing. It is used to balance related ideas, to stress contrasting ones, or to create a memorable rhythm.

Read the following excerpts from famous speeches. Write *Parallelism* in the blank before each item that contains parallelism. Write *No parallelism* in the blank before each item that does not contain parallelism.

1. _____ We have petitioned and our petitions have been scorned. We have entreated and our entreaties have been disregarded. We have begged and they have mocked when our calamity came. We beg no longer. We entreat no more. We petition no more. We defy them. (from William Jennings Bryan's Cross of Gold speech, 1896)

2. _____ Our progress out of the depression is obvious. But that is not all that you and I mean by the new order of things. Our pledge was not merely to do a patchwork job with secondhand materials. By using the new materials of social justice we have undertaken to erect on the old foundations a more enduring structure for the better use of future generations. (from Franklin D. Roosevelt's Second Inaugural Address, 1937)

3. _____ Now, so there will be no misunderstanding, it is not my intention to do away with government. It is, rather, to make it work—work with us, not over us; to stand by our side, not ride on our back. Government can and must provide opportunity, not smother it; foster productivity, not stifle it. (from Ronald Reagan's First Inaugural Address, 1981)

4. _____ We may not share a common past, but we surely do share a common future. Building one America is our most important mission, the foundation for many generations of every other strength we must build for this new century. Money cannot buy it, power cannot compel it, technology cannot create it. It can only come from the human spirit. (from William Clinton's State of the Union address, 1998)

© Pearson Education, Inc., publishing as Pearson Prentice Hall.

# Parallelism

Read the Gettysburg Address, a speech delivered by President Abraham Lincoln on November 19, 1863. Underline any examples of parallelism that you see in the speech. Then, answer the question that follows.

### Gettysburg Address

Four score and seven years ago our fathers brought forth on this continent, a new nation, conceived in Liberty, and dedicated to the proposition that all men are created equal.

Now we are engaged in a great civil war, testing whether that nation, or any nation so conceived and so dedicated, can long endure. We are met on a great battle-field of that war. We have come to dedicate a portion of that field, as a final resting place for those who here gave their lives that that nation might live. It is altogether fitting and proper that we should do this.

But, in a larger sense, we can not dedicate—we can not consecrate—we can not hallow—this ground. The brave men, living and dead, who struggled here, have consecrated it, far above our poor power to add or detract. The world will little note, nor long remember what we say here, but it can never forget what they did here. It is for us the living, rather, to be dedicated here to the unfinished work which they who fought here have thus far so nobly advanced. It is rather for us to be here dedicated to the great task remaining before us—that from these honored dead we take increased devotion to that cause for which they gave the last full measure of devotion—that we here highly resolve that these dead shall not have died in vain—that this nation, under God, shall have a new birth of freedom—and that government of the people, by the people, for the people, shall not perish from the earth.

How does parallelism increase the effectiveness of the Gettysburg Address?

_____

_____

_____

_____

_____

_____

_____

© Pearson Education, Inc., publishing as Pearson Prentice Hall.

# Paraphrasing

To **paraphrase** means to restate something in your own words. Paraphrasing can often help you understand poetry, which sometimes contains difficult passages and ideas. If you are unsure of a poem's meaning, reread the difficult parts. Follow these steps:

- Look up unfamiliar words and replace them with words you know.
- Look for the main idea of the passage.
- Restate the line or passage using your own everyday words.
- Reread the passage to check that your version accurately restates the meaning.

**A** Read the following lines from "This Moment Yearning and Thoughtful" by Walt Whitman. Then, answer the questions. Use your dictionary if you need help.

This moment yearning and thoughtful sitting alone,
It seems to me there are other men in other lands yearning
    and thoughtful,
It seems to me I can look over and behold them in Germany,
    Italy, France, Spain,
Or far, far away, in China, or in Russia or Japan, talking other
    dialects,
And it seems to me if I could know those men I should become
    attached to them as I do to men in my own lands,
O I know we should be brethren. . . .

1. What is the meaning of the word *yearning*? _____

2. What is the meaning of the word *behold*? _____

3. What is the meaning of the word *brethren*? _____

4. What is the meaning of the word *dialects*? _____

5. What is the main idea of this passage? _____

_____

**B** On a separate sheet of paper, write your own paraphrase of these lines from "This Moment Yearning and Thoughtful."

© Pearson Education, Inc., publishing as Pearson Prentice Hall.

# Paraphrasing

**A** Read the following lines from "The Ecchoing Green" by William Blake. Then, answer the questions. Use your dictionary if you need help.

The Sun does arise,
And make happy the skies.
The merry bells ring
To welcome the Spring.
The sky-lark and thrush,
The birds of the bush,
Sing louder around,
To the bells' cheerful sound.
While our sports shall be seen
On the Ecchoing Green.

Till the little ones weary
No more can be merry.
The sun does descend,
And our sports have an end. . . .

**1.** The word *ecchoing* is an old-fashioned spelling of which word? _____

**2.** A *thrush* is what kind of animal? _____

**3.** What is the meaning of *descend* as it is used in the poem? _____

**4.** What is the likely meaning of "Green" in this poem? _____

**5.** What is the main idea of this poem? _____

_____

_____

**B** Write your own paraphrase of these lines from "The Ecchoing Green."

_____

_____

_____

_____

_____

_____

_____

© Pearson Education, Inc., publishing as Pearson Prentice Hall.

# Parody

A **parody** is a humorous work that makes fun of another piece of writing by imitating it. Writers can parody different aspects of a work, including the following:

- **style,** or the way a writer uses words. For example, stories about private detectives are told in a tough-guy style and use striking comparisons. To parody this style, a writer can imitate this conversational language but use it to tell about silly events.

- **characters,** the people taking part in a story. For example, private-eye stories are filled with mean characters with tough-sounding nicknames. To parody such characters, a writer might exaggerate a character's bad qualities and give him a silly nickname.

- **plot,** or the sequence of connected events that make up a story. For example, private-eye stories may tell of a man who is being pursued by bad guys. A parody might imitate this plot but have the bad guys decide they like the man too much to do anything to him.

- **theme,** or the main message. For example, the theme of some mobster stories is that a person is better off not trusting anyone. To parody this theme, a writer might have everyone let the main character down—even his pet canary.

Each item is a parody of a private-eye story. Circle the letter of the element or elements that are most clearly being parodied. Then, underline one example of each parodied element.

I opened the warehouse door and saw why five men had been following me for the last week. The warehouse was filled with gold. It was also filled with gangsters.

"Hey, it's the private eye," said Louie the Goldfish. Louie was so mean that his own dog growled at him. He got his nickname because he liked to blow bubbles in his bathtub.

**1. A.** character **B.** plot

It was 9:00 on a sunny San Diego morning when she walked into my office. One look at her and my heart stopped. My socks bunched up, and my shoelaces untied themselves. Her smile was so bright it made the sun hide behind a cloud. Of course, that might have been the metal braces on her teeth. She opened her mouth and reached in with her graceful, dainty hand to pull out a fat wad of chewing gum.

"You got a garbage for this?" she said in a voice like a parrot's. Suddenly, I was in love.

**2. A.** style and character **B.** theme and character

© Pearson Education, Inc., publishing as Pearson Prentice Hall.

# Parody

**A** For each question, circle the letter of the best answer.

**1.** Which is the best definition of a parody?

    **A.** a work that makes fun of other works by imitating them

    **B.** a humorous work written to entertain

    **C.** a story that makes fun of mobsters and private eyes

**2.** Which best explains how writers parody another writer's style?

    **A.** They humorously imitate the type of events in the other writer's works.

    **B.** They humorously imitate the way the other writer uses words.

    **C.** The humorously imitate the other writer's message.

**B** For each item, tell what type of story is being parodied. Then, circle the letter of the element that is most clearly being parodied. Finally, underline one example.

> I ran down the alley, a dead end. I turned to face the men chasing me.
> "Hey, Mr. Detective," said Louie the Goldfish, catching up to me. "You knows what happens to guys what knows too much, don't you?"
> "No, Louie," I said, suddenly feeling very tired. "Why don't you tell me?"
> "Why, they go on television game shows to answer questions for cash prizes," said Louie. "Ain't that right, boys?"
> "That's right, Louie," said the four hoodlums who had joined us.
> "We got you a contract to go on the new quiz show," said Louie. "Waddya say?"

**1. Type of story being parodied:** _____

    **Element parodied: A.** plot         **B.** style

> Young Sam Starhopper gasped as the Dark One swung his sword down. The sword missed him, but it was a close call. Suddenly, the voice of Master Oaktree spoke in Sam's mind. "Sam, use your hidden dark powers."
> "But master, we Sun Lords are forbidden to use such powers. We only use light."
> "True," said the voice of Master Oaktree. "'light makes right,' and all. Still, if you're about to be squashed like a bug, who cares if you break the rules? But it's up to you."

**2. Type of story being parodied:** _____

    **Element parodied: A.** plot         **B.** theme

© Pearson Education, Inc., publishing as Pearson Prentice Hall.

# Picturing the Action

Practice

When you are reading a narrative, pause occasionally to **picture the action,** or form a mental image of what you are reading. Imagine in your mind's eye the details you are reading—the images, shapes, colors. See the movements described by the verbs.

> Read the following passage from "The Listeners," a poem by Walter de la Mare. Then, answer the questions and complete the activities that follow.

"Is there anybody there?" said the Traveler,
    Knocking on the moonlit door;
And his horse in the silence champed the grasses
    Of the forest's ferny floor;
And a bird flew up out of the turret,
    Above the Traveler's head;
And he smote upon the door again a second time;
    "Is there anybody there?" he said.

**1.** Point out two verbs or other words that help you see the actions in the first four lines.

_____

_____

**2.** Describe the picture created by the phrase, *the forest's ferny floor.* What does that phrase tell you about where the house with the "moonlit door" is located?

_____

_____

_____

**3.** What is the only response to the Traveler's first knock?

_____

_____

**4.** In your own words, describe the picture created in this passage, and summarize what happens.

_____

_____

_____

_____

© Pearson Education, Inc., publishing as Pearson Prentice Hall.

# Picturing the Action

**A**   Read the following passage from "The Story of the Flood" from the Mesopotamian epic *Gilgamesh,* translated by N. K. Sanders. Then, answer the questions and complete the activities that follow.

(1) For six days and six nights the winds blew, torrent and tempest and flood overwhelmed the world, tempest and flood raged together like warring hosts. (2) When the seventh day dawned the storm from the south subsided, the sea grew calm, the flood was stilled; I looked at the face of the world and there was silence, all mankind was turned to clay. (3) The surface of the sea stretched as flat as a roof-top; I opened a hatch and the light fell on my face. (4) Then I bowed low. (5) I sat down and I wept, the tears streamed down my face, for on every side was the waste of water.

1. What picture does the speaker create in Sentence 1 when he says that "tempest and flood raged together like warring hosts"? _____

_____

2. According to Sentence 2, what is the speaker telling us when he says, "all mankind was turned to clay"? What picture do these words create? _____

_____

3. How does the phrase *flat as a roof-top* in Sentence 3 contrast with the description of the storm in Sentence 1?

_____

_____

4. What does the speaker say he does in Sentences 4 and 5, and what picture of himself does he create? _____

_____

**B**   On a separate sheet of paper, summarize what happens in this passage. What feeling does this description create?

© Pearson Education, Inc., publishing as Pearson Prentice Hall.

# Point of View

**Point of view** is the perspective from which a story is told. In **first-person point of view,** the story is told by a character who is involved in the story and is part of the action. The narrator uses the pronouns *I, we, me,* and *us.* In **third-person point of view,** the story is told by someone outside the action. This narrator uses third-person pronouns such as *he, she, they,* and *them* to refer to all characters.

Read the story excerpts. Write **F-P** if the excerpt is told from the first-person point of view. Write **T-P** if the excerpt is told from the third-person point of view.

1. _____ Ernie says that being a good stage magician isn't easy. He and Gert practice their tricks for hours a day. Sometimes they watch themselves in the mirror as they do the tricks. Other times, they invite an audience to watch. "The hand is quicker than the eye!" Ernie always says.

2. _____ Laura and I were completely silent. We crouched down behind the garbage cans afraid to even breathe. Who was that masked figure sneaking through the garage? Suddenly my nose started tingling. "Ah, ah, ah-choo!" I sneezed.

3. _____ I watched Jason as he took his time putting on the roller skates. Why had he told LeTeena he could really skate? I noticed that she hadn't been that impressed. Why did Jason always have to make up stories? I could tell that Jason was feeling nervous. He looked at me with a weak smile and sighed.

4. _____ Identical twins Manu and Mico used to dress the same way, speak the same way, and go everywhere together. However, ever since they met Sylvia, the twins look quite different. Manu dresses in khakis and button-down shirts. Mico nearly always wears jeans and T-shirts.

5. _____ "A storm is coming," said Cassie. "We better pack up and get off the beach." Dark clouds were forming, and the wind was getting stronger. Cassie, Tina, and Jake quickly folded the towels while Deena called used her cell phone to call her dad. When Mr. Jackson heard the phone ring, he was already about to leave to pick up the kids at the lake.

© Pearson Education, Inc., publishing as Pearson Prentice Hall.

# Point of View

**A**  Circle the letter of the best answer.

**1.** In a first-person point of view, who is the person telling the story?

    **A.** a character in the story     **B.** a person outside the action of the story

**2.** In the third-person point of view, who is the person telling the story?

    **A.** a character in the story     **B.** a person outside the action of the story

**3.** If the reader cannot be sure whether to believe the person telling the story, from what point of view is the story probably being told?

    **A.** the first-person point of view     **B.** the third-person point of view

**4.** When a story is told from the third-person point of view, what do readers know?

    **A.** only what the narrator experiences
    **B.** what many of the characters do and say

**B**  Read each passage. Then, answer the questions.

I really do not like Daniel. He is always rude to customers and coworkers. Plus, he always shows off whenever the boss is around. There he goes again. He might as well wear a sign that says, "Look at me! I'm the greatest!" Oh, no. He is heading this way! I'm going to get out of here fast.

**1.** What is the point of view? _____

**2.** Do readers know whether the narrator's view of Daniel is correct? Why or why not?

_____

Sasha and Arnie volunteer at the Humane Society after school three days a week. First, they check to make sure that all the dogs' cages are clean and that every dog has fresh water. Then, the boys see which dogs are scheduled for a walk. They may walk as many as eight dogs before Arnie's mom comes to pick them up at 5:30.

**3.** What is the point of view? _____

© Pearson Education, Inc., publishing as Pearson Prentice Hall.

# Political Poetry

**Political poetry** connects personal emotions to political or social issues. A poet might write a poem about his mother's work cleaning people's houses. He might tell his feelings about his mother. He might also make the following political point: It is unfair for society to pay people so little that they have to work all the time.

When reading a political poem, think about the feelings it shares. Think also about the point it makes about the effect of events or social conditions on people's lives.

Langston Hughes wrote when African Americans did not have full rights and faced many obstacles to success. Read the following poem by Hughes. Then, answer the questions that follow.

## A Dream Deferred

What happens to a dream deferred?
Does it dry up
like a raisin in the sun?
Or fester like a sore —
And then run?
Does it stink like rotten meat?
Or crust and sugar over —
like a syrupy sweet?
Maybe it just sags
like a heavy load.
Or does it explode?

1. Underline five images to which Hughes compares a dream deferred.

2. What three personal feelings does this poem express?

   **A.** frustration, anger, despair
   **B.** doubt, resignation, fear
   **C.** grief, longing, hope

3. What connection do you see between Hughes's poem and the political situation of African Americans at the time?

_____

_____

© Pearson Education, Inc., publishing as Pearson Prentice Hall.

# Political Poetry

Assess

**A** Answer the following questions.

1. What is political poetry? _____
_____

2. Give one example of a situation that might motivate a poet to write a
political poem.
_____

**B** Read this passage from "Song to the Men of England" by Percy Bysshe Shelley. Then,
answer the questions.

> Men of England, wherefore plough
> For the lords who lay ye low?
> Wherefore weave with toil and care
> The rich robes your tyrants wear?
> Wherefore feed, and clothe, and save,
> From the cradle to the grave,
> Those ungrateful drones who would
> Drain your sweat — nay, drink your blood?
> Wherefore, Bees of England, forge
> Many a weapon, chain, and scourge
> That these stingless drones may spoil
> The forced produce of your toil?

1. Which "men of England" does Shelley address in this poem?

   **A.** the wealthy ruling class          **B.** the exploited working class

2. To what does Shelley compare the men of England? Why do you think he

   makes this comparison? _____
_____

3. How does Shelley feel about the ruling class? Circle three words and
phrases in the passage that support your answer.
_____
_____

© Pearson Education, Inc., publishing as Pearson Prentice Hall.

# Reading Between the Lines

**Reading between the lines** reveals the meaning of actions, words, and events in literary works. For example, a father in a play might want his sons to join the business. His eldest son refuses, and the two no longer speak. The father might try to persuade his younger son to join the family business, saying "Of course, you could always do what your brother did." Reading between the lines, you can tell that the father is saying, "You could not join the business—and hurt my feelings, just as your brother did."

To read between the lines, follow these steps as you read:

- Make inferences, or educated guesses, about the meanings of whole lines or passages.

- Find clues about the characters, setting, mood, and symbolism.

- Examine specific word choices, including words in the title.

The following items explain the characters' circumstances and tell what one character says. Explain what the character probably means by his or her words.

1. **Situation** In Shakespeare's play *Julius Caesar*, Portia, Brutus' wife, sees that her husband is troubled. She wants to know what is wrong. Brutus will not say.

    **What the Character Is Talking About** Portia says that when people are married, they share each other's troubles and secrets.

    **Character's Lines** Portia says that if Brutus will not share his secret with her, she is not really his wife.

    **Meaning Between the Lines?** _____

    _____

2. **Situation** John and David work part-time and are shopping for gifts for their best friend. John selects an expensive watch from the jewelry case. He asks David if he should buy it.

    **What the Character Is Talking About** John wants David's advice.

    **Character's Lines** David says, "John, that watch costs two weeks' salary!"

    **Meaning Between the Lines?** _____

    _____

© Pearson Education, Inc., publishing as Pearson Prentice Hall.

# Reading Between the Lines

Each item explains the characters' circumstances and tells what one character says. Explain what the character probably means by his or her words.

1. **Situation** In Shakespeare's play *Julius Caesar*, Cassius asks Brutus about his recent change of mood. He has been withdrawn and quiet.

   **What the Character Is Talking About** Cassius wants to know if Brutus is troubled.

   **Character's Lines** Brutus says that he is at war with himself.

   **Meaning Between the Lines?** _____

   _____

2. **Situation** Cathy and Beth are building a tree house. Cathy accidentally hits her thumb with the hammer. She thinks that she has a broken thumb. Beth thinks back to other situations when Cathy thought her injuries were worse than they actually were.

   **What the Character Is Talking About** Cathy thinks that she is seriously injured.

   **Character's Lines** Beth says, "I think that you're making a mountain out of a molehill."

   **Meaning Between the Lines?** _____

   _____

3. **Situation** Paul tells Bob that they must rescue the kitten from the tree. Bob knows that Paul rushes into situations he cannot handle.

   **What the Character Is Talking About** Paul wants Bob to hold the rickety old ladder he has found while he climbs up to the kitten.

   **Character's Lines** Bob says, "Paul, I think you need to look before you leap."

   **Meaning Between the Lines?** _____

   _____

© Pearson Education, Inc., publishing as Pearson Prentice Hall.

# Reading Drama

## Practice

When **reading drama,** pay special attention to the stage directions. Stage directions are usually printed in italic type. They can appear before, after, or even in the middle of dialogue. Stage directions give critical information about the setting of a scene, about what characters do, how they speak, how they move, and what is happening around them.

Stage directions can help you imagine what the play would look like on stage. Plays are written to be performed, not just read silently, so it is important to imagine the action as you read. Stage directions can also help you understand the actions and feelings of the characters in a play. Here is an example of part of a play featuring stage directions:

Scene i. *A small apartment filled with objects of African art, including masks, musical instruments, and sculptures. There is a small kitchen in the background. The front door is on the left. The door to the bedroom is on the right. As the curtain rises, a loud knocking is heard on the front door. Walter comes through the bedroom door to answer it.*

Walter *[walking groggily, still dressed in his pajamas]* All right, all right! I heard you the first time. *[He yawns.]*

**A** Circle the letter of the item that best completes the statement.

1. When reading a drama, you can recognize stage directions because they

   **A.** occur at the end of the play.        **B.** are printed in italic type.

2. Stage directions may provide information about

   **A.** the characters' behavior.        **B.** the playwright's biography.

**B** Write *SD* for each item that names information you could find in the stage directions for a play. If the item does not relate to stage directions, leave the space blank.

1. _____ a character's physical appearance

2. _____ the furniture for the stage set

3. _____ the identity of the actor playing a character

4. _____ a character's tone of voice

5. _____ a change in lighting

© Pearson Education, Inc., publishing as Pearson Prentice Hall.

## Reading Drama

Read the following passage. Then, answer the questions that follow.

**Scene ii.** *The curtain rises to show the interior of a cave. An eerie blue light reveals strange rock formations hanging from its ceiling. At stage left, there is a large, fancy four-poster bed with curtains. Suitcases and large trunks surround the bed. At stage right, the pirates lie on the floor of the cave, sleeping. Squidge, one of the pirates, stirs in his sleep, mumbles, and then jumps up, still caught up in his dream.*

**Squidge.** *[With wild eyes, yelling incoherently while he waves his arms about]* Avast me hearties! Belay! Fire below decks! Launch the lifeboats!

*[Inkle leaps up from the group of sleepers.]*

**Inkle.** *[In a loud, hoarse whisper]* Squidge, you idiot! Stow it, afore you wake her majesty! Squidge! *[He runs up to Squidge and clamps a hand firmly across Squidge's mouth.]*

*[Suddenly, the curtains around the bed are thrown open. Her Majesty, Queen of the Pirates, is revealed sitting up and stretching within.]*

**Queen of the Pirates.** *[Speaking slowly and with deceptive mildness. She is clearly angry and ready to pounce.]* How charming! A little entertainment! And who, may I ask, is the brilliant author of this skit?

**1.** Where does this scene take place? _____

**2.** What kind of light fills the stage? _____

**3.** Who is sleeping on the right side of the stage? _____

**4.** Who is sleeping in the curtained bed? _____

**5.** What does Squidge do as he speaks? _____

**6.** Why is Squidge acting this way? _____

**7.** What does Inkle do to keep Squidge quiet? _____

**8.** How does the Queen of the Pirates feel about Squidge's outburst?

_____

# Reading in Sentences

## Practice

Most poems are written in sentences. A poet does not always complete a sentence at the end of a line, however. Instead, a sentence may stretch across several lines. To understand the meaning of a poem, **read in sentences.** Notice the punctuation. If there is no punctuation at the end of the line, read on to the next line without pause. Pause slightly for a comma. Do not make a full stop at the end of a line unless there is a period, colon, semicolon, or dash there.

**A** Read the following excerpt from "I Wandered Lonely as a Cloud" by William Wordsworth. Circle the letter of the correct answer to each question.

> I wandered lonely as a cloud
> That floats on high o'er vales and hills,
> When all at once I saw a crowd,
> A host, of golden daffodils;
> 5 Beside the lake, beneath the trees,
> Fluttering and dancing in the breeze.

**1.** According to the punctuation, what should you do at the end of line 1?

**A.** stop          **B.** pause          **C.** continue without stop or pause

**2.** According to the punctuation, what should you do at the end of line 2?

**A.** stop          **B.** pause          **C.** continue without stop or pause

**3.** According to the punctuation, what should you do at the end of line 6?

**A.** stop          **B.** pause          **C.** continue without stop or pause

**B** Read the following excerpt from "Harlem Night Song" by Langston Hughes. Then, answer the questions.

> Come,
> Let us roam the night together
> Singing.
> I love you.

**1.** _____ How many lines are in this excerpt?

**2.** _____ How many sentences are in this excerpt?

**3.** How should the punctuation at the end of line 1 affect your reading?

© Pearson Education, Inc., publishing as Pearson Prentice Hall.

Name _____ Date _____

# Reading in Sentences

**A** Read the following excerpt from "Rocking" by Gabriela Mistral. Circle the letter of the correct answer to each question.

The wind wandering by night
Rocks the wheat.
Hearing the loving wind,
I rock my son.

**1.** According to the punctuation, after which line should you pause?

   **A.** line 1          **B.** line 2          **C.** line 3

**2.** According to the punctuation, after which line should you continue without stop or pause?

   **A.** line 1          **B.** line 3          **C.** line 4

**3.** According to the punctuation, after which lines should you stop?

   **A.** lines 1 and 2      **B.** lines 2 and 4      **C.** lines 3 and 4

**B** Read the following excerpt from "Grandma Ling" by Amy Ling. Then, answer the questions.

If you dig that hole deep enough
you'll reach China, they used to tell me,
a child in a backyard in Pennsylvania.
Not strong enough to dig that hole,
5  I waited twenty years,
then sailed back, half way around the world.

**1.** _____ How many lines are in this excerpt?

**2.** _____ How many sentences are in this excerpt?

**3.** _____ At the end of which lines should you stop?

**4.** Read the first line and stop. Then, read the first and second lines together without stopping. What information becomes clear when you read the lines together?

# Reading Stanzas as Units of Meaning

Practice

Many poems take the form of stanzas, or formal groupings of lines. A stanza usually expresses a single main idea, much like a paragraph in prose writing. To aid your understanding of poetry, **read stanzas as units of meaning,** just as you read prose paragraphs. You might pause after each stanza to consider its main thought.

Read the following stanzas from "The River-Merchant's Wife: A Letter" by Li Po, translated by Ezra Pound. Then, answer the questions and complete the activities that follow.

> At fourteen, I married My Lord you.
> I never laughed, being bashful.
> Lowering my head, I looked at the wall.
> Called to, a thousand times, I never looked back.
>
> 5 At fifteen, I stopped scowling.
> I desired my dust to be mingled with yours
> Forever and forever and forever.
> Why should I climb the look out?

**1.** Restate in your own words what the first stanza says.

_____

_____

**2.** Restate in your own words what the second stanza says.

_____

_____

**3.** How has the River-Merchant's Wife changed from one stanza to the next? Consider her age, her possible experience, and her attitude toward her husband.

_____

_____

_____

© Pearson Education, Inc., publishing as Pearson Prentice Hall.

## Reading Stanzas as Units of Meaning

Assess

**A**   Read the following opening stanzas from Canto I of *The Inferno* by Dante Alighieri, translated by John Ciardi. Then, answer the questions and complete the activities that follow.

> Midway in our life's journey, I went astray
>    From the straight road and woke to find myself
>    alone in a dark wood. How shall I say
>
> what wood that was! I never saw so drear,
> 5     so rank, so arduous a wilderness!
>    Its very memory gives a shape to fear.
>
> Death could scarce be more bitter than that place!
>    But since it came to good, I will recount
>    all that I found revealed there by God's grace.

**1.** Restate in your own words what the first stanza says.

_____

_____

_____

**2.** Restate in your own words what the second stanza says.

_____

_____

_____

**3.** Restate in your own words what the third stanza says. What purpose does it state for the stanzas that will follow?

_____

_____

_____

**B**   The three stanzas in **A** are the beginning of a long poem about a man's spiritual journey. What job do these three stanzas do for the rest of the poem? Write your answer on a separate sheet of paper.

© Pearson Education, Inc., publishing as Pearson Prentice Hall.

# Recognizing Author's Bias

## Practice

**Bias** refers to a person's unstated or unsupported judgments. For example, imagine that a person who does not like cats is asked to write a description of a cat. The person might write "a scrawny nuisance with fur and claws." This description might suggest that the person has a bias against cats.

If you **recognize the author's bias,** or point of view on details and events, you will be able to understand why he or she stresses certain facts or makes certain statements. Clues to bias include a writer's use of phrases with negative or positive associations.

**A**    Read each of the following passages. Underline any phrases or assertions with positive or negative associations. Write *P* on the line if the association is positive or *N* if it is negative.

1. _____ Ellen's calm presence helped restore order after the unexpected storm.

2. _____ The tyrannical rulers whipped any citizen unfortunate enough to disagree with their unjust laws.

3. _____ Having to move every six to eight months is like having a scab that won't heal.

**B**    Read the passage below. Then, answer the questions.

> Tracie stands out as one of the most remarkable young ladies on campus. Unlike her less refined peers, she prefers the superior fit and feel of designer clothing. When she attends awards ceremonies and other important school functions, she always wears the most flattering designer dresses. Her shoes and handbags are made by quality designers as well, and her fine jewels perfectly complement her wardrobe.

1. Circle the words the author uses to describe Tracie's peers, and underline the words used to describe Tracie and her wardrobe. What associations does each set of words have?

_____

2. What fact does the author stress? _____

3. Why do you think the author stresses this fact? _____

_____

© Pearson Education, Inc., publishing as Pearson Prentice Hall.

# Recognizing Author's Bias

Assess

**A**  Answer the following questions. Write your answer on the lines provided.

**1.** Why is it useful to recognize an author's bias? _____

_____

**2.** What clues can help you identify an author's bias? _____

_____

**B**  Read the passage below. Then, answer the questions.

Val and her friends spent the night at Samantha's house, watching videos and "window shopping" online. There were piles of snack foods littering the tables: doughnuts, crackers, chips, and candy. A pepperoni pizza and two bottles of soda (raspberry flavored) would arrive any minute.

Everyone but Val munched happily away. As usual, Val had to make a point of being fussy. She dared to nibble on a cracker but tossed it away after scanning the box and discovering it was only wheat, not *whole* wheat. The strawberries looked good, but unless they were organic she wouldn't go near them.

"Your dad is a doctor," said Val to Samantha. "I'm surprised he would let you have so much junk food in the house. Maybe he didn't pay attention in medical school when they got to the part about nutrition." As usual, Val's prim lecturing just made the others uncomfortable. Did Val know the difference between caring about her own health—and spoiling others' good time?

**1.** What bias does the author reveal in this passage? _____

_____

_____

**2.** Give four clues that reveal this bias.

_____

_____

_____

_____

© Pearson Education, Inc., publishing as Pearson Prentice Hall.

# Recognizing Dramatic Tension

## Practice

Dramatic tension is the sense of suspense that an audience feels while watching a drama unfold. To **recognize dramatic tension,** monitor the anticipation you feel while reading each scene. Ask questions such as these:

- Why are these characters in conflict with one another?
- How does the main characters' situation get worse as the play progresses?

---

**A** Circle the letter of the best answer to each question.

1. Which feeling is most closely related to dramatic tension?

   **A.** joy                 **B.** grief                 **C.** suspense

2. Which element would most likely produce dramatic tension?

   **A.** a conflict between characters         **C.** a long speech about the past
   **B.** a rhyming speech

---

**B** Read these brief plot summaries. Circle the number of the item that you think would offer the best opportunities for creating dramatic tension. Then, briefly explain your choice.

1. A young woman and a young man fall in love. Their parents enthusiastically approve of the match, and the young people become engaged. A year later, they are happily married.

2. Two young people are in love, but their parents are against their getting married because they are from different religious and ethnic backgrounds. They make a secret plan to elope, but the young woman's father learns about the plan and aims to stop them.

3. A young man and a young woman think they have fallen in love with each other. They discover, however, that they are really very different people. After a humorous series of misunderstandings, they settle down, accept each other for what they are, and get married.

_____

_____

_____

          © Pearson Education, Inc., publishing as Pearson Prentice Hall.

# Recognizing Dramatic Tension

Assess

**A** Circle the letter of the best answer to each question.

**1.** The term "dramatic tension" is used to describe a reader's response to which of the following?

    **A.** sonnets         **B.** novels         **C.** plays

**2.** Which of the following is most closely associated with dramatic tension?

    **A.** flashback         **B.** conflict         **C.** soliloquies

**3.** What emotional response does dramatic tension produce?

    **A.** regret         **B.** joy         **C.** suspense

**4.** To recognize dramatic tension, which of the following should you do?

    **A.** Monitor your sense of anticipation as you read each scene.
    **B.** Become familiar with the playwright's biography.
    **C.** Sketch a diagram of the way the scene might look on stage in performance.

**B** Read these brief plot summaries. Circle the number of the item that you think would offer the best opportunities for creating dramatic tension. Then, briefly explain your choice.

**1.** A young pianist is determined to achieve fame. Inspired by talented teachers, he practices daily for hours. At the age of nineteen, he wins an international piano competition. From that point onward, his career is assured.

**2.** A hard-working young pianist is encouraged by his teachers, who believe he has a great future. At the age of nineteen, he wins an international competition. Everyone believes he is on his way to stardom. A year later, however, a mysterious nervous disease affecting his hands is diagnosed.

**3.** A young musician, ambitious for fame, is encouraged by his teachers. His parents, however, know that the odds against "making it" in a musical career are enormous. They encourage their son to develop other career plans, but they reluctantly go along with his dream, at least for the moment.

_____

_____

_____

© Pearson Education, Inc., publishing as Pearson Prentice Hall.

# Relating to Your Own Experiences

## Practice

Many common experiences know no cultural boundaries. If you have ever taken a journey, yearned for the past, or experienced an inner awakening, you can find a connection between your experiences and those that an author may describe. **Relating to your own experiences** will increase your understanding and enjoyment of literary works.

> Read the story summaries. Then, write a few notes about how you might relate the characters and events in the story to your own experience.

1. In "The Monkey's Paw" by W.W. Jacobs, an old soldier visits an elderly couple and tells them a story about a monkey's paw he acquired in India. The spell on the paw allows three men to each have three wishes. Despite the soldier's warnings, Mr. White is eager to own the paw and wish on it. He gets his wish for money, but he also loses something priceless.

   _____

   _____

2. In "Through the Tunnel" by Doris Lessing, a thirteen-year-old boy visits the seashore with his mother. The boy notices some older youngsters who take turns swimming through a rocky tunnel underwater. Eager for the older boys' approval, day after day he practices holding his breath so that he too can make the swim. Finally, he succeeds. Meeting the challenge has given him a new sense of confidence and independence from his mother.

   _____

   _____

3. In "The Interlopers" by Saki, two men meet at night in the woods during a storm. The men are from families who have feuded over property rights for three generations. They are eager to fight, but then a large tree falls, trapping them both. Both men agree to end their feud. After they shout for help, they see figures approaching them. They think they are saved, but then one of the men recognizes that the figures are really wolves.

   _____

   _____

© Pearson Education, Inc., publishing as Pearson Prentice Hall.

## Relating to Your Own Experiences

Assess

Read the story summaries. Then, write a few notes about how you might relate the characters and events in the story to your own experience.

**1.** An older man who lives alone decides the time has come when he must surrender his independence. He visits his daughter. She and her family invite him to live with them, but he chooses instead to move into a home for the elderly. His daughter and granddaughter take him to the old-folks' home, where he lies down and thinks about the struggle against death that his future holds.

_____

_____

_____

**2.** In "Two Kinds" by Amy Tan, a Chinese American girl is locked into conflict with her mother. Her mother wants her to be a star pianist. She takes piano lessons with a deaf teacher who cannot evaluate her playing properly. At a recital, she plays poorly, embarrassing herself and her family. The conflict reaches a bitter climax when the mother accuses the daughter of disobedience. Years later, the daughter is able to understand better her own behavior, as well as that of her mother.

_____

_____

_____

**3.** In "The Amigo Brothers" by Piri Thomas, two boys are devoted to boxing. They are the best of friends and often work out with each other. Then, they sign up for a championship competition. They realize that the contest may destroy their friendship, so they prepare for the match separately. At the contest, they box their hearts out. At the end of the fight, though, they put their arms around each other's shoulders and leave the ring before the referee can announce the winner.

_____

_____

_____

© Pearson Education, Inc., publishing as Pearson Prentice Hall.

# Reread for Clarification

**Rereading** passages can often help clarify the character's identities, the relationships among characters, the sequence of events, and even puzzling language. Sometimes earlier passages contain the key to understanding information that seems confusing.

**Passage:** "With the help of Sassouma Berete's intrigues, Dankaran Touman was proclaimed king."
**What Is Unclear?** the relationship between the two characters
**Earlier Passage I Reread:** "Dankaran Touman, the son of Sassouma Berete, was now a fine youth."
**What Is Now Clear:** Dankara Touman is Sassouma Berete's son.

---

**A** | Read the passage, and then respond to the items that follow.

A few years ago, Martha and Pam shared a life-changing experience. Martha was trapped in a sinking boat. Pam risked her own life and rescued Martha. This year, Martha learned that Pam's mother had fallen ill. Pam wanted to visit her sick mother but could not afford the airfare. As soon as Martha found out, she bought a round-trip ticket and mailed it to Pam. Two weeks later, Martha received a postcard with a short message: "Thank you!"

1. Reread the passage. Underline the sentence that clarifies why Martha bought Pam the airline ticket.

2. Reread the passage to clarify who sent the postcard, and why. Write your response below.

_____

---

**B** | Read the passage, and then respond to the items that follow.

Mark was the son of the influential, powerful, and famous Senator Michael Harris. Even though Mark was not a good student, he managed to gain admission into a top university. No one was surprised. Someone noted that "Iron Mike" had been at work again.

1. Reread the passage. Underline the words that clarify who "Iron Mike" is.

2. Reread the passage to clarify why Mark was admitted into a top university even though he was not a good student. Write your response below.

_____

© Pearson Education, Inc., publishing as Pearson Prentice Hall.

# Reread for Clarification

**A**  Read the passage below. Answer the questions that follow.

As Mary walked through the garden with her father on her wedding day, the strong scent of jasmine awakened an old, almost forgotten memory. It reminded Mary of one warm summer day when she was busy playing out in the backyard as a young girl, and the scent of jasmine surrounded her. It was then that a tall, handsome man bent down and scooped her into his arms. "Daddy!" said Mary with excitement. "You're home!"

**1.** Reread the passage. What does Mary associate with the scent of jasmine?

_____

**2.** Reread the passage. In the episode from her childhood, why doesn't Mary notice her father immediately? _____

_____

**B**  Read the passage. Answer the questions that follow.

Linda loves helping people. For thirty years, Linda worked as an emergency room nurse. During that time, she gained valuable experience in treating victims of car accidents. She developed an ability to work well under extreme pressure in life-threatening situations.

One night, as Linda drove home, she witnessed a terrible car accident. She immediately pulled over to the side of the road and ran toward the wreck. She saved the lives of two people.

**1.** Reread the passage. What makes Linda pull over to the side of the road?

_____

**2.** Reread the passage. How was Linda able to save the lives of two people?

_____

© Pearson Education, Inc., publishing as Pearson Prentice Hall.

# Responding

When you **respond** to a work of literature, you connect it to your own experiences. You feel the emotions in the work; you see and hear its images. Lyric poems nearly always use images of the senses—taste, touch, sight, hearing, and smell—to convey ideas and emotions. To **respond to imagery,**

- Identify the sensory word pictures in the poem.
- Take time to consider how these images relate to your own life.

Notice what you are feeling and what causes you to respond—the words that stirred your emotions or captured your imagination.

Read this passage from Walt Whitman's *Song of Myself.* Then, answer the questions that follow.

The spotted hawk swoops by and accuses me, he complains of
    my gab and my loitering.
I too am not a bit tamed, I too am untranslatable,
I sound my barbaric yawp over the roofs of the world. . . .
I bequeath myself to the dirt to grow from the grass I love,
If you want me again look for me under your boot soles. . . .
Failing to fetch me at first keep encouraged,
Missing me one place search another,
I stop somewhere waiting for you.

1. What do you hear when you read the words *gab* and *barbaric yawp?*

_____

_____

2. What is your response when the poet tells you to look for him under your "boot soles"?

_____

_____

3. List two or three other expressions in the passage that particularly struck you. What did these words make you feel or see or hear?

_____

_____

© Pearson Education, Inc., publishing as Pearson Prentice Hall.

## Responding

**A** Read the following passage from Stephen Crane's Civil War story, "An Episode of War," in which a young lieutenant, wounded in the arm, heads toward the hospital tents in his camp. Then, answer the questions that follow.

The low white tents of the hospital were grouped around an old schoolhouse. . . . In the foreground two ambulances interlocked wheels in the deep mud. The drivers were tossing the blame of it back and forth, gesticulating and berating, while from the ambulances, both crammed with wounded, there came an occasional groan. An interminable crowd of bandaged men were coming and going. Great numbers sat under the trees nursing heads or arms or legs. . . . Sitting with his back against a tree a man with a face as grey as a new army blanket was serenely smoking. . . . The lieutenant wished to rush forward and inform him that he was dying.

1. What images in the description of the ambulances did you find especially striking? Why?

_____

_____

_____

2. The passage ends with the image of the dying soldier. How does this description make you feel? What do you think the wounded lieutenant feels as he looks at this man?

_____

_____

_____

3. What emotions did you experience as you read the passage from beginning to end? What words in the passage triggered those emotions?

_____

_____

_____

**B** On a separate sheet of paper, write a short note to the author, Stephen Crane, about your response to the above passage.

© Pearson Education, Inc., publishing as Pearson Prentice Hall.

# Romanticism

**Romanticism** is a literary and artistic movement that is characterized by the following elements:

- The Romantics favored emotion over reason. They preferred intuition, or "gut feeling," over intellect. They valued the subjective life of feeling and imagination over objective facts.

- They celebrated creativity, individuality, imagination, and the lives of ordinary people.

- Their writings reflect nature, self-knowledge, folklore, and the mysterious and exotic.

Read each of the following passages from William Wordsworth's *Literary Ballads*. Then, write the letter of the passage that best answers each question about Romanticism.

A. One impulse from a vernal wood / May teach you more of man; / Of moral evil and of good, / Than all the sages can.

B. It is the first mild day of March: / Each minute sweeter than before, / The red-breast sings from the tall larch / That stands beside our door.

C. Love, now an universal birth, / From heart to heart is stealing, / From earth to man, from man to earth, / —It is the hour of feeling. / One moment now may give us more / Than fifty years of reason; / Our minds shall drink at every pore / The spirit of the season.

1. _____ Which passage best reflects a love of nature?

2. _____ Which passage best reflects a preference for intuition over intellect?

3. _____ Which passage best reflects a preference for emotion over reason?

© Pearson Education, Inc., publishing as Pearson Prentice Hall.

# Romanticism

**A** Write a *T* beside each true statement or an *F* beside each false statement.

1. ____ The Romantics valued the mysterious and exotic.

2. ____ The Romantics favored reason over emotion.

3. ____ The Romantics favored the subjective over the objective.

4. ____ The Romantics celebrated the lives of ordinary people.

**B** Circle the letter of the best answer to each question.

1. What is the best description of Romanticism?

   **A.** a political movement
   **B.** a religious movement
   **C.** a literary and artistic movement

2. What element of Romanticism does this passage reflect?

   The birds around me hopp'd and play'd:
   Their thoughts I cannot measure,
   But the least motion which they made,
   It seem'd a thrill of pleasure.
   —from "Lines Written in Spring" by William Wordsworth

   **A.** It reflects the love of nature.
   **B.** It reflects the importance of individuality.
   **C.** It reflects the emphasis on intuition over intellect.

3. What aspect of Romanticism is reflected in the following passage?

   Enough of science and of art;
   Close up these barren leaves;
   Come forth, and bring with you a heart
   That watches and receives.
   —from "The Tables Turned" by William Wordsworth

   **A.** It reflects the love of nature.
   **B.** It reflects the importance of individuality.
   **C.** It reflects the emphasis on intuition over intellect.

© Pearson Education, Inc., publishing as Pearson Prentice Hall.

## Satire

**Satire** is writing that makes fun of the foolishness and faults of individuals, institutions, or humanity in general. Writers use satire to amuse readers. They also use satire to bring about positive change. The following are literary devices that writers often use in works of satire:

- **Exaggeration**—making something seem better, bigger, or more important than it really is. By using exaggeration, a writer can make a person's faults or a society's problems seem obvious to readers. *Example:* In a movie, a couple buys a sport utility vehicle. It is so huge, their children can play softball in the back.

- **Sarcasm** or **irony**—language that means the opposite of what it says. *Example:* The mayor says that he will rebuild the city. Businesses continue to close, though. Downtown becomes a ghost town. A writer comments, "Congratulations, Mr. Mayor, for your new addition to downtown—tumbleweeds rolling down the empty streets."

■ Read the passage. Then, put a check mark next to the correct answer for each question.

Lots of people reported our [dog] to the police . . . but Mother told them it hadn't been Muggs' fault but the fault of the people who were bitten. "When he starts for them, they scream," she explained, "and that excites him." The cops suggested that it might be a good idea to tie the dog up, but mother said that it mortified [embarrassed] him to be tied up and that he wouldn't eat when he was tied up.
—from "The Dog That Bit People" by James Thurber

1. What group of people is James Thurber satirizing in this passage?

_____ mothers

_____ pet owners

_____ police officers

_____ people who are afraid of dogs

2. Which phrase from the passage is an example of exaggeration?

_____ it hadn't been Muggs' fault but the fault of the people who were bitten

_____ When he starts for them, they scream

_____ it might be a good idea to tie the dog up

_____ it mortified [embarrassed] him to be tied up

© Pearson Education, Inc., publishing as Pearson Prentice Hall.

# Satire

**A**  For each question, circle the letter of the best answer.

**1.** What is the main purpose of satire?

   **A.** to present factual information    **C.** to make fun of a person or society

   **B.** to explain causes and effects    **D.** to explain a process

**2.** What is exaggeration?

   **A.** making fun of a person or society

   **B.** making something seem more than it is

   **C.** making something seem less than it is

   **D.** words that mean the opposite of what they say

**3.** What is irony?

   **A.** words that mean what they say

   **B.** words that mean the opposite of what they say

   **C.** words that appeal to the five senses

   **D.** words that are meant to change how people think

**B**  Read the passage. Then, put a check mark next to the correct answer for each question.

It is allowed on all hands, that the primitive way of breaking eggs before we eat them, was upon the larger end; but his present Majesty's grandfather, while he was a boy, going to eat an egg, and breaking it according to the ancient practice, happened to cut one of his fingers. Whereupon the Emperor, his father, published an edict, commanding all his subjects, upon great penalties, to break the smaller end of their eggs. The people so highly resented this law that our histories tell us there have been six rebellions raised on that account; wherein one emperor lost his life, and another his crown.

—from *Gulliver's Travels* by Jonathan Swift

**1.** What is Jonathan Swift satirizing in this passage?

_____ eating eggs     _____ wars over beliefs     _____ ancient kings

**2.** Which is an ironic comment on the passage?

_____ Cutting a finger on an eggshell is not a real danger.

_____ It does not matter which end of the egg you break.

_____ What better reason to fight than to decide how to break an egg!

© Pearson Education, Inc., publishing as Pearson Prentice Hall.

# Setting

The **setting** is the time and place of the story's events. To establish a setting, writers use description, or word-pictures appealing to the senses. Settings shape stories in a few ways:

- Settings may determine plot. In a story set in the Arctic wilderness, characters will face challenges not found in a Caribbean resort hotel.

- Setting may shape a character's concerns and values. A character from the days of knights might be concerned with honor.

---

**A** Read the description of each problem. On the line, write the letter of the most likely setting.

**1.** _____ A colony of tourists has lost communication with Earth.

   **A.** the past in New York
   **B.** the future of the moon
   **C.** the present in San Diego

**2.** _____ A group of men in America want to be free of England.

   **A.** the future in Boston
   **B.** the present in Detroit
   **C.** the past in Boston

**3.** _____ A sixteen-year-old wants to work at a computer store, but his parents say no.

   **A.** ancient Egypt
   **B.** Florida today
   **C.** Italy in 1955

---

**B** Match each event on the left with the most likely setting on the right.

**1.** _____ A ship hits an iceberg.

**2.** _____ A student graduates.

**3.** _____ A mountain climber is lost in a snowstorm.

**4.** _____ A caterpillar becomes a butterfly.

   **A.** the first day of spring, in the middle of a forest
   **B.** the middle of a frigid winter season, high up in the Colorado Rockies
   **C.** near South Bend, Indiana, on the University of Notre Dame campus
   **D.** two hours after dusk, in the Ross Sea off the coast of Antarctica

© Pearson Education, Inc., publishing as Pearson Prentice Hall.

# Setting

**A**   Circle the letter of the best answer.

**1.** The setting of a story is the _____ of its events.

    **A.** time and place           **C.** meat and potatoes

    **B.** rise and fall              **D.** best and worst

**2.** Which of the following most clearly conveys a setting?

    **A.** I loved to paint when I was a child, but now I prefer to play the piano.

    **B.** Patricia was a master photographer who was on her way to a lucrative career.

    **C.** It was a dark and stormy night in late June 1952, and the rain hit the roof like a thousand horses.

    **D.** The boys and girls could not wait until the last day of school.

**B**   Read each description. Then, write the letter of the most likely setting.

**1.** _____ A group of civil rights activists march to a rally held by Martin Luther King, Jr.

    **A.** Washington, D.C., in the 1960s     **C.** New Jersey in colonial times

    **B.** Oklahoma in the frontier days

**2.** _____ thousands of people with noisemakers, streamers, and confetti

    **A.** Sunday morning in a churchyard, early fall

    **B.** a college library the night before final exams

    **C.** Times Square in New York City on New Year's Eve

**3.** _____ a crowd of young children with backpacks and lunchbags

    **A.** a sandy beach in Mexico         **C.** a supermarket in New Jersey

    **B.** a schoolyard in San Francisco

**C**   Match each event on the left with the most likely setting on the right.

**1.** _____ A horse grazes in a field.     **A.** the first day of spring, in the middle of a forest

**2.** _____ A bee pollinates a flower.     **B.** a family farm in Boise, Idaho

**3.** _____ A book is placed on a shelf.     **C.** near South Bend, Indiana, in the library of the University of Notre Dame

© Pearson Education, Inc., publishing as Pearson Prentice Hall.

# Setting a Purpose for Reading

### Practice

When you **set a purpose for reading**, you decide beforehand why you are reading and what to focus on as you read. Here are some examples of purposes for reading and of suitable types of material and reading style:

| Purpose | Type of Material | Type of Reading |
|---|---|---|
| reading to be entertained | an adventure story; a poem | read at a comfortable speed; reread when necessary |
| reading to find information | an encyclopedia; a Web site | skip around until you find the information you need, then read more carefully |
| reading to understand | a chapter in a history book | read slowly and carefully, pausing to summarize or clarify points |

Previewing the text can help you establish a purpose for reading. Quickly look at titles, captions, and beginnings of passages to see what sort of material it is and what sort of reading you will be doing.

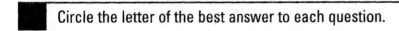 Circle the letter of the best answer to each question.

1. If an article is titled "The Life Cycle of Mosquitoes," and you notice charts, photos, and scientific captions in it, what purpose for reading would you set?

   **A.** to be inspired
   **B.** to be entertained
   **C.** to gain a new skill
   **D.** to learn about a subject

2. Your purpose in reading a book is to understand the causes of the Civil War. How should you read?

   **A.** at a comfortable pace, skipping over the boring parts
   **B.** at a fast pace, slowing down for details about specific dates
   **C.** at a slow, steady pace, pausing to summarize ideas
   **D.** at a slow, steady pace, speeding up when you reach exciting parts

© Pearson Education, Inc., publishing as Pearson Prentice Hall.

# Setting a Purpose for Reading

### Assess

**A**  Read the following passage. Then, answer the questions.

## Some Facts About Owls

Owls are birds of prey that are usually active at night and at rest during the day. There are over 130 species of owls in the world.

All owls have large heads and very large eyes. One interesting fact about owls' eyes is that they are immobile: they do not move in their eye sockets. An owl must turn its head to see things to the side of it or behind it.

Because their feathers are extremely thick, owls make almost no noise when they fly. Their stealth helps them surprise their prey, which they catch with hooked claws and beaks. Many types of owls hunt mice and other rodents; others hunt reptiles or large insects.

1. What does the title suggest about this selection?

   **A.** The selection is a short story.
   **B.** The selection gives information.
   **C.** The selection will inspire the reader.
   **D.** The selection is about current events.

2. Based on the title and the first paragraph, which is the best purpose to set for reading this passage?

   **A.** to be entertained
   **B.** to learn how to do something
   **C.** to be informed about a topic
   **D.** to get help with a personal problem

**B**  Read this introduction to an encyclopedia entry on Leeds Castle. Then, name two different purposes readers might have for reading the entry.

**Leeds Castle** Leeds Castle, located in the county of Kent in England, was originally built as a Saxon fortress in A.D. 857. It was later converted to a royal palace by Henry VIII. Throughout the years, it served as a residence to six medieval queens. Today, it is a popular tourist destination offering visitors a chance to view an important part of history along with a nature trail, an aviary, and a dog collar museum.

_____

_____

# Sonnet

A **sonnet** is a fourteen-line poem focused on a single theme. The Petrarchan sonnet is one kind of sonnet. It has these characteristics:

- It is divided into an eight-line *octave* followed by a six-line *sestet*.
- The octave usually has a rhyme scheme of *abba abba* or *abab abab*.
- The sestet usually has a rhyme scheme of *cdecde, cdcdcd,* or *cdedce.*
- The sestet often responds to a question or statement in the octave.

Here is part of the octave from Petrarch's "The White Doe." It shows the octet rhyme scheme *abab* and describes the speaker's encounter with a doe:

A pure-white doe in an emerald <u>glade</u> / Appeared to me, with two antlers of *gold,* / Between two streams, under a laurel's <u>shade,</u> / At sunrise, in the season's bitter *cold.*

Here is the sestet from this sonnet. Notice the different rhyme scheme: *cdcdcd.*

Around her lovely neck "Do not touch *me*" / Was written with topaz and diamond <u>stone,</u> / "My Caesar's will has been to make me *free.*" / Already toward noon had climbed the <u>sun,</u> / My weary eyes were not sated to *see,* / When I fell in the stream and she was <u>gone.</u>

> **Read each part of Petrarch's "Laura," and then answer the questions that follow.**

She used to let her golden hair fly free / For the wind to toy and tangle and molest; / Her eyes were brighter than the radiant west. / (Seldom they shine so now.) I used to see / Pity look out of those deep eyes on me. / ("It was false pity," you would now protest.) / I had love's tinder heaped upon my breast; / What wonder that the flame burned furiously?

**1.** Group together the words that rhyme. What octet rhyme scheme is used?

_____

_____

**2.** What part of his life does the speaker describe in the octet?

_____

_____

She did not walk in any mortal way, / But with angelic progress; when she spoke, / Unearthly voices sang in unison. / She seemed divine among the dreary folk / Of earth. You say she is not so today? / Well, though the bow's unbent, the wound bleeds on.

**3.** What does "the wound bleeds on" tell you about how the speaker feels now?

_____

   © Pearson Education, Inc., publishing as Pearson Prentice Hall.

# Sonnet

**A** Read the octave from Petrarch's "Spring." Then, answer the questions.

Zephyr[1] returns, and scatters everywhere
New flowers and grass, and company does bring,
Procne and Philomel, in sweet despair,
And all the tender colors of the Spring.
Never were fields so glad, nor skies so fair;
And Jove exults in Venus' prospering.
Love is in all the water, earth and air,
And love possesses every living thing.

1. **Zephyr** the west wind.

**1.** Circle the words that rhyme with "everywhere." Underline the words that

rhyme with "bring." What octet rhyme scheme is used? _____

**2.** What statement about love does the speaker make in this octet? Bracket the
lines that support your answer.

_____

**B** Read the sestet from Petrarch's "Spring." Then, answer the questions.

But to me only heavy sighs return
For her who carried in her little hand
My heart's key to her heavenly sojourn.[1]
The birds sing loud above the flowering land;
Ladies are gracious now.—Where deserts burn
The beasts still prowl on the ungreening sand.

1. **sojourn** visit or stay.

**1.** Circle the words that rhyme with "return." Underline the words that rhyme

with "hand." What sestet rhyme scheme is used? _____

**2.** Why is the speaker sad, even though spring has arrived? Bracket the lines

that support your answer. _____

_____

**3.** In what way does the sestet respond to the octave in Activity A? _____

_____

© Pearson Education, Inc., publishing as Pearson Prentice Hall.

# Speaker

The **speaker** of a work is the character who "says" its words, or the voice of the work. Here are some of the various types of speaker:

- a fictional character—including the "I" who speaks in many poems
- the writer's representation of himself or herself

The speaker of a work reveals himself or herself through the information he or she gives and the words he or she uses. Generally, you should only conclude that the speaker is the writer if the speaker includes facts about his or her own life, as in an essay.

| Essay | Speaker |
|---|---|
| Home is where the heart is. . . . I love my home with a ferocity totally out of proportion to its appearance or location.   —from "Homeless" by Anna Quindlen | The speaker is the writer herself. Quindlen presents herself as a thoughtful, lively person. She uses casual words like *totally* to express her feelings. |

| Poem | Speaker |
|---|---|
| That's my last Duchess painted on the wall, Looking as if she were alive. . . .   —from "My Last Duchess" by Robert Browning | The speaker is a made-up character. You can tell that he is a Duke showing a visitor a painting of his dead wife. |

For each passage, tell whether the speaker is a fictional character or the writer. Then, give two words or phrases that describe the speaker's personality.

My mother was born like me—in Chicago but of Mexican descent. It would be her tough, streetwise voice that would haunt all my stories and poems. An amazing woman who loves to draw and read books and can sing an opera. A smart cookie.   —from "Straw Into Gold" by Sandra Cisneros

**1.** Fictional Character / Writer _____

I have looked down the saddest city lane. / I have passed by the watchman on his beat / And dropped my eyes, unwilling to explain.

—from "Acquainted With the Night" by Robert Frost

**2.** Fictional Character / Writer _____

   © Pearson Education, Inc., publishing as Pearson Prentice Hall.

Name _____ Date _____

# Speaker

**A** In the blank, write *T* if the statement is true or *F* if it is false.

**1.** _____ The speaker of a poem or an essay is the "voice" of the work.

**2.** _____ In poems, the speaker is always the poet.

**3.** _____ The speaker in a poem may be a generalized voice, without many specific characteristics.

**4.** _____ The speaker of an essay is often the writer himself or herself.

**B** Read the following passage from the essay "Shooting an Elephant" by George Orwell. Then, tell whether the speaker is the writer or a fictional character. Explain what you learn, about the speaker's personality in the passage, and tell how you know.

In Moulmein, in lower Burma, I was hated by large numbers of people— the only time in my life that I have been important enough for this to happen to me. I was subdivisional police officer of the town, and in an aimless, petty kind of way anti-European feeling was very bitter.

_____

_____

_____

**C** Read the following lines by Alfred, Lord Tennyson. Then, explain who the speaker of the poem is. Tell how you know.

I slip, I slide, I gloom, I glance,
Among my skimming swallows;
I make the netted sunbeam dance
Against my sandy shallows.

. . .

5　And out again I curve and flow ·
To join the brimming river,
For men may come and men may go,
But I go on forever.

_____

_____

© Pearson Education, Inc., publishing as Pearson Prentice Hall.

# Speech

A **speech** is an oral presentation on an important issue. The speaker determines the content of the speech by considering the speech's *purpose*, the *occasion* for which it is being given, and the *audience* to whom it is addressed. An effective speaker uses a variety of techniques to emphasize key points in a speech:

- **Restatement:** repeating an idea in a variety of ways
- **Repetition:** restating an idea using the same words
- **Parallelism:** repeating grammatical structures
- **Rhetorical question:** asking a question whose answer is self-evident

**A**  Write *T* if the statement is true or *F* if it is false.

1. _____ Speeches are delivered orally.

2. _____ A rhetorical question is one that has no answer.

3. _____ Parallelism involves the repetition of grammatical structures.

4. _____ In repetition, you restate an idea using different words.

5. _____ Speakers may use restatement of an idea in a variety of ways to emphasize a key point.

**B**  For each passage, circle the letter of the technique it uses.

"I came, I saw, I conquered." (Julius Caesar)

**1. A.** rhetorical question          **B.** parallelism

"Our brethren are already in the field! Why stand we here? What is it that gentlemen wish? What would they have? Is life so dear, or peace so sweet, as to be purchased at the price of chains and slavery?" (Patrick Henry)

**2. A.** repetition          **B.** rhetorical question

". . . we here highly resolve that these dead shall not have died in vain—that this nation, under God, shall have a new birth of freedom—and that government of the people, by the people, and for the people shall not perish from the earth." (Abraham Lincoln)

**3. A.** parallelism          **B.** repetition

© Pearson Education, Inc., publishing as Pearson Prentice Hall.

# Speech

## Assess

**A**  Write the letter of the item in Column B that correctly matches each item in Column A.

| Column A | Column B |
|---|---|
| 1. _____ restatement | **A.** repeating grammatical structures |
| 2. _____ repetition | **B.** question with a self-evident answer |
| 3. _____ parallelism | **C.** repeating an idea in a variety of ways |
| 4. _____ rhetorical question | **D.** using the same words to repeat an idea |

**B**  Read the following passages from the Inaugural Address of President John F. Kennedy, delivered on January 20, 1961. Then, circle the letter of the technique used in each one.

1. Let every nation know whether it wishes us well or ill, that we shall pay any price, bear any burden, meet any hardship, support any friend, oppose any foe, to assure the survival and success of liberty.

   **A.** parallelism          **B.** repetition          **C.** rhetorical question

2. To that world assemblage of sovereign states, the United Nations, our last best hope in an age where the instruments of war have far outpaced the instruments of peace, we renew our pledge of support—to prevent it from becoming merely a forum for invective—to strengthen its shield of the new and the weak—and to enlarge the area in which its writ may run.

   **A.** rhetorical question          **B.** parallelism          **C.** restatement

3. In the long history of the world, only a few generations have been granted the role of defending freedom in its hour of maximum danger. I do not shrink from that responsibility—I welcome it. I do not believe that any of us would exchange places with any other people or any other generation. The energy, the faith, the devotion which we bring to this endeavor will light our country and all who serve it. And the glow from that fire can truly light the world.

   **A.** rhetorical question          **B.** parallelism          **C.** restatement

# Summarizing

A summary is a brief statement that expresses the key details of a literary work. **Summarizing** helps you review and understand what you are reading. To summarize, identify the details that are essential to your understanding of a story. Then, organize those details into a concise statement.

**Read the paragraphs below. Then, answer the questions.**

[1] The peculiar bright light, which shone through the attic door, bothered Kelly as she passed the doorway to the attic stairs. Every night she walked past the doorway on her way to wash up for bed, but this was the first time she had noticed this strange orange glow.

[2] As she crept carefully, but nervously, toward the door, Kelly had the feeling her curiosity might get her into trouble. Her mother and father were due back from a meeting at school, and she knew she should wait and let them explore the cause of the light. Patience had never been one of her strongest virtues, though.

1. Which detail is *not* essential to your understanding of paragraph 1?

   **A.** A peculiar bright light shone through the attic door.
   **B.** The peculiar bright light bothered Kelly.
   **C.** Every night Kelly walked past the doorway on her way to wash up for bed.
   **D.** Kelly had never noticed this strange orange glow before.

2. Which detail is *not* essential to your understanding of paragraph 2?

   **A.** Kelly's parents are at a meeting at her school.
   **B.** Kelly is very curious about the bright light.
   **C.** Kelly is very nervous about the bright light.
   **D.** Kelly is not a very patient person.

3. Which is the best summary of both paragraphs?

   **A.** Kelly is a nervous girl who washes up for bed every night.
   **B.** Kelly is home alone at night when she discovers she is not very patient.
   **C.** Kelly sees a bright light in the attic that makes her nervous but curious.
   **D.** Kelly is not doing very well at school, which is why her parents are meeting with her teachers.

© Pearson Education, Inc., publishing as Pearson Prentice Hall.

# Summarizing

**A**  Circle the letter of the best answer.

**1.** A summary is a _____ statement about the key details of a literary work.

   **A.** long          **B.** brief          **C.** thorough          **D.** sad

**2.** How can summarizing help a reader understand a passage or work?

   **A.** Summarizing forces a reader to read details aloud.
   **B.** Summarizing helps a reader increase his or her vocabulary.
   **C.** Summarizing helps a reader improve his or her spelling.
   **D.** Summarizing helps a reader identify details that are essential to the understanding of a story.

**B**  Read the following paragraph. Then, respond to the items below.

The Willow Grove botanical garden is famous for having a rare breed of purple rose bushes. These purple roses are so rare that the gardeners are not allowed to cut flowers from them. However, this botanical garden does have many other beautifully colored roses—every color of the rainbow, in fact, from shades of white and ivory to pale oranges and golds to deepest reds. From these varieties the gardeners are allowed to cut freely, and they often donate rose bouquets to local hospitals. In fact, the rare purple roses help the hospital, too: each year, the Willow Grove botanical garden donates one small purple rose bush to the hospital's fund-raising auction.

**1.** Which detail is *not* essential to your understanding of the paragraph?

   **A.** The Willow Grove botanical garden is famous for its purple rose bushes.
   **B.** The Willow Grove botanical garden has roses in shades of white and ivory to pale oranges and golds to deepest reds.
   **C.** The Willow Grove botanical garden donates one small purple rose bush to the hospital's fund-raising auction every year.
   **D.** The Willow Grove botanical garden's purple roses are so rare that the gardeners are not allowed to cut flowers from them.

**2.** Write a summary of this paragraph on the lines provided.

_____

_____

_____

© Pearson Education, Inc., publishing as Pearson Prentice Hall.

# Surrealism

**Surrealism,** which means "beyond realism," refers to a twentieth-century artistic movement. Surrealist works generally portray people, animals, and objects in realistic detail. But they go "beyond realism" by putting images together that do not logically belong with each other. In this way, Surrealist works create dreamlike images and stories.

> Read the following passage from "She used to throw her old crockery . . . " a poem by Vénus Khoury-Ghata, translated by Marilyn Hacker. (*Crockery* means "dishware.") Then, answer the questions and complete the activities.

She used to throw her old crockery at the moon
which mends chipped plates
darns wedding sheets
and sorts lamplight-yellowed snapshots by degrees of sadness

The whole universe shared my mother's household chores
contrary winds blew into her bureau drawers
bargained between her shutters
and swept towards town the dream-crumbs she nibbled in her sleep

1. In the first stanza, what things does the moon do? Are these activities logical? Explain.

_____

_____

2. In the second stanza, what do the "contrary winds" do? What makes this portrayal of the winds' activities dreamlike?

_____

_____

3. If "Surrealism" means "beyond realism," explain how the two stanzas above could be called surrealistic.

_____

_____

_____

© Pearson Education, Inc., publishing as Pearson Prentice Hall.

## Surrealism

**Read the following passage. Then, answer the questions and complete the activities.**

The child stood in her backyard blowing bubbles
And each bubble was filled with wonderful things.
One bubble contained nothing but dark, velvety violets;
Another, a family of squeaking, pink-mouthed mice.
A third, a very, very small girl blowing very small bubbles.
The bubbles sometimes broke and what was in them fell out
And landed on oak trees and traffic lights.
But this didn't stop the child from blowing more bubbles.

**1.** Tell in your own words what is happening in the poem.

_____

_____

_____

**2.** Point out two concrete details that add an air of realism to the poem.

_____

**3.** Why are the blown bubbles part of an illogical, dreamlike world?

_____

**4.** What is dreamlike about the child himself or herself?

_____

**5.** Explain why this is a surrealistic poem.

_____

_____

_____

_____

_____

_____

_____

© Pearson Education, Inc., publishing as Pearson Prentice Hall.

# Symbols

Practice

A **symbol** is a person, a place, or an object that has its own meaning but also suggests a larger or secondary meaning.

- The American flag is a *symbol* of the United States.

- In a story, a dog might be a *symbol* of friendship or loyalty.

To recognize symbols in literature, look for characters, places, or objects that are mentioned repeatedly or linked to larger concepts.

**A**    For each item, name one thing for which it might be a symbol.

1. _____ a bald eagle

2. _____ a person's fist with the thumb sticking up

3. _____ a fancy white dress with a long veil

4. _____ a picture of a bird sewn onto an athlete's uniform

5. _____ a cheetah

**B**    For each question, circle the letter of the best answer.

1. In a story about two friends, Sally and Ashley, the friends share a portable CD player. Sally uses it one week, and Ashley uses it the next. Sally and Ashley have an argument. The next day, the CD player breaks. What is the CD player a symbol of?

     **A.** the girls' friendship           **C.** the girls' music

     **B.** the girls' argument           **D.** the girls' unhappiness

2. In a story, Sue goes to the city to become an actress. Before she leaves, her mother gives her an old hairbrush. It first belonged to Sue's grandmother, who gave it to Sue's mother. In the city, Sue uses the brush whenever she needs good luck. What is the hairbrush a symbol of?

     **A.** family love and pride           **C.** acting

     **B.** the grandmother's hair           **D.** the city

© Pearson Education, Inc., publishing as Pearson Prentice Hall.

# Symbols

**A**  For each item, name one thing for which it might be a symbol.

1. _____ a red circle with a slanted red line through it

2. _____ a skull with two crossed bones beneath it

3. _____ a stork carrying a bundle in its beak

4. _____ a pumpkin

5. _____ an owl

**B**  For each question, circle the letter of the best answer.

1. In a story, a little boy's grandfather falls ill. The little boy is sad and worried. One day, the boy finds a bird with a broken wing outside his house. He takes the bird inside and helps it heal. A few weeks later, he learns that his grandfather is better. That same day, the bird flies away, its wing fully healed. What is the bird a symbol of?

   A. the boy's worries about his grandfather
   B. the grandfather's worries about the boy
   C. the boy's father
   D. the grandfather's doctor

2. In a story, a young man is in love with a young woman. Every evening, he sits outside her home and plays songs for her on his guitar. She tells him that she likes his music. One day, the young man comes to her home and sees a wedding taking place. The young woman is getting married to another man. The young man goes home and puts his guitar away. He swears he will never play it again. What is the guitar a symbol of?

   A. the young woman's marriage
   B. the young man's life
   C. the young man's love for the young woman
   D. the young woman's love of music

© Pearson Education, Inc., publishing as Pearson Prentice Hall.

# Theme

The **theme** of a literary work is the central message it communicates. For example, a simple story might have the theme, "Honesty is the best policy." A more complex work might show that "Human suffering cannot be justified or explained." To express a theme, a writer may take one of these approaches:

- **Directly state** the theme of the work, or have a character directly state it.
- Create patterns of story elements to **imply** a larger meaning—for instance, by contrasting a generous man and his selfish brother to communicate a message about generosity.

**A** Read the following passage. Then, circle the best answer to each question.

Wilma Rudolph was an athlete who had a difficult childhood. After she came down with scarlet fever and double pneumonia at the age of four, she could not use her left leg. She learned to walk again at age seven and ran in races when she was twelve. Later, she won gold medals running in the Olympics. Wilma's life is proof that if people try hard, they can overcome great handicaps.

1. What is the message, or theme, in this paragraph?

   A. Wilma Rudolph got pneumonia when she was four.
   B. You can overcome a lot of difficulties if you try.

2. Which sentence from the paragraph directly states the theme?

   A. Wilma's life is proof that if people try hard, they can overcome great handicaps.
   B. Wilma Rudolph was an athlete who had a difficult childhood.

**B** Read the following paragraph. Then, circle the letter of the theme.

The ladder was still propped against the house. Everywhere there was the smell of smoke. Luckily, the three children had been carried to safety by a passing mail carrier who noticed the flames shooting through the roof. The father had been overcome by smoke. Now, he was recovering in the hospital.

A. It is sad when a family loses their home because of a fire.
B. Sometimes, being in the right place at the right time makes all the difference.

© Pearson Education, Inc., publishing as Pearson Prentice Hall.

# Theme

**A**  Read the following passage. Then, circle the letter of the theme.

Sam is a pilot. His plane was in a midair accident over a large city. He was in danger of losing his own life, his copilot's life, and perhaps the lives of others on the ground. He started to panic. Then, he calmed himself, grabbed the controls, and headed for an open area he saw down below. Carefully, he landed the plane.

**A.** A small plane should never be allowed to fly over a city.
**B.** Sometimes, a person must remain calm to survive in a crisis.

**B**  Read each passage, and then answer the questions that follow.

The main reason to explore outer space is to keep our curiosity and our courage alive. We cannot say what good things will come from sending a mission to Mars. There may be many, or there may be few. What is most important is that once again, we leap into the unknown.

**1.** Is the theme of this passage implied or directly stated?

**A.** implied                    **B.** directly stated

**2.** What is the theme?

_____

_____

An old fisherman and a young fisherman went fishing. Near the end of the day, the old fisherman hooked a huge fish. The two fishermen struggled for an hour to get the fish on their boat. The fish was too strong, though, and it got away. The young fisherman was upset that they did not catch the fish after so much work. The old fisherman laughed and said, "Now you have a reason to go fishing tomorrow—to catch that big fish!"

**2.** Is the theme of this passage implied or directly stated?

**A.** implied                    **B.** directly stated

**2.** What is the theme?

_____

_____

# Tragedy

**A tragedy** is a play in which the main character experiences a deep loss or a reversal of fortune, such as the loss of his or her family or kingdom. The tragedy ends in the downfall or even the death of the hero.

- In classical tragedies, the **tragic hero** is almost always a person of noble birth or high rank. The tragic hero usually demonstrates greatness in other ways as well. He or she may be a brilliant military leader, a great king or queen, or the savior of a people.

- The tragic hero often has a **tragic flaw.** A tragic flaw is a personality trait that contributes to his or her doom. For example, the tragic hero may display excessive rage, blindness to the truth, or a thirst for revenge.

**A** For each question, circle the letter of the best answer.

1. Which is the best definition of a tragic hero?

   **A.** a person of low rank but fine inner qualities who sacrifices for others
   **B.** a person who hides bad qualities behind high rank or power
   **C.** a person of high rank and noble quality who suffers a reversal of fortune
   **D.** a person of low rank who rises to a position of power

2. Which is the best definition of a tragic flaw?

   **A.** a personality weakness that the hero does not recognize in himself
   **B.** a personality weakness that contributes to a hero's doom
   **C.** a personality trait that is both good and bad
   **D.** a personality trait that motivates the hero to take action

**B** Read the summary below. Then, answer the questions.

   King Oedipus is the savior of his city, a great warrior and leader. In order to rid his land of a plague he vows to find and punish the murderer of the former king. Oedipus continues the search, even as it uncovers the terrible truth that he is the killer he seeks. In the end, Oedipus blinds himself and is banished.

1. In what ways is Oedipus a classic tragic hero?

   _____

   _____

2. Briefly describe the reversal of fortune that Oedipus experiences.

   _____

   _____

  © Pearson Education, Inc., publishing as Pearson Prentice Hall.

# Tragedy

Assess

---

**A** For each item, circle the letter of the answer that best completes the definition.

**1.** A tragedy is a play in which

    **A.** a noble person suffers for a time but finally finds happiness.
    **B.** a noble person suffers a terrible reversal of fortune.
    **C.** a person of low rank sinks even lower.
    **D.** a deserving person achieves success after conquering many obstacles.

**2.** A tragic hero is a character

    **A.** of high rank who is otherwise ordinary.
    **B.** who does not know his own origins.
    **C.** of high rank or noble birth who also reveals greatness in other ways.
    **D.** who seeks out his own destruction.

**3.** A tragic flaw is a personality trait in the hero that

    **A.** makes the audience feel pity.     **C.** is both a blessing and a curse.
    **B.** the hero tries to hide.     **D.** leads to the hero's downfall.

---

**B** Read the summary below. Then, answer the questions.

    Antigone is a princess in the kingdom of Thebes. Her uncle Creon is now king. Antigone is angry with Creon because he has denied burial to Antigone's brother Polyneices, who had fought against Thebes. Even though Creon promises death to anyone who tries to bury the body, Antigone buries her brother. She says she must obey the laws of the gods, who require burial, more than the laws of man. Despite pleas for mercy from his son Haimon, who was Antigone's fiancé, and others, Creon will not change his mind. He has Antigone killed. After her execution, Haimon kills himself. Creon's wife also kills herself. In the end, Creon is alive but deeply grieved. His family and his pride have been destroyed.

**1.** How does the character of Antigone fit the definition of a tragic hero?

_____

**2.** Judging from the summary, what might be Creon's tragic flaw?

_____

**3.** Briefly describe the reversal of fortune that Creon experiences.

_____

© Pearson Education, Inc., publishing as Pearson Prentice Hall.

# Understanding Spatial Relationships

## Practice

The location of things in a story can be important. For instance, if you understand that the hero is hiding under the couch on which the villains sit, you will appreciate the story's excitement more. **Spatial relationships** include the locations and sizes of things, as well as the distances between them. As you read, keep track of these details to **understand spatial relationships.**

**A**  Circle the letter of the best answer to each question.

**1.** To describe a tree effectively, how might you organize your description?

    **A.** from left to right           **B.** from bottom to top

**2.** What spatial organization might you use to describe the sight of the ocean at a beach?

    **A.** from near to far           **B.** from left to right

**3.** To clarify the size of a specific dinosaur, what would be more effective?

    **A.** describing the animal as "huge"    **B.** comparing it to an elephant

**B**  Read the following description. Then, answer the questions.

> Over to his right a thin, black horse was running across the ploughland towards the hill, its head down, neck stretched out. It seemed to be running on its toes like a cat, like a dog up to no good.
> From the high point on which he stood the hill dipped slightly and rose to another crested point fringed with the tops of trees, three hundred yards to his right. As he watched it, the horse ran up to that crest, showed against the sky— for a moment like a nightmarish leopard—and disappeared over the other side.
> —from "The Rain Horse" by Ted Hughes

**1.** In which direction from the man is the horse? _____

**2.** Is the man looking down on or up at the horse? Explain how you know.

_____

_____

**3.** Is the horse near the man or some distance away? Explain how you know.

_____

_____

    © Pearson Education, Inc., publishing as Pearson Prentice Hall.

# Understanding Spatial Relationships

## Assess

**A** Circle the letter of the best answer to each question.

**1.** Which of the following can noting spatial relationships help clarify?

   **A.** size, distance, and location    **B.** order of importance

**2.** Which method of spatial organization would best describe a skyscraper?

   **A.** from left to right    **B.** from bottom to top

**3.** You see a sailboat on the horizon. As you quickly approach it in a powerboat, what change in spatial relationship takes place?

   **A.** from far to near    **B.** from top to bottom

**4.** In which item might a focus on spatial relationships be especially valid?

   **A.** a description of a computer    **B.** a description of a canyon

**B** Read the following description. Then, answer the questions.

   . . . One could not help looking, that summer afternoon, in the long glass[1] that hung outside in the hall. Chance had so arranged it. From the depths of the sofa in the drawing room one could see reflected in the Italian glass not only the marble-topped table opposite, but a stretch of the garden beyond. One could see a long grass path leading between banks of tall flowers until, slicing off an angle, the gold rim cut it off.

   1. **glass** mirror.
      —from "The Lady in the Looking Glass: A Reflection" by Virginia Woolf

**1.** Is the mirror inside or outside the drawing room? Explain how you know.

_____

**2.** Where is the marble-topped table in relation to the mirror? Explain.

_____

_____

**3.** How can the mirror show a reflection of the garden to someone on the sofa?

_____

_____

# Using Context Clues

## Practice

If you are having trouble understanding the meaning of unfamiliar words in a story or passage, you can **use context clues** to help you define them. Context clues are surrounding words, phrases, and sentences that can help you determine the meanings of unfamiliar words as you read.

For example, look at the word *glittering* in the following sentence.

> The front of the building was covered with glittering, eye-catching decorations, and people stopped to admire them.

From the context clues, you can determine that *glittering* must mean something related to *eye-catching*. You can also see that people might want to look at something glittering.

Read the following sentences, using the context clues to help you determine the meanings of the underlined words. Select the best meaning for each word from the list below. Write its letter on the line in front of the sentence.

**1.** _____ She was loath to admit that her shameful failure had been her own fault.

**2.** _____ His jocose account of the meeting had us all laughing.

**3.** _____ The man bartered a fine horse in exchange for a sack of flour.

**4.** _____ Her duties as president were so onerous that they left her little time or energy for herself.

**5.** _____ A scholar from the museum was consulted to determine the provenance, or origin, of the manuscript.

**6.** _____ Centuries ago, the cost of eyeglasses was so exorbitant that only the wealthy could afford them.

**A.** humorous          **D.** unwilling
**B.** source            **E.** burdensome
**C.** expensive         **F.** traded

   © Pearson Education, Inc., publishing as Pearson Prentice Hall.

## Using Context Clues

**A** In the following sentences, *dog* is used in several different ways. Use the context clues to help you determine which word from the list below best fits the meaning of *dog* in each sentence. Write the letter of your choice on the line in front of the sentence.

1. _____ The great detective would *dog* his enemy to the ends of the earth.

2. _____ I asked the waiter for a *dog* with mustard and onions.

3. _____ "Some *dog* has emptied all the ice trays and not refilled them," she shouted from the kitchen.

    **A.** frankfurter      **B.** follow      **C.** rascal

**B** Read the following sentences. Use the context clues to help you select the best meaning for each of the italicized words from the choices below. Write the letter of your choice on the line in front of the sentence.

1. _____ Several days without food and water had greatly *debilitated* him.

    **A.** helped                **C.** fattened
    **B.** rested                **D.** weakened

2. _____ At the back of the stage was a *flat* painted to look like a prison wall.

    **A.** apartment         **C.** plain
    **B.** piece of scenery    **D.** note

3. _____ The couple liked the house but thought that the *figure* its owner was asking was much too high.

    **A.** person           **C.** design
    **B.** price             **D.** diagram

4. _____ Ending the day with his breakfast was only one of his many *quirks*.

    **A.** strong feelings    **C.** cheerful smiles
    **B.** old friends        **D.** odd habits

© Pearson Education, Inc., publishing as Pearson Prentice Hall.

# Vedic Hymn

## Practice

A **hymn** is a poem or song of praise. Vedic hymns summarize the importance of gods and nature in Indian life and ponder timeless questions, such as the origin of the universe. These hymns were originally meant to be chanted, and they were passed down through the ages by spoken word before they were written down. While reading a Vedic hymn, look for devices that reflect this oral tradition, such as the repetition of words or of grammatical structures.

**A**   Write *T* if the statement is true or *F* if it is false.

1. _____ Hymns are typically poems or songs of praise.

2. _____ Vedic hymns were written down as soon as they were composed.

3. _____ Vedic hymns often deal with gods and nature.

4. _____ Repetition of words does not often occur in Vedic hymns.

5. _____ Vedic hymns ponder timeless questions, such as the origin of the universe.

**B**   Write *V* if you think the topic would be suitable for a Vedic hymn. If not, leave the space blank.

1. _____ how animals came into existence

2. _____ the stars in the night sky

3. _____ how to milk a cow

4. _____ whether guavas or oranges are more delicious

5. _____ the approach of twilight

6. _____ the way the god Shiva saved the world by swallowing poison

7. _____ how to build a small temple or wayside shrine

© Pearson Education, Inc., publishing as Pearson Prentice Hall.

Name _____ Date _____

# Vedic Hymn

**A** Circle the letter of the best answer to each question.

**1.** A hymn typically focuses on which of the following?

   **A.** sorrow            **B.** love            **C.** praise

**2.** Vedic hymns deal with life in which of the following?

   **A.** Japan            **B.** India            **C.** China

**3.** In which category do Vedic hymns belong?

   **A.** oral tradition       **B.** scholarly allusions    **C.** epic poetry

**4.** Which element might you likely find in a Vedic hymn?

   **A.** disrespect for the gods   **B.** repetition      **C.** punning statements

**5.** Which of the following are often the subjects of Vedic hymns?

   **A.** the poet's ancestors    **B.** village laws      **C.** timeless questions

**B** Write **V** if you think the topic would be suitable for a Vedic hymn. If not, leave the space blank.

**1.** _____ the sun as a life-giving force for all things

**2.** _____ how the god Vishnu assumed the form of a tortoise

**3.** _____ whether or not to eat fresh fruit in hot weather

**4.** _____ medications for treating snakebite

**5.** _____ settled life vs. nomadic life

**6.** _____ how to become an expert weaver

**7.** _____ children's duties toward their parents

© Pearson Education, Inc., publishing as Pearson Prentice Hall.

Reading Kit **187**

# Zen Parables

A **parable** is a short story that teaches a moral or spiritual lesson. **Zen parables** teach the principles of Zen Buddhism. They do so by inspiring contemplation rather than by expressing a clear moral. A parable usually offers an entertaining tale, but it lacks a statement summarizing the story's lesson.

**A**   Circle the letter of the best answer to each question.

**1.** A parable is a type of which of the following?

   **A.** epic poem          **B.** short story          **C.** lyric poem

**2.** Parables usually teach which of the following?

   **A.** history          **B.** a moral lesson          **C.** mathematics

**3.** Which of the following is most closely related to Zen parables?

   **A.** Buddhism          **B.** Taoism          **C.** Hinduism

**4.** You might expect a Zen parable to be which of the following?

   **A.** lengthy          **B.** brief          **C.** confusing

**5.** Zen parables usually lack which of the following?

   **A.** humor          **B.** characters          **C.** a directly stated moral

**B**   Read the following parable. Then, on the lines below, state the lesson of the story in your own words.

   After the power failed, a man went into the storeroom to get candles to light. He found four candles, but they each refused to be lit so that light could fill the house. The first candle said to the man, "I am too tired." The second one said, "I am too busy." The third one said, "I am too unstable, with a bad temper." The fourth candle said, "There are other things I would like to do." So the man shook his head, closed the storeroom door, and the house remained dark that night.

_____

_____

_____

© Pearson Education, Inc., publishing as Pearson Prentice Hall.

# Zen Parables

**A** Write *T* if the statement is true or *F* if it is false.

1. _____ Zen parables are usually quite lengthy.

2. _____ The purpose of a Zen parable is to teach a moral or spiritual lesson.

3. _____ A parable is a type of short story.

4. _____ Parables can often be entertaining.

5. _____ A Zen parable usually spells out the moral in an explicit statement.

**B** Choose one of these statements. On the lines below, write a brief parable of your own illustrating the moral or spiritual lesson summed up by the statement you have chosen.

(1) Look before you leap.
(2) Pride goes before a fall.
(3) A friend in need is a friend indeed.
(4) Don't count your chickens before they're hatched.

_____

_____

_____

_____

_____

_____

_____

_____

_____

_____

_____

_____

_____

© Pearson Education, Inc., publishing as Pearson Prentice Hall.

# Anglo-Saxon Word Parts *fore-* and *-less*

Practice

The **Anglo-Saxon prefix *fore-*** means "before in time, place, order, or rank." The word *forethought* means "careful thought before acting."

The **Anglo-Saxon suffix *-less*** means "without," "not able to," or "not able to be." A *restless* child is a child who is unable to rest.

**A**   Add the prefix *fore-* to each word in the box. Then, write a definition for each new word.

| man | word | head | noon |
|-----|------|------|------|

1. Word _____ Meaning _____

2. Word _____ Meaning _____

3. Word _____ Meaning _____

4. Word _____ Meaning _____

**B**   On the first line, write a definition for each numbered word. Be sure to show how the suffix *-less* is used in the word to mean either "without" or "not able to." Then, write a sentence using each word.

1. careless **Meaning** _____

   **Sentence:** _____

2. flawless **Meaning** _____

   **Sentence:** _____

3. restless **Meaning** _____

   **Sentence** _____

4. tireless **Meaning** _____

   **Sentence** _____

   © Pearson Education, Inc., publishing as Pearson Prentice Hall.

## Anglo-Saxon Word Parts *fore-* and *-less*

Assess

**A** Answer each question about the underlined word. Explain your answer.

**1.** Are a person's <u>forefathers</u> his or her grandfathers or grandchildren?

_____

**2.** Is the <u>forewoman</u> of a jury in charge of the jury or just a member?

_____

**3.** Is a <u>forerunner</u> to a storm a dark sky or a sunny sky?

_____

**4.** Which time comes in the <u>forenoon</u>, 2 P.M. or 10 A.M.?

_____

**B** Read each set of sentences. Then, write in the best word from the box.

| ageless | noiseless | shameless | faultless |
|---|---|---|---|

**1.** My grandmother is a person who never seems to get old. My grandmother

has a(n) _____ face.

**2.** The thief was not concerned that he was robbing the convenience store in

broad daylight. The thief's bold act was _____.

**3.** A library provides a place for people to go where there are no loud sounds

that distract readers. A library is a _____ place to study.

**4.** Our new volleyball coach can spike a ball over the net with no error. Our

new volleyball coach has a _____ spike.

© Pearson Education, Inc., publishing as Pearson Prentice Hall.

# Coined Words

**Coined words** are new words invented by speakers or writers, often by combining or blending two existing words. Here are some examples:

data ("information") + base ("operations center") = database, "a large collection of information stored in a central place—on a computer"

gate ("entrance to a performance or an exhibition") + crash ("enter uninvited") = gatecrash, "to enter a performance or an exhibition uninvited"

camera + recorder = camcorder, "an electronic device that takes pictures like a camera and also records sound"

**A** Write the two words that have been combined or blended to form the underlined coined word in each sentence.

1. They will <u>homeschool</u> Kay until ninth grade, but then they will send her to a

public high school. _____

2. I have not investigated the price, but my <u>guesstimate</u> is over a thousand

dollars. _____

3. The <u>infomercial</u> spokesman explained how the gadget worked and then tried

to sell it. _____

4. On a computer with a dial-up modem, it may take hours to <u>download</u> the

information. _____

**B** Write the letter of its meaning before each coined word. To figure out the meaning of the coined word, think about the two words it combines or blends.

1. ____ docudrama     **A.** farm production by large corporations

2. ____ agribusiness     **B.** the interlinked network of online computers

3. ____ fanzine     **C.** a nonfiction film or TV show that tells a good story

4. ____ cyberspace     **D.** a publication put out by fans of music, comics, and so on

© Pearson Education, Inc., publishing as Pearson Prentice Hall.

# Coined Words

Assess

**A** Write the letter of its meaning before each coined word. To figure out the meaning of the coined word, think about the two words it combines or blends.

1. ____ database

2. ____ download

3. ____ guesstimate

4. ____ infomercial

**A.** a commercial providing, or seeming to provide, factual details about the product or service being sold

**B.** a reasonable idea or speculation about a number or an amount

**C.** to transfer information from a central computer or file to another computer

**D.** a collection of retrievable information stored on a computer

**B** Combine or blend the word pairs in the box to form four recently coined words. Then, use one of the coined words to complete each sentence below.

cybernetic + space   documentary + drama   fan + magazine   gate + crash

1. I watched an interesting _____ about global warming.

2. When she could not find a ticket to the exhibition, Carole tried to

   _____.

3. Sherman subscribes to a monthly _____ about model railroads.

4. There are thousands and thousands of Web sites in _____.

**C** Make up three coined words of your own. For each, explain which two words you have combined. Give a definition for each of your own words, based on the meanings of the words you have combined.

_____

_____

_____

_____

© Pearson Education, Inc., publishing as Pearson Prentice Hall.

# Connotations and Denotations

A word's **denotation** is its basic, literal meaning. For example, the words *gaze* and *stare* have the same basic denotation: "look at something or someone steadily." The **connotations** of a word are the ideas and feelings associated with it. *Gaze* carries the connotations of *calm, thoughtfulness,* or *meditation.* You might expect someone to gaze at a painting or at the person he or she loves. *Stare* has connotations of *amazement, hostility,* and other disturbing emotions. You might expect someone to stare when he or she sees a surprising or upsetting sight.

> Read each pair of sentences. The underlined words have the same basic denotation.
> Write the different connotations of each word. The first item has been completed for you.

**1. A.** My brother <u>reminded</u> me to take out the garbage.
   **B.** My brother <u>nagged</u> me to take out the garbage.

**Basic Denotation:** caused someone to remember

**Connotations:**

**A. reminded** <u>caused someone to remember, in a friendly or an official way</u>

**B. nagged** <u>caused someone to remember, in an annoying, persistent way</u>

**2. A.** Scientists <u>warn</u> that Earth will grow warmer.
   **B.** Scientists <u>predict</u> that Earth will grow warmer.

**Basic Denotation:** tell of a future event

**Connotations:**

**A. warn** _____

**B. predict** _____

**3. A.** Mary and I <u>chatted</u> about college.
   **B.** Mary and I <u>discussed</u> college.

**Basic Denotation:** talk with someone

**Connotations:**

**A. chatted** _____

**B. discussed** _____

© Pearson Education, Inc., publishing as Pearson Prentice Hall.

# Connotations and Denotations

## Assess

In these sentences, each underlined word means "looked" or "directed the eyes." Write the connotations of each word, basing your answer on the context of the sentence.

**1.** The eye doctor's patient <u>squinted</u> at the eye chart.

_____

**2.** The child <u>peeped</u> through the closet door to see if anyone knew where he was hiding.

_____

**3.** The foolish people <u>gawked</u> with their mouths open at the celebrities walking by.

_____

**4.** When no one was looking, he <u>peeked</u> at the answers in the back of the book.

_____

**5.** Our cat <u>stared</u> without blinking at the bird hopping outside the window.

_____

**6.** The knight <u>gazed</u> fondly at the princess he had rescued from the dragon.

_____

**7.** I <u>glanced</u> through the newspaper, but I did not find any stories worth reading.

_____

**8.** Several doctors <u>examined</u> the X-rays of the football player's broken leg.

_____

**9.** My big sister <u>glared</u> at me when I teased my little sister.

_____

# Connotations: Words for Crowds

Practice

The word *throng* is one of several words meaning "crowds." Each word for crowds has different connotations, or ideas and feelings associated with it.

*Throng* may have a positive connotation, suggesting a bustling crowd, such as shoppers.
*Horde* has a negative connotation, suggesting an invasion of warriors.
*Mob* has negative connotations, suggesting an out-of-control group that is ready to act senselessly or violently.
*Masses* may have negative connotations. It may suggest a group in which people lose their individuality. It may also suggest people of common tastes and abilities.
*Swarm* suggests insects. It has a negative connotation of mindlessness or a destructive appetite.
*Herd* usually refers to a group of animals, such as cows, in which individuals follow one another. It has a negative connotation of conformity.
*Flock* also refers to a group of animals, such as sheep. *Flock* often has a positive connotation. It may suggest the affection that members of a group have for their leader or the protection that a leader gives a group.
*Pack* normally refers to a group of hunting animals, such as wolves or dogs. It may have a negative connotation of a threat of harm.

---

**A**  Read each sentence, and write *Positive* or *Negative* to describe the connotations associated with the underlined word. Use the context of the sentence for clues.

1. _____ The mobs threw rocks at cars after their team lost.

2. _____ Herds of shoppers lined up to buy the latest bestseller.

3. _____ Throngs of dancers crowded the dance floor.

4. _____ This sensitively directed film is not for the masses.

---

**B**  Use each word from the box once to correctly complete each sentence.

| flock | pack | swarm |

1. After the storm, a _____ of abandoned dogs looked for food.

2. A _____ of bees buzzed near the picnic table.

3. A _____ of children gathered around the Santa Claus at the mall.

  © Pearson Education, Inc., publishing as Pearson Prentice Hall.

# Connotations: Words for Crowds

**A**   To complete each sentence, choose the word with the most appropriate connotations from the box. Use each word only once.

| | | | |
|---|---|---|---|
| flock | herds | hordes | masses |
| mob | packs | swarms | throngs |

**1.** The writer said that the _____ would never understand his latest novel.

**2.** The kindergarten teacher crossed the street, surrounded by her

_____ of small children.

**3.** _____ of invaders swept down from the hills to attack the town.

**4.** The _____ that had gathered outside the store was growing restless, and Jimmy thought about calling the police.

**5.** _____ of shoppers surrounded the bargain tables like flies at a picnic.

**6.** _____ of happy spectators lined the city streets, waiting for the parade.

**7.** _____ of fans followed the celebrity wherever he went.

**8.** Small _____ of troublemakers were prowling the park, so people stayed away.

**B**   Write one sentence describing a scene at a mall, using one of the words in the box above. Then, write a new description of the scene using another one of the words. Finally, explain the difference in the connotations, or suggested meaning, of each sentence.

_____

_____

_____

_____

© Pearson Education, Inc., publishing as Pearson Prentice Hall.

Name _____ Date _____

# Echoic Words

**Echoic words** are words that sound like the sounds they name. They *echo* these sounds. For example, the word *hiss* sounds like the sound it names, the sound made by a snake or a leaking tire.

**A** Pronounce each of the following words. Pay attention to the sound that each word imitates. Then, use the sound of each word to write a brief definition of the word.

**1.** hoot _____

**2.** screech _____

**3.** rustle _____

**4.** snap _____

**5.** squawk _____

**6.** crash _____

**B** Circle the correct word to answer each question.

**1.** Which of these is NOT an echoic word that makes you think of a farm?

    whinny   cackle   barn   snort

**2.** Which of these is NOT an echoic word that makes you think of water?

    gush   drain   gurgle   patter

**3.** Which of these is NOT an echoic word that makes you think of dishes falling off a table?

    pots   clatter   crash   smash

© Pearson Education, Inc., publishing as Pearson Prentice Hall.

## Echoic Words

**A**  Wrie the echoic word from the box that sounds most like the sound described.

| | | | |
|---|---|---|---|
| blat | pop | crunch | thump |
| buzz | murmur | crinkle | click |

1. _____ the sound of biting down on a mouthful of peanuts

2. _____ the sound of shooting a picture with a camera

3. _____ the sound made by a wasp

4. _____ the sound of a balloon breaking

5. _____ the sound of a very loud trumpet note

6. _____ the sound of people speaking in low tones

7. _____ the sound of unwrapping a candy bar

8. _____ the sound of the thrown newspaper hitting the front door in the morning

**B**  To complete each sentence, write the best echoic word.

1. We heard the _____ of the batter hitting a home run.

   boom        whack        roar

2. The door kept _____, so I oiled the hinges.

   splashing        creaking        rumbling

3. Our dog Bones gave one quick _____ and the piece of meat was gone.

   bark        whine        gulp

4. The avalanche _____ down the mountain like thunder.

   dribbled        roared        clanged

© Pearson Education, Inc., publishing as Pearson Prentice Hall.

# Forms of *reciprocity*; Related Words: *awe*

Practice

The **noun** *reciprocity* means "mutual exchange." For instance, two friends who trade desserts from their lunches every day have a relationship of reciprocity. The **noun** *awe* means "a feeling that mixes wonder, admiration, and fear." The sight of a space shuttle might inspire a feeling of awe in someone.

Both of these nouns have related forms or words.

| *reciprocity* | ADJECTIVE: *reciprocal* | In a <u>reciprocal</u> agreement, two countries agree to exchange a service. |
|---|---|---|
| | VERB: *reciprocate* | If a friend gives me a gift, I <u>reciprocate</u> by giving him one. |
| | ADVERB: *reciprocally* | An argument usually starts <u>reciprocally</u>, with each person giving the other a reason to quarrel. |
| *awe* | ADJECTIVE: *awful* | For the witnesses, the explosion of the first atomic bomb was an <u>awful</u> sight (a sight that inspires *awe*). |
| | VERB: *awe* | Her abilities as a skater <u>awe</u> me. |
| | ADVERB: *awfully* | He drives <u>awfully</u>, speeding up when he should slow down. (The words *awful* and *awfully* have come to mean "terrible" and "terribly.") |

**A**   Write a form of the word *reciprocity* from the box above to complete each sentence.

**1.** The two nations agreed to _____ trade agreements.

**2.** If the mayor apologizes to the city council, they will _____ with an apology of their own.

**B**   Write a form of the word *awe* from the box above to complete each sentence.

**1.** I think that his painting is _____ bad and might be the worst I have ever seen.

**2.** In the play, the king is quite impressive and gestures with

_____ majesty.

© Pearson Education, Inc., publishing as Pearson Prentice Hall.

Name _____ Date _____

**A** Match each word with its definition.

1. ____ reciprocal     **A.** give in return

2. ____ awe     **B.** relationship of mutual exchange

3. ____ reciprocate     **C.** inspiring feelings of wonder and terror

4. ____ reciprocally     **D.** in return

5. ____ awful     **E.** fill with wonder and fear

6. ____ reciprocity     **F.** involving mutual exchange

**B** Answer each question about the underlined word with *Yes* or *No*, and then explain your answer.

1. _____ If you do not pay your brother back for the money you borrowed, are you acting <u>reciprocally</u>?

**Explanation:** _____

_____

2. _____ If you agree to dog-sit for your neighbor and she agrees to cat-sit for you, is it a <u>reciprocal</u> arrangement?

**Explanation:** _____

_____

3. _____ If looking down on the Grand Canyon fills you with wonder and a little fear, is it an <u>awful</u> sight?

**Explanation:** _____

_____

4. _____ If you laugh a little while watching a movie and then forget what it was about the next day, did it fill you with <u>awe</u>?

**Explanation:** _____

_____

© Pearson Education, Inc., publishing as Pearson Prentice Hall.

# Greek Prefix *hypo-*; Latin Prefix *re-*

## Practice

The **Greek prefix *hypo-*** means "under," "less than," or "slightly." For example, a person with a *hypothyroid* condition has a thyroid gland that is less active than it should be.

The **Latin prefix *re-*** means "again" or "back." For example, the word *retreat* means "to draw back," as when an army draws back from the field of battle.

---

**A** Match each description with one of the English words in the box.

| hypothermia | hypodermic | hypotension | hypoglycemia |
|---|---|---|---|

1. _____ from *hypo-* and *-ten-*, meaning "to stretch." It refers to low blood pressure.

2. _____ from *hypo-* and *derma*, meaning "skin." It refers to an injection given under the skin.

3. _____ from *hypo-* and *therme*, meaning "heat." It refers to a condition in which the body temperature falls too low.

4. _____ from *hypo-* and *glykys*, meaning "sweet," and *haima*, meaning "blood." It refers to a condition of low blood sugar.

---

**B** Replace each underlined word with a synonym from the box.

| resurface | repeat | reemploy | retrieve | repel | reload |
|---|---|---|---|---|---|

1. _____ My dog loves to <u>bring back</u> the ball when I throw it.

2. _____ I waited a long time for the ball to <u>come to the top of the lake again</u>.

3. _____ Will you help me <u>put new film in</u> my camera?

4. _____ The factory has said it will <u>hire</u> my cousin <u>again</u> after he finishes school.

5. _____ The fierce warriors will <u>drive back</u> the invaders.

6. _____ Will you <u>play</u> that piece <u>again</u>, please?

© Pearson Education, Inc., publishing as Pearson Prentice Hall.

# Greek Prefix *hypo-*; Latin Prefix *re-*

Assess

**A**  Match each description with one of the English words in the box.

| hypoallergenic | hypogastrium | hypoactive | hypokinesis |
|---|---|---|---|

1. _____ from *hypo-* and *gaster,* meaning "the stomach." It refers to the lower middle region of the abdomen.

2. _____ from *hypo-* and the German *allergie,* meaning "sensitivity to a specific substance." It means "less likely to cause an allergic reaction."

3. _____ from *hypo-* and the Greek *kinesis,* meaning "the study of bodily movements." It refers to a condition of weakened muscles.

4. _____ from *hypo-* and the Latin *activus.* It means "less than normally active."

**B**  Match each description with one of the English words in the box.

| repeal | reflect | retrieve | resonate |
|---|---|---|---|

1. _____ from *re-* and *flectere,* "to bend."

2. _____ from *re-* and the French *apeler,* "to call."

3. _____ from *re-* and *sonare,* "to sound."

4. _____ from *re-* and the French *trouver,* "to find."

**C**  Using the meaning of *re-* and the descriptions given in exercise B, write a definition for each word below.

**1.** reflect _____

**2.** repeal _____

**3.** retrieve _____

**4.** resonate _____

© Pearson Education, Inc., publishing as Pearson Prentice Hall.

# Greek Word Parts -logy and -path-

The **Greek word part -logy** means "the science, theory, or study of." *Criminology* is the study of crime. The **Greek root -path-** means "feeling" or "suffering." The word *empathize* means "to feel what another person is feeling or suffering." The root *-path-* also means "disease."

**A** Combine the word part *-logy* with one of the Greek word parts in the box to form a new word to complete each sentence.

| -geo- ("earth")   -bio- ("life")   -ornitho- ("bird")   -anthropo- ("human being") |

1. Someone studying _____ learns about the migration of snow geese.

2. A person studying _____ can understand other people's cultures.

3. The study of _____ tells about the rock layers on the planet.

4. Someone studying _____ learns about the variety of living things.

**B** Each word in the box contains the Greek root *-path-* and matches one of the numbered word descriptions. Write the correct word for each description.

| apathy   pathogen   pathology   sympathetic   osteopath |

1. _____ from *path-* and *-logy-*, "the science or study of"

2. _____ from *path-* and *a-*, "without"

3. _____ from *path-* and *syn-*, "together"

4. _____ from *path-* and *-genes*, "producing"

5. _____ from *path-* and *osteon*, "bone"

© Pearson Education, Inc., publishing as Pearson Prentice Hall.

# Greek Word Parts -logy and -path-

Assess

**A** For each definition, circle the letter of the word that best fits the definition. Use your knowledge of the Greek word parts -logy and -path-.

**1.** the study of the stories of ancient peoples

   **A.** mythology                   **B.** empathy

**2.** the study of ancient artifacts

   **A.** apathy                      **B.** archaeology

**3.** kind and understanding; sharing feelings with

   **A.** psychological            **B.** empathic

**4.** the study of family histories

   **A.** genealogy                 **B.** pathogen

**5.** a lack of feeling or interest

   **A.** apathy                      **B.** vulcanology

**B** Underline the correct synonym for each numbered word. Then, write a sentence using the numbered word.

**1.** pathologist        (doctor, mechanic)

_____

**2.** apathetic          (heavy, uncaring)

_____

**3.** pathogen          (virus, medicine)

_____

**4.** empathic          (foul, understanding)

_____

**5.** pathology         (recreational activity, study of disease)

_____

© Pearson Education, Inc., publishing as Pearson Prentice Hall.

# Latin Prefixes *ab-* and *sub-*

Practice

The **Latin prefix *ab-*** means "away," "off," or "from." It is part of the word *absorb*, which means "to take in <u>from</u> a place," as a sponge absorbs water from the floor.

The **Latin prefix *sub-*** means "under," "below," or "down." It is part of the word *submarine*, which means "<u>below</u> the sea," or "a vehicle that moves <u>under</u> the sea."

**A**  For each definition, circle the word that best fits the definition.

**1.** took away from; kidnapped

**A.** abducted                **B.** submerged

**2.** away from the ordinary; unusual or unhealthy

**A.** abnormal                **B.** subcutaneous

**3.** below the surface of the earth

**A.** subterranean            **B.** abraded

**4.** pushed or sank underwater

**A.** abjured                 **B.** submerged

**5.** under the speed of sound

**A.** subsonic                **B.** aberrant

**6.** having the details taken away; general

**A.** sublime                 **B.** abstract

**B**  Choose the circled word from Exercise A that best completes each sentence.

**1.** The diving capsule _____ to view the wreck on the seafloor.

**2.** The robbers _____ the sheriff and held him for ransom.

**3.** She was famous for exploring _____ caves.

**4.** Most airplanes fly at _____ speeds.

**5.** Some _____ growths on the skin may require surgery.

**6.** _____ ideas like *justice* can be hard to define.

                © Pearson Education, Inc., publishing as Pearson Prentice Hall.

## Latin Prefixes *ab-* and *sub-*

**A**  Match each numbered word with the letter of its meaning.

1. ____ submerge

2. ____ abnormal

3. ____ subtotal

4. ____ subsoil

5. ____ absent

**A.** not ordinary; away from what is usual

**B.** a number less than complete

**C.** layer of earth under the surface layer

**D.** away from a place; not present

**E.** plunge or dive

**B**  The words in the box each begin with the Latin prefix *ab-* or *sub-*. Use one of the words to complete each sentence.

| | | | |
|---|---|---|---|
| subnormal | absent | subtitle | abjure |
| subterranean | absorb | subtract | abnormal |

1. Her temperature was too low. It was _____.

2. The _____ earthquake made dishes fall from our table.

3. The main title of my essay is "My Recycling Project." The

   _____ is "From Glass to Plastic."

4. When you _____ 24 from 78, what is your answer?

5. The doctor saw the _____ break in the bone X-ray.

6. Several students were _____ from school because they had the flu.

7. This cloth will _____ that spilled juice from the table better than newspaper.

8. I _____ candy, and I promise to stay away from cake, too.

© Pearson Education, Inc., publishing as Pearson Prentice Hall.

Name _____ Date _____

# Latin Prefixes *ante-/anti-* and *en-*

## Practice

The **Latin prefix *ante-*** means "before" or "preceding in time." For example, *antedate* means "come before in time."

The prefix *ante-* is sometimes spelled *anti-*, as in *anticipate*, which means "look forward to." Be careful not to confuse this spelling of the prefix with the Greek prefix *anti-*. The Greek prefix means "against" or "opposed to" and may be found in words such as *antiwar* and *antigravity*.

The **Latin prefix *en-*** means "put into," "cover with," or "make into." The word *endanger* means "put into danger." The prefix *en-* can also mean "cause to be." The word *enlarge* means "cause to be large."

**A** Match each description with one of the *ante-/anti-* words in the box. Then, give a definition of the word, using the description and your knowledge of the prefix.

| antebellum | antechamber | antipasto |
| --- | --- | --- |

1. _____ from the Latin *anti-* and *pasto*, meaning "food"

_____

2. _____ from the Latin *ante-* and *chamber*, meaning "bedroom"

_____

3. _____ from the Latin *ante-* and *bellum*, meaning "war"

_____

**B** Use the meanings of *en-* to define each of these words.

1. encode _____

2. entrust _____

3. entangle _____

**208** Reading Kit

© Pearson Education, Inc., publishing as Pearson Prentice Hall.

## Latin Prefixes *ante-/anti-* and *en-*

Assess

**A** Answer *Yes* or *No* to the question about each underlined word. Then, explain how you used the meaning of the prefix *ante-* or *anti-* to find the answer.

1. _____ If you are <u>anticipating</u> an event, are you remembering how exciting it was after it has ended?

_____

2. _____ If the Golden Age of Greece <u>antedates</u> the Roman Empire, does it come before the Roman Empire?

_____

3. _____ Is an order of <u>antipasto</u> a dessert?

_____

4. _____ If a book describes <u>antebellum</u> life in America, is it written about life before the Civil War?

_____

**B** Answer *Yes* or *No* to the question about each underlined word. Then, explain how you used the meaning of the prefix *en-* to find the answer.

1. _____ If you <u>encourage</u> someone, do you help him or her gain courage?

_____

2. _____ If you <u>enrage</u> someone, do you calm his or her rage?

_____

3. _____ If you <u>entomb</u> a body, do you put it in a tomb?

_____

4. _____ If you <u>enable</u> someone to drive home, do you take his or her car keys?

_____

© Pearson Education, Inc., publishing as Pearson Prentice Hall.

## Latin Prefixes *con-/com-*, *ex-*, and *im-/in-*

The **Latin prefixes *con-* and *com-*** mean "with" or "together." When you add *com-* to *bat*, from a Latin word meaning "to battle," you get *combat*, "to fight with one another." It can also add emphasis to a basic meaning. When you add *con-* to *fidence*, from a Latin word for "trust," you get *confidence*, "deep or sure trust in yourself or others."

**A**   Match each numbered word with the letter of its meaning.

1. _____ conduct

2. _____ conspire

3. _____ compact

**A.** to plot together

**B.** an agreement made with another

**C.** to lead together, as an orchestra

The **Latin prefix *ex-*** means "out." If you add *ex-* to a word part from the Latin *tendere*, "to stretch," you get the word *extend*, or "to stretch out." The Latin word *clamare* means "to cry out," *claudere* means "to shut or close," and *trahere* means "to draw or pull."

**B**   Add the prefix *ex-* to each word part in the box, and use each word to fill the blanks.

| claim | tract | clude |
|-------|-------|-------|

1. If you answer all the questions except one, you _____ that question.

2. If you hear a sudden loud noise, you might _____ in surprise.

3. If you draw out a splinter from your thumb, you _____ it.

The **Latin prefixes *im-* and *in-*** mean "not" or "the opposite of." If you add *im-* to *possible* and *in-* to *active*, you get *impossible*, "not possible," and *inactive*, "not active."

**C**   Answer *Yes* or *No* to each question about the underlined word.

1. _____ Is a jewel with a flaw in it <u>imperfect</u>?

2. _____ Is making fun of someone an <u>immature</u> behavior?

3. _____ Is a skilled gymnast <u>inflexible</u>?

© Pearson Education, Inc., publishing as Pearson Prentice Hall.

# Latin Prefixes con-/com-, ex-, and im-/in-

Assess

**A**  Answer each question about the underlined word. Then, explain your answer.

**1.** Which would you wear to an informal dance, jeans or a fancy dress?

_____

Why? _____

**2.** Is a conversation a talk between two friends or a speech made by one

person? _____

Why? _____

**3.** If you expose a plot, do you cover it up or reveal it? _____

Why? _____

**B**  Use one of the words in the box to complete each sentence.

| | | |
|---|---|---|
| exhale | impatient | excel |
| incomplete | immortal | convention |

**1.** The students will meet together at the human rights _____.

**2.** If you rise above your normal state, you _____ at whatever
you do.

**3.** Jack didn't finish his college course, so he received an _____.

**4.** I have always been _____. I don't like to wait in line.

**5.** The gods were said to be _____. They could live forever.

**6.** We breathe in oxygen and _____ carbon dioxide.

© Pearson Education, Inc., publishing as Pearson Prentice Hall.

# Latin Prefixes *mal-* and *dis-*

## Practice

The **Latin prefix *mal-*** means "bad" or "badly" and comes from the Latin word *malus*, which means "evil." To *malfunction* is to function badly, or break down.

---

**A** Answer each question about the underlined word, and then explain your answer.

**1.** Which substance would you call <u>malodorous</u>, perfume or garbage?

_____ **Explanation:** _____

**2.** Which would you describe as <u>malformed</u>, a symmetrical vase or a twisted tree?

_____ **Explanation:** _____

**3.** If someone has a <u>malicious</u> personality, is he or she spiteful or friendly?

_____ **Explanation:** _____

**4.** If someone suffers from <u>malnutrition</u>, is he or she eating healthful food or junk food?

_____ **Explanation:** _____

The **Latin prefix *dis-*** means "apart" or "not" and changes the meaning of a word to its opposite. *Disconnect* means "to undo a connection," and *disappear* means "to vanish."

---

**B** Add the prefix *dis-* to each word in the box, and use each word to complete a sentence.

| honest | believe | continue | entangle | locate |
|---|---|---|---|---|

**1.** Help me _____ Rusty from his chain.

**2.** I hope the store doesn't _____ this brand of clothing.

**3.** I _____ your story because it just doesn't make sense.

**4.** If you jump off that boulder, you could _____ your knee.

**5.** An investigation showed the politician to be _____.

© Pearson Education, Inc., publishing as Pearson Prentice Hall.

# Latin Prefixes *mal-* and *dis-*

**Assess**

**A**    Fill in the blank in each sentence with a word from the box.

| malfunction | malice | malaria | malignant | malpractice | maltreat |
|---|---|---|---|---|---|

**1.** We were relieved to learn the tumor was not _____.

**2.** The disease _____ got its name because people used to believe it was caused by bad air.

**3.** That plantation owner was one of the few who did not _____ his slaves.

**4.** Our neighbors sued for _____ when their grandfather died in surgery.

**5.** I hope our VCR doesn't _____ when that terrific adventure movie is on.

**6.** The villain in the horror movie was full of _____.

**B**    Write the word from the box that is a synonym for each of the numbered words.

| displease | dissolve | disagree | disloyal | disappear | disclose |
|---|---|---|---|---|---|

**1.** melt _____

**2.** reveal _____

**3.** vanish _____

**4.** argue _____

**5.** unfaithful _____

**6.** annoy _____

© Pearson Education, Inc., publishing as Pearson Prentice Hall.

# Latin Roots -firm-, -tort-, and -voc-/-vok-

## Practice

The word *distort* contains the **Latin root -tort-**, which means "twist." To *distort* something is to twist it or change it from its usual shape or form.

Knowing the meaning of a root can help you understand the meanings of words in which the root appears. Learn all three of these Latin roots:

> *-firm-* means "strengthen" or "strong"
> *-tort-* means "twist"
> *-voc-* or *-vok-* means "speak," "voice," or "call"

**A** On the top lines, write the root of each underlined word and the root's meaning. Then, write the meaning of the word, using clues in the sentence and your knowledge of the root.

**1.** He answered in the <u>affirmative</u>, nodding his head vigorously.

Root: _____ Meaning: _____

_____

**2.** The acrobat <u>contorted</u> her body so that her head came between her legs.

Root: _____ Meaning: _____

_____

**3.** The talented <u>vocalist</u> has released another recording.

Root: _____ Meaning: _____

_____

**B** Write *T* if the statement is true or *F* if it is false.

**1.** ____ When you <u>vocalize</u> something, you probably think it without speaking.

**2.** ____ To <u>confirm</u> the meaning of a word, you might check a dictionary.

**3.** ____ A <u>tortuous</u> path is probably a straight line.

**4.** ____ A religious person might <u>invoke</u> a higher power to ask for help.

© Pearson Education, Inc., publishing as Pearson Prentice Hall.

## Latin Roots -firm-, -tort-, and -voc-/-vok-

Assess

**A** Write the letter of its meaning next to each root.

1. ____ -firm-          **A.** speak; voice; call

2. ____ -tort-          **B.** twist

3. ____ -voc-           **C.** strengthen; strong

**B** Use your knowledge of these roots to help you match each numbered word with its correct meaning on the right. Write the letter of the meaning on the line before the word.

1. ____ vocalize        **A.** to put in words

2. ____ affirm          **B.** to twist

3. ____ contort         **C.** to call forth

4. ____ evoke           **D.** to reinforce

**C** Complete each sentence with one of the words from the box. Use your knowledge of roots to help you.

| confirmed | vocal | invoked | tortuous |
|-----------|-------|---------|----------|

1. They were _____ about the problem and complained to the manager.

2. The dirt path twisted and turned on its _____ route through the jungle.

3. We called the supplier again and _____ that the shipment had been sent.

4. The ancient Greek warrior _____ the goddess of wisdom to help him.

© Pearson Education, Inc., publishing as Pearson Prentice Hall.

# Latin Roots -naviga-, -temp-, and -ject-

Practice

The Latin word *tempus* means "time." From it comes the **Latin root -temp-**, which appears in several English words. Here are three examples:

temporary, "lasting, used, or enjoyed for a time only"
tempo, "speed at which music is played or something is done"
contemporary, "living or happening in the same time period" or "someone of the same age or time"

Study the following three Latin roots, which are used in many English words:

> *-naviga-* means "to steer a ship"
> *-temp-* means "time"
> *-ject-* means "to throw"

**A** Read this paragraph. Then, answer the questions about the passage.

As the sailing ship slowly navigated around the globe, one sailor tried to inject some fun into the long voyage. He picked up a flute and began to play an Irish jig. The lively tempo soon had the other sailors tapping their feet and singing along.

1. _____ Which word has a root meaning "to throw"?

2. _____ Which word has a root meaning "time"?

3. _____ Which word has a root meaning "to steer a ship"?

**B** Use your knowledge of roots to help you match each numbered word with its correct meaning on the right. Write the letter of the meaning on the line before the word.

1. _____ navigator        **A.** a machine that throws an image onto a screen

2. _____ projector        **B.** a person who steers a ship or maps its course

3. _____ temporary        **C.** occurring in the same era

4. _____ contemporary     **D.** short lived; not permanent

© Pearson Education, Inc., publishing as Pearson Prentice Hall.

# Latin Roots -naviga-, -temp-, and -ject-

Assess

**A** Write the letter of its meaning next to each root.

1. _____ -naviga-                    **A.** to steer a ship

2. _____ -temp-                      **B.** to throw

3. _____ -ject-                      **C.** time

**B** Use your knowledge of these roots to help you decide if each statement is true or false. Write *T* if the statement is true or *F* if it is false.

1. _____ A temporary job is likely to last forever.

2. _____ A nurse is likely to use a needle to give you an injection.

3. _____ A map is a useful tool for a navigator.

4. _____ In a movie theater, the projector is high up at the back of the room.

**C** Circle the letter of the word that best completes each sentence. Use your knowledge of roots to help you.

1. In olden times, sailors used the stars to help with the _____ of their ships.

   **A.** navigation          **B.** projection          **C.** tempo

2. A good stage actor can _____ his or her voice so that the audience can hear it without a microphone.

   **A.** navigate            **B.** project             **C.** temporize

3. England's great writer William Shakespeare and Spain's great writer Miguel

   de Cervantes were _____ who both lived during the Renaissance.

   **A.** navigators          **B.** conjectures         **C.** contemporaries

4. The rain pattered on the roof at a steady _____.

   **A.** injection           **B.** navigation          **C.** tempo

© Pearson Education, Inc., publishing as Pearson Prentice Hall.

Name _____ Date _____

Many English words have roots that come from Latin or Old English words. Latin was the language of the ancient Romans. Old English was the language spoken by the Anglo-Saxons who invaded and settled in England.

| | |
|---|---|
| **The Latin root -pel-** means "push into motion" or "drive." | **Impel** means "**push** something forward." |
| **The Latin root -vert-** means "turn." | **Inverted** means "**turned** upside down." |
| **The Latin root -trem-** means "tremble." | **Tremendous** originally meant "big enough or powerful enough to make people tremble with fear." |
| **The Anglo-Saxon root -stead-** means "place." | **Homestead** means "the **place** where a family makes their home." |

**A** Write the letter of its meaning next to each numbered word.

**1.** ___ revert

**A.** a shivering or shaking

**2.** ___ tremor

**B.** turn back to an original state or condition

**3.** ___ steadfast

**C.** drive away

**4.** ___ repel

**D.** staying in one place; loyal

**B** Each item gives the meaning of a word. Form the word that has each meaning by adding one of the roots above to one of the following word parts.

| di- | -ble | in- | pro- |

**1.** in place of; as a substitute _____

**2.** distract, or turn someone's attention elsewhere _____

**3.** shake _____

**4.** drive a rocket or an airplane forward _____

© Pearson Education, Inc., publishing as Pearson Prentice Hall.

## Latin Roots -pel-, -vert-, and -trem-; Anglo-Saxon Root -stead-

Assess

**A** Write the letter of its meaning next to each word root.

1. _____ -pel-          **A.** place

2. _____ -vert-         **B.** turn

3. _____ -trem-         **C.** shake

4. _____ -stead-        **D.** push into motion; drive

**B** Using your knowledge of word roots, write *Yes* or *No* to answer each question.

1. _____ If you are <u>repelled</u> by something, are you likely to stand next to it without moving?

2. _____ If a police officer <u>diverts</u> your car, does he or she turn you in another direction?

3. _____ Is someone who goes into a snowstorm wearing a bathing suit likely to start <u>trembling</u>?

4. _____ If a lion gave you a <u>steadfast</u> stare, would it likely be blinking?

**C** Use your knowledge of word roots to write the word that best completes each sentence.

| home<u>stead</u>  com<u>pel</u>led  <u>trem</u>ors  di<u>vers</u>ions  <u>vert</u>igo |
| --- |

1. I wanted to stay at home, but I was _____ by urgent business to travel.

2. The earthquake caused severe _____, and the bridge started to shake.

3. People need _____ like movies to turn their attention away from their worries.

4. People who suffer from _____ feel as if the world is turning around and around.

5. The settlers plotted out a place in the woods for their _____.

© Pearson Education, Inc., publishing as Pearson Prentice Hall.

# Latin Roots -port-, -stup-, and -patr-/-pater-

Practice

The Latin word *pater* means "father." As a root in English words, it sometimes appears as *-patr-*. Here are some examples:

paternal, "relating to fathers or fatherhood"
patriarch, "the father or ruler of a family or tribe; a respected older man"
patriot, "someone who loves and strongly supports his or her fatherland"

Study the following three Latin roots, which are used in many English words:

> *-port-* means "carry" or "move"
> *-stup-* means "stunned" or "amazed"
> *-patr-* or *-pater-* means "father"

**A** On the lines after each sentence, write the root of the underlined word and the root's meaning.

**1.** Shocked by events, he failed to respond and seemed to be in a stupor.

**Root:** _____ **Meaning:** _____

**2.** The shipper imports many different goods from overseas.

**Root:** _____ **Meaning:** _____

**3.** On the paternal side of my family tree I showed all my father's ancestors.

**Root:** _____ **Meaning:** _____

**B** Circle the letter of the synonym for each underlined word. Use your knowledge of roots and the clues in Activity A to help you.

**1.** stupor:   **A.** weight   **B.** movement   **C.** daze   **D.** love

**2.** patriotic:   **A.** supporting the fatherland   **B.** moving a weight   **C.** deep in sleep   **D.** running a race

**3.** imports:   **A.** supports the fatherland   **B.** carries into the country   **C.** falls asleep   **D.** runs a race

**4.** paternal:   **A.** of a father   **B.** of an aunt   **C.** of movement   **D.** of shock

© Pearson Education, Inc., publishing as Pearson Prentice Hall.

## Latin Roots -port-, -stup-, and -patr-/-pater-

Assess

**A** Underline the word in parentheses that best completes each sentence. Use your knowledge of roots to help you.

1. The islanders use a ferry to (transport, stupefy, patronize) them to the mainland.

2. Desktop computers remain in one place, but laptop computers are (portable, paternal, stupid).

3. To be a true (exporter, patriot, stupefaction), a politician should put the good of the country before the good of his or her party.

4. Dazzled by the headlights, the deer seemed to be in a (patriarch, deportment, stupor).

**B** Circle the letter of the most likely answer. Use your knowledge of roots to help you.

1. The prefix *im-* can mean "in." What does someone who imports a car probably do?

   **A.** brings it into the country
   **B.** repairs it
   **C.** gives it to his father

2. The prefix *ex-* can mean "out." What does someone who exports rice probably do?

   **A.** sends it outside the country
   **B.** grows it
   **C.** is allergic to it

3. Which of the following would people most likely describe as stupendous?

   **A.** a boring day
   **B.** a tasteless food
   **C.** an exciting concert

4. Which of these is Jay's paternal grandfather?

   **A.** Jay's mother's father
   **B.** Jay's father's father
   **C.** Jay's stepmother's father

© Pearson Education, Inc., publishing as Pearson Prentice Hall.

# Latin Roots -sacr-, -lustr-, and -cred-

Practice

Many English words have their origins in Latin, the language of ancient Rome. Here, for example, are three Latin roots that appear in many English words.

> -sacr- means "holy"
> -lustr-, sometimes spelled -luster-, means "light" or "shine"
> -cred- means "believe"

Knowing a root's meaning can help you understand the meanings of words in which it appears. For example, knowing that -cred- means "believe" can help you figure out that something *credible* is something most people will believe. If you also know that the prefix *in-* can mean "not," you can figure out that something *incredible* is hard to believe. And if you know that the prefix *dis-* means "the opposite of," you can figure out that to *discredit* is to show that something is not believable or to prove that it is untrue.

**A** On the lines after the sentence, write the root of the underlined word and the root's meaning.

1. The temple was a <u>sacred</u> place to the people who worshipped there.

   **Root:** _____ **Meaning:** _____

2. The <u>lustrous</u> silk fabric caught the warm glow of the sun.

   **Root:** _____ **Meaning:** _____

3. The politician used many negative ads to try to <u>discredit</u> his opponent.

   **Root:** _____ **Meaning:** _____

**B** Circle the letter of the synonym for each underlined word.

1. <u>sacrosanct</u>: **A.** holy **B.** shining **C.** unbelievable **D.** noisy

2. <u>incredulous</u>: **A.** sinful **B.** bright **C.** astonished **D.** hungry

3. <u>credible</u>: **A.** believable **B.** dim **C.** dishonest **D.** religious

4. <u>luster</u>: **A.** reason **B.** glow **C.** doubt **D.** faith

© Pearson Education, Inc., publishing as Pearson Prentice Hall.

# Latin Roots -sacr-, -lustr-, and -cred-

Assess

**A** Write the letter of its meaning before each word root.

1. _____ -sacr-        **A.** light; shine

2. _____ -lustr-       **B.** holy

3. _____ -cred-        **C.** believe

**B** Use your knowledge of roots to help you match each numbered word with its correct meaning on the right. Write the letter of the meaning on the line before the word.

1. _____ credulous     **A.** easily believing whatever one is told; gullible

2. _____ discredit     **B.** shiny; glowing

3. _____ sacred        **C.** fail to believe in; reject as untrue or untrustworthy

4. _____ lustrous      **D.** holy

**C** Underline the word in parentheses that best completes each sentence. Use your knowledge of roots to help you.

1. The (sacrament, credit, luster) of the warriors' spears was like a thousand suns shining in the sky.

2. We believed the witness because her account of events was so (credible, sacrificial, lackluster).

3. Each step of the holy ritual was (sacrosanct, credulous, lustrous) to those who performed it.

4. When I heard the unbelievably amazing news, I was (sacred, incredulous, illustrious).

© Pearson Education, Inc., publishing as Pearson Prentice Hall.

# Latin Suffixes -ence, -ity, -ment, and -tion

**Practice**

A **suffix** is a word part that attaches to the end of a word or a root.

### Latin Suffixes -ence, -ity, ment, and -tion

-*ity* means "the quality or state of" or "an instance or example of"
-*ence* means "the quality, state, or act of" or "an instance or example of"
-*ment* means "the state or act of" or "an instance or example of"
-*tion* means "the state or act of" or "the result of an act of"

A suffix can change the part of speech of a word. All four of these suffixes form nouns when added to verbs or adjectives.

authentic + -ity = authenticity, "the quality or state of being authentic"
differ + -ence = difference, "an instance of being different"
agree + -ment = agreement, "the act of agreeing" or "an instance of agreeing"
inflate + -tion = inflation, "the act of inflating" or "the state of being inflated"

---

**A** Complete each sentence with the noun form of the word in parentheses. Form the noun by adding the suffix indicated. Check your spellings in a dictionary.

**1.** (real) + -ity     The boy did not fully understand the _____ of the situation.

**2.** (insist) + -ence     The child's steady _____ finally led us to agree to take her to the zoo.

**3.** (achieve) + -ment     Getting straight A's is a wonderful

_____ .

**4.** (illuminate) + -tion     A good light bulb provides many hours of

_____ .

---

**B** Use your knowledge of suffixes to help you match each numbered word with its correct meaning on the right. Write the letter of the meaning on the line before the word.

**1.** ____ employment     **A.** the state of looking forward to something

**2.** ____ capability     **B.** an instance of wanting one thing more than another

**3.** ____ preference     **C.** the state of having a job

**4.** ____ anticipation     **D.** the state of having a skill

© Pearson Education, Inc., publishing as Pearson Prentice Hall.

## Latin Suffixes -*ence*, -*ity*, -*ment*, and -*tion*

Assess

**A**  Write the letter of its meaning on the line before each word.

1. ____ innocence      **A.** the act of making a demand

2. ____ equality       **B.** the quality of being without guilt

3. ____ insistence     **C.** an instance of reaching a goal

4. ____ achievement    **D.** the quality of being equal

**B**  Use the meaning of the suffix to write a brief definition for each underlined noun. Indicate to what word the suffix was added to form the noun.

1. My <u>preference</u> is to eat dinner first and go to the movie afterward.

_____

2. We loved listening to the actor's <u>narration</u> of the story.

_____

3. In a movie, dinosaurs might walk the earth, but in <u>actuality</u>, they are extinct.

_____

4. My sister is looking for <u>employment</u> as a supermarket manager.

_____

**C**  Write a few sentences correctly using the words listed below.

eminence, from *eminent* ("respected" or "powerful") + -*ence*
capability, from *capable* ("having the ability to do something") + -*ity*
adornment, from *adorn* ("decorate" or "dress up with") + -*ment*
elation, from *elate* ("fill with joy") + -*tion*

_____

_____

_____

_____

© Pearson Education, Inc., publishing as Pearson Prentice Hall.

# Legal Terminology: Latin Roots -domin-, -jur-, and Others

## Practice

Lawyers, judges, and lawmakers use **legal terminology,** a specialized vocabulary. Many legal terms contain Latin roots. You can use your knowledge of roots to figure out their meanings.

| Latin Roots in Legal Terms | |
|---|---|
| **-dict-** means "state" or "say" | In a **verdict,** a jury *states* whether a person is guilty or not. |
| **-domin-** means "rule" or "authority" | International law determines which part of the sea a country has **dominion** over, or *rules*. |
| **-jur-** means "oath" or "law" | **Perjury** is the crime of lying while under *oath*. |
| **-sec-** usually means "follow" or "pursue" | A **prosecutor** is a lawyer who *"pursues"* a suspect through the court system. |

**A**    For each sentence, write the root in the underlined term and give the meaning of the root.

1. The prosecutor tried to prove the guilt of the accused person.

   **Root:** _____ **Meaning:** _____

2. The queen has dominion over all her subjects.

   **Root:** _____ **Meaning:** _____

3. The indictment listed three crimes of which Joan was accused.

   **Root:** _____ **Meaning:** _____

4. The judge had studied jurisprudence for years.

   **Root:** _____ **Meaning:** _____

**B**    Match each numbered word with its correct meaning.

1. ____ prosecutor      **A.** the science of law

2. ____ dominion      **B.** legal authority over

3. ____ indictment      **C.** one who pursues the court case against

4. ____ jurisprudence      **D.** statement detailing charges against a person

 © Pearson Education, Inc., publishing as Pearson Prentice Hall.

Name _____ Date _____

Assess

**A**   Write the root in the underlined word, and give the meaning of the root.

**1.** In the <u>verdict</u>, the jury pronounced a harsh sentence on the accused person.

   **Root:** _____   **Meaning:** _____

**2.** The government has <u>domain</u> over this wildlife preserve.

   **Root:** _____   **Meaning:** _____

**3.** The <u>prosecution</u> of the case took a full year.

   **Root:** _____   **Meaning:** _____

**4.** The judge had studied the law for years and was a respected <u>jurist</u>.

   **Root:** _____   **Meaning:** _____

**B**   Using your knowledge of roots and the clues in Activity A, match each numbered word with its meaning.

**1.** ___ verdict          **A.** area over which a person or state rules

**2.** ___ domain           **B.** one who studies and judges the law

**3.** ___ prosecution      **C.** pursuit of a legal case against an accused person

**4.** ___ jurist           **D.** a final statement of guilt or innocence

**C**   Complete each sentence with one of the legal terms from the box.

| dominion | indicted | juror | prosecutor |
| --- | --- | --- | --- |

**1.** When a person is _____, a statement of the charges may be read aloud.

**2.** As part of the case she presented in court, the _____ called two witnesses.

**3.** The king's _____ stretched across the sea.

**4.** A _____ helps decide how the law applies to a case.

© Pearson Education, Inc., publishing as Pearson Prentice Hall.

# Prefixes *eu-*, *pro-*, and *mono-*

Practice

The **prefix *eu-*** means "good" or "well." The word *eulogy* comes from the prefix *eu-* and *-logy*, "speech." A *eulogy* is a talk delivered at a memorial service. The **prefix *pro-*** means "forward" or "before in place or time." The word *promote* comes from the prefix *pro-* and the Latin *movere*, "to move." The **prefix *mono-*** means "alone," "one," or "single." A *monologue* is a speech in a play by a single actor alone on the stage.

**A** Match the numbered words with the definitions. Use your knowledge of the prefix *eu-* and the following definitions of root words.

> *phone* ("sound")    *pepsis* ("cooking; digestion")    *pheme* ("speaking")

1. _____ euphemism      **A.** a pleasing sound

2. _____ euphony        **B.** a pleasant word in place of a harsh one

3. _____ eupepsia       **C.** a healthy digestion

**B** Write each *pro-* word next to its definition.

promote      produce      propel

1. _____ move forward; publicize or advocate

2. _____ lead forward into being; make

3. _____ push ahead

**C** On the first line, answer each question. Then, explain how the meaning of *mono-* helped determine your answer.

1. If someone spoke in a <u>monotone</u>, would you likely be bored or interested?

_____ **Explanation:** _____

2. Does a <u>monoplane</u> have two pairs of wings?

_____ **Explanation:** _____

© Pearson Education, Inc., publishing as Pearson Prentice Hall.

# Prefixes *eu-*, *pro-*, and *mono-*

Assess

**A** Write each word in the box next to its definition below.

| proceed | monocle | eulogize | projectile |

1. _____ to speak well of a person, as at a memorial service

2. _____ to move ahead with an activity

3. _____ something that is shot forward with great force

4. _____ an eyeglass for one eye

**B** Write *T* if the statement is true or *F* if it is false. Then, explain how the meaning of the prefix determined your answer.

1. _____ A promotion means an advancement for an employee.

Explanation: _____

2. _____ Eupepsia is digestion that is unhealthy.

Explanation: _____

3. _____ A monolith is a single large stone.

Explanation: _____

**C** Write the letter of the correct meaning of each word.

1. ____ euphoria          **A.** control of an industry by a single corporation

2. ____ provoke           **B.** a feeling of joy or great happiness

3. ____ monopoly          **C.** a train system that runs on a single track

4. ____ monorail          **D.** to call forth an action

© Pearson Education, Inc., publishing as Pearson Prentice Hall.

# Related Words: *glaze* and *glimmering; prime*

### Practice

The words **glaze** and **glimmering** come from an ancient root meaning "to shine." *Glaze* can mean "fit glass (a shiny substance) to a window." *Glimmering* means "a faint glow." Other related English words include the following:

gleam, "a faint <u>light</u>"; "a <u>flash</u> of reflected light"; "to <u>flash</u> with light"
glint, "a <u>flash</u> of reflected light"; "to <u>flash</u> with reflected light"
glimpse, "a brief look at something, as when something <u>flashes</u> by"

The word **prime** and its relatives all involve the idea of being first. The word *prime* may be used as an adjective meaning "first in time, rank, importance, or quality." It may also be used as a verb meaning "to prepare or get started" or a noun meaning "the time of greatest importance or value." Many other English words are related to *prime*.

primal, "original"; "fundamental"; "from the <u>earliest</u> times"
primacy, "the state of being <u>first</u> in time, rank, or importance"
primary, "<u>first</u> in time or importance"; "main"
primitive, "from <u>earliest</u> times"; "simple and rough or crude"

Circle the letter of the best answer to each question.

1. When is a political <u>primary</u> held?

   **A.** before the main election
   **B.** during the main election
   **C.** after the main election

2. What do you think a schoolbook called a <u>primer</u> teaches?

   **A.** the basics
   **B.** high-school literature
   **C.** advanced studies

3. Which is probably a <u>primal</u> characteristic of human beings?

   **A.** a desire for computers
   **B.** the ability to drive
   **C.** the habit of walking upright

4. How long does a <u>gleam</u> last?

   **A.** a year
   **B.** all day
   **C.** a brief moment

5. Which is likeliest to <u>glint</u> in the sun?

   **A.** a cardboard box
   **B.** an aluminum can
   **C.** a wet towel

6. If you have a <u>glimmer</u> of an idea, what is the condition of the idea?

   **A.** completely worked out
   **B.** already widespread
   **C.** faint and not yet pinned down

© Pearson Education, Inc., publishing as Pearson Prentice Hall.

## Related Words: *glaze* and *glimmering; prime*

Assess

**A** Write *T* if the statement is true or *F* if it is false. Use your knowledge of words related to *prime* to help you decide.

1. ____ The primary colors are most likely the ones from which all other colors are mixed.

2. ____ A primer probably teaches the most basic lessons in school.

3. ____ The life of someone in his or her prime is probably of poor quality.

**B** Write *T* if the statement is true or *F* if it is false. Use your knowledge of words related to *glaze* and *glimmering* to help you decide.

1. ____ The glaze on baked ham is probably a dark, muddy-looking crust.

2. ____ A good table lamp gives out a glimmer of light.

3. ____ If someone has gleaming eyes, his or her eyes are probably bright with excitement.

**C** Complete each sentence with the best word from the box. Use each word only once.

| glazier | glimmering | glint | primacy | primary | prime |
|---------|------------|-------|---------|---------|-------|

1. The _____ benefit of traveling by plane instead of by car is that you get where you are going much more quickly.

2. Because of its strength and power, the lion established its

   _____ over the other creatures in the area.

3. The hot coals in the barbeque grill gave off a _____ light.

4. The coach worked hard to _____ the team before the game.

5. A _____ is someone who cuts glass to fit windows.

6. When he opened the treasure chest, he saw the _____ of gold.

© Pearson Education, Inc., publishing as Pearson Prentice Hall.

# Words Related to *vulgar* and *languish*

The **adjective *vulgar*** comes from the Latin word *vulgus*, which means "the public" or "the common people." It is related to the verb *divulge*, which means "to make public." Over time, *vulgar* came to mean "common" in the sense of "coarse" or "improper." Study these other words related to *vulgar:*

> vulgarity (noun), "the act of being coarse or improper"; "an instance of being coarse or improper"
> vulgarize (verb), "to make coarse or improper"

The **verb *languish*** means "to become weak" or "to fail in health or vitality." Study these other words related to *languish:*

> languishing (verbal), "becoming weak"; "failing in health or vitality"
> languor (noun), "the feeling of being weak or lacking energy"
> languid (adjective), "weak"; "without energy or vitality"

**A** Complete each sentence with the correct word from the box.

| vulgar | vulgarity | vulgarize | divulge |
|---|---|---|---|

**1.** The comedian offended some people with his _____ remarks.

**2.** I will not _____ the answer but instead will keep you in suspense.

**3.** Do not _____ the script by adding coarse humor.

**4.** People should avoid _____ in polite conversation.

**B** Underline the word in parentheses that best completes each sentence.

**1.** The hot weather may cause some people to (languish, languishing, languor).

**2.** The invalid raised a (languish, languid, languor) arm and waved goodbye.

**3.** After (languish, languishing, languid) in a corner for several hours, she finally regained her strength.

**4.** A healthy diet may help you recover from your (languid, languor, languish).

© Pearson Education, Inc., publishing as Pearson Prentice Hall.

## Words Related to *vulgar* and *languish*

Assess

**A**  Circle the letter of the best answer to each question.

**1.** Which is the original meaning of *vulgar*?

   **A.** public; of the common people      **B.** in bad taste

**2.** Which meaning did *vulgar* later come to have?

   **A.** public; of the common people      **B.** in bad taste

**3.** Which is the basic meaning of *languish*?

   **A.** to panic                          **B.** to become weak

**B**  Circle the letter of the word that best completes each sentence.

**1.** The elderly woman was shocked by the store clerk's _____.

   **A.** vulgar        **B.** vulgarity        **C.** vulgarize        **D.** divulge

**2.** Sharon promised not to _____ the secret to anyone else.

   **A.** vulgar        **B.** vulgarity        **C.** vulgarize        **D.** divulge

**3.** I was shocked by his _____ bragging about how rich he was.

   **A.** vulgar        **B.** vulgarity        **C.** vulgarize        **D.** divulge

**4.** The cheap costumes and loud music may _____ the celebration.

   **A.** vulgar        **B.** vulgarity        **C.** vulgarize        **D.** divulge

**C**  Underline the word in parentheses that best completes each sentence.

**1.** The tired woman moved with a (languish, languid, languor) grace across the room.

**2.** The prisoner was (languish, languishing, languor) in a dark cell.

**3.** After she began taking vitamins, she recovered from her (languid, languor, languish).

**4.** Do not leave the plants to (languish, languishing, languid) in the hot sun.

© Pearson Education, Inc., publishing as Pearson Prentice Hall.

# Absolute Phrases

An **absolute phrase** consists of a noun or a noun phrase modified by a participle or a participial phrase. An absolute phrase modifies an entire clause instead of just a noun or a pronoun within a clause. It is always set off from the clause by a comma.

Present participles end in *-ing* (*opening, closing, shutting*); most past participles end in *-ed*, although some are irregular (*opened, closed, shut*). A participial phrase consists of a participle with a helping verb (*having opened; being shut*) In the following examples, *Pr P = present participle*, and *Pa P = past participle*.

|  | Noun | Pa P Phrase | Noun Phrase | Pr P |
|---|---|---|---|---|
| Absolute phrases: | school having closed; a new store opening | | | |
| Sample sentences: | The kids went to the beach, school having closed. | | | |
| | A new store opening, we decided to go into town. | | | |

**A**    Draw parentheses around each absolute phrase. Then, underline the noun or noun phrase once, and the participle or participial phrase twice.

**Example:** (The express train speeding along,) we knew we'd arrive on time.

**1.** We stayed inside watching DVDs, the night being rainy and cold.

**2.** The chocolate cake baked, Mrs. Patruni turned to the decorations.

**3.** The refugees can return from the mountains, the war finally ending.

**4.** The judges went home, the prizes having been awarded.

**5.** The coach singing their praises, the athletes felt proud.

**B**    Write a sentence using each of these absolute phrases:

the paint having dried     the holes being dug     the project still not done

**1.** _____

**2.** _____

**3.** _____

© Pearson Education, Inc., publishing as Pearson Prentice Hall.

Name _____  Date _____

# Absolute Phrases

**Assess**

**A** Draw parentheses around each absolute phrase. Then, underline the noun or noun phrase once, and the participle or participial phrase twice.

**Example:** (The play having begun,) we crept quietly to our seats.

1. The alarm set, I turned off the light and went to sleep.

2. Sandra Cisneros began her second book, the first one having been published.

3. The ice finally frozen solid, we grabbed our skates and headed for the pond.

4. The plane took off, the pilot having been given the all-clear.

5. The anthem being sung, the game began.

6. Ali was quick to go to the store, DVD recorders being sold for half price.

7. The air conditioner broken, the hotel provided fans for the guests.

8. The autumn air smelling crisp and fresh, Ben and Maggie went for a walk.

**B** Write a sentence using each absolute phrase.

1. the crime having been solved

_____

2. the winds getting stronger

_____

3. the gas tank filled

_____

4. the cast having rehearsed

_____

© Pearson Education, Inc., publishing as Pearson Prentice Hall.

Reading Kit **235**

# Action and Linking Verbs

An **action verb** tells the action that the subject of a sentence is doing. The action can be physical (*run, dance, jump*) or mental (*think, love, worry*). A **linking verb** connects the subject of a sentence with another word that identifies or describes the subject. The most common linking verbs are forms of *be* (*am, is, are, was, were, has/have been, had been*). Other linking verbs include *feel, look, seem, become, smell, taste, grow.*

    Action verbs:   Casey <u>swung</u> his bat. The <u>fans</u> <u>thought</u> he would hit the ball.

    Linking verbs:  Casey <u>was</u> a star. Today <u>he</u> <u>looked</u> strong. The <u>fans</u> <u>grew</u> quiet.

Some linking verbs can often be action verbs, depending on how they are used.

    Action verbs:   Casey <u>looked</u> at his fans. The <u>fans</u> <u>tasted</u> victory.

---

**A**   Underline the action verb in each sentence.

**1.** Rice grows in China, Japan, and India.

**2.** The people in Asia usually prefer rice to potatoes.

**3.** In Central America, much of the population eats rice with beans.

**4.** They believe in the healthfulness of these two foods.

---

**B**   Underline the linking verb in each sentence.

**1.** Rice and beans are an important part of the Central American diet.

**2.** Rice and beans taste good.

**3.** Sometimes the beans seem spicy.

**4.** They feel sharp on your tongue.

---

**C**   Underline the verb in each sentence. Then, write *A* if it is action or *L* if it is linking.

**1.** ____ I looked up "foods of Asia" on the Internet.

**2.** ____ In the photographs, the Chinese dishes looked very tasty.

**3.** ____ Walking by Indian restaurants, I smell the curry spices.

**4.** ____ Those Indian curries smell delicious.

© Pearson Education, Inc., publishing as Pearson Prentice Hall.

# Action and Linking Verbs

**A**  Underline the action verb in each sentence.

**1.** Charities appreciate the work of volunteers.

**2.** In fact, they need the help of volunteers in order to succeed.

**3.** They often grow their funds by sending out requests for donations.

**4.** Most charities look for ways to spend their money wisely.

**5.** They understand the importance of their good works.

**B**  Underline the linking verb in each sentence. Then, draw an arrow to the subject from the word that identifies or describes the subject.

**Example:** A telethon is a televised fund-raiser for a charity.

**1.** Television fund-raisers are popular at holiday time.

**2.** Many viewers seem happy to call in their donations.

**3.** Each donation will be a help to a needy person or organization.

**4.** Most people feel good about making a donation.

**C**  Underline the verb in each sentence. Then, write *A* if it is action or *L* if it is linking.

**1.** ____ Local clubs collected food and clothing for hurricane victims.

**2.** ____ The boxes of donations grew larger every day.

**3.** ____ The organizers worried about shipping the items.

**4.** ____ However, they remained confident about finding help.

**5.** ____ Then, a truck rental business offered to take the items.

**6.** ____ "Helping hands" became their motto.

© Pearson Education, Inc., publishing as Pearson Prentice Hall.

# Adjectival Modifiers

**Adjectival modifiers** are phrases and clauses that modify nouns or pronouns. They can have different grammatical structures. In these examples, the phrases and clauses are underlined. The boldfaced words are the preposition, the participle, the infinitive, and the relative pronoun that introduces the adjective clause.

> Prepositional phrase: The actor **on** the stage bowed. (modifies *actor*)
> Participial phrase: I saw it **lying** on the table. (modifies the pronoun *it*)
> Infinitive phrase: It was an alarm **to wake** the town. (modifies *alarm*)
> Adjective clause: We felt the calm **that** follows a storm. (modifies *calm*)

**A**  Underline each adjectival modifier, and then draw parentheses around the noun or pronoun it modifies. Then, write *prep.* if the modifier is a prepositional phrase, *part.* if it is a participial phrase, *inf.* if it is an infinitive phrase, or *cl.* if it is an adjective clause.

**Example:** (Squirrels) in the attic made scratching noises.

1. _____ It was the letters that the soldiers appreciated most.

2. _____ After working hard all day, we were happy to relax.

3. _____ The time to end the debate is now.

4. _____ Fans cheered for the team that won the championship.

5. _____ Rain falling from the sky beat upon the rooftops.

6. _____ The decorations in the window made a lovely display.

7. _____ The new mayor was a politician to admire.

8. _____ The shop around the corner sells newspapers and candy.

**B**  Use each phrase or clause as an adjectival modifier in a sentence.

1. swimming in the lake _____

2. that the customer ordered _____

3. across the street _____

© Pearson Education, Inc., publishing as Pearson Prentice Hall.

## Adjectival Modifiers

Assess

**A** Underline each adjectival modifier, and then draw parentheses around the noun or pronoun it modifies.

**Example:** (The people) <u>celebrating their freedom</u> danced in the streets.

1. It is the bad weather that kept us at home.

2. Saying their last goodbyes, the friends parted.

3. The old people sat on benches along the boardwalk.

4. Trail mix to give you energy should always be in your backpack.

5. The road that we take runs next to the river.

6. Picnickers were amazed at the fireworks exploding in the sky.

7. It was a day to remember.

8. You will find a treasure buried under that rock.

9. Badly burned, Max determined never to forget his sunscreen again.

10. She had a time-saving plan to order gifts online.

**B** Use each phrase or clause as an adjectival modifier in a sentence.

1. that Kyle is listening to for the first time _____

_____

2. from her best friend _____

_____

3. working out every day _____

_____

4. to repaint the walls _____

_____

© Pearson Education, Inc., publishing as Pearson Prentice Hall.

# Adjective Clauses

A **clause** is a group of words containing a subject and a verb. A **subordinate clause** is one that contains a subject and a verb but does not express a complete thought.

An **adjective clause** is a subordinate clause that is used as an adjective. In a sentence, it modifies a noun or a pronoun by telling what kind or which one. Adjective clauses begin with relative pronouns (*who, whom, whose, which,* or *that*) or relative adverbs (*when, where, why, before,* or *after*).

I bought the book *which was on sale.*

The man *whom you described* is my uncle.

We need a place *where we can relax.*

---

**A**  Underline the adjective clause in each sentence. Then, circle the noun or pronoun it modifies.

1. The book that you mentioned is no longer in print.

2. It is they who should be ashamed.

3. The capital, which is beautiful, is not a very big city.

4. This is the style that she prefers.

5. The man whom you questioned is the general manager.

---

**B**  Underline the relative pronoun or relative adverb in each adjective clause.

1. He is the same man who stole our newspaper last Sunday morning.

2. She traveled with Ida in Italy, where they attended school.

3. On a day when there was almost no smog, Uncle Stanley went jogging in the park.

4. Willow, who came from the city pound, is the prettiest cat in our building.

5. I wanted a list of places where I could travel alone safely.

© Pearson Education, Inc., publishing as Pearson Prentice Hall.

# Adjective Clauses

Assess

**A**  Circle the letter of the correct answer.

**1.** Which of the following is a relative pronoun?

    **A.** but         **B.** than         **C.** who         **D.** and

**2.** Which of the following is a relative adverb?

    **A.** when        **B.** then        **C.** and         **D.** because

**3.** Which sentence contains an adjective clause?

    **A.** Millie's favorite subject is math, but she does better in English.
    **B.** Volleyball is harder to play in the sand than it is to play in a gymnasium.
    **C.** My brother plays the guitar and the harmonica.
    **D.** I like being home, where I feel most comfortable.

**B**  Underline the adjective clause in each sentence. Then, circle the noun or pronoun it modifies.

**1.** Is this the map that he wanted?

**2.** The woman whom you wanted to see is on her lunch break.

**3.** The man whose car is outside will be disappointed.

**4.** The jacket, which was on sale, was the first item I purchased.

**5.** The woman who is coming over is my Aunt Jane.

**C**  Underline the relative pronoun or relative adverb in each adjective clause.

**1.** She is the same woman who walks her dog past our house every morning.

**2.** I wanted to buy a few CDs that I could listen to at night.

**3.** The newlyweds returned to Italy where they first met.

**4.** On a day when there was a perfect sunset, the photographer took some great photos.

**5.** The brown coat that hangs in the front closet is my favorite one.

© Pearson Education, Inc., publishing as Pearson Prentice Hall.

# Adverb Clauses

A **subordinate clause** contains a subject and a verb but does not express a complete thought. It is often introduced by a subordinating conjunction such as *after, because,* or *if.* An **adverb clause** is a subordinate clause that is used as an adverb. In a sentence, it modifies a verb, an adjective, or another adverb. Adverb clauses explain *how, where, when, why, to what extent,* or *under what circumstances.*

To vary your writing, you can combine two sentences by turning one of them into an adverb clause. Notice that when an adverb clause comes at the beginning of a sentence, it is followed by a comma.

> Two sentences: The jury returned its verdict. The prisoner was set free.
> Combined: When the jury returned its verdict, the prisoner was set free.
> adverb clause

**A** Underline each adverb clause.

**1.** Pete opened his back door because he heard a cat crying.

**2.** Before Pete could blink, the cat was in the kitchen.

**3.** The cat purred gratefully when Pete offered it some leftovers.

**4.** Pete was able to find the cat's owner when he put an ad in the newspaper.

**B** Combine each pair of sentences, using the subordinating conjunction indicated.

**1.** We left on vacation. We took the dogs to the kennel. (before)

_____

**2.** You can make the trip. You will enjoy the scenery. (if)

_____

**3.** She finished her homework. Cathy played basketball. (after)

_____

**4.** I hurried home. I was hungry. (because)

_____

© Pearson Education, Inc., publishing as Pearson Prentice Hall.

# Adverb Clauses

Assess

**A** Underline the each adverb clause, and then circle the subordinating conjunction.

1. Dana awakened before the winter sun rose.

2. She skated where her coach had told her.

3. She practiced daily because she wanted to be champion.

4. Before he left, Tom closed and locked the window.

5. When the clock struck six, Carrie started home for dinner.

6. My sister had long hair when she was in college.

7. Unless I call you, I will take the bus from the station.

8. She was late because the train was delayed.

9. A storm developed after we reached the turnpike.

10. While we're in Virginia, we should visit Williamsburg.

**B** Combine each pair of sentences, using the subordinating conjunction indicated.

1. Bob was late to the show. He missed part of the first act. (because)

_____

2. They picked two bushels of blueberries. They fell asleep. (after)

_____

3. We can begin the conference. All the participants have arrived. (since)

_____

4. She developed laryngitis. She caught a cold. (whenever)

_____

5. We played brilliantly. We lost the game. (although)

_____

© Pearson Education, Inc., publishing as Pearson Prentice Hall.

# Adverb Phrases (Sentence Beginnings)

### Practice

A **prepositional phrase** is a group of words that includes a preposition and a noun or a pronoun that is the object of the preposition.

> In the beautiful, spacious lobby, volunteers welcomed visitors to the museum.

An **adverb phrase** is a prepositional phrase that modifies a verb, an adjective, or an adverb. Adverb phrases tell *where, when, in what way,* or *to what extent.*

> Dozens of modern paintings were hung on the walls.
> [The adverb phrase *on the walls* modifies the verb *were hung.*]

> The curator, upset about the repeated mistakes, fired both employees.
> [The adverb phrase *about the repeated mistakes* modifies the adjective *upset.*]

> The exhibit opened late due to a shipping problem. [The adverb phrase *due to a shipping problem* modifies the adverb *late.*]

One way writers create sentence variety and interest is by beginning some sentences with adverb phrases.

> In just three short years, Helen had earned her degree in art history.
> Upon the walls of the gallery hung paintings by several modern masters.

---

■ Underline each adverb phrase, and then circle the word or words it modifies. A sentence may contain more than one adverb phrase.

**1.** This morning two flocks of Canadian geese flew over our house.

**2.** For many years Howard diligently practiced the craft of writing.

**3.** Concerned about the bad weather, Dad postponed his trip.

**4.** The flight will arrive soon because of favorable tail winds.

**5.** Kathy competed in the chess tournament, and she was happy with her performance.

© Pearson Education, Inc., publishing as Pearson Prentice Hall.

# Adverb Phrases (Sentence Beginnings)

**Assess**

**A**  Complete each sentence by inserting an adverb phrase from the following list.

during the student council meeting    for two long hours
by the large crowd    across the open field
due to a mechanical problem

1. _____ the wind howled and the rain pelted the plains.

2. Were you surprised _____ when you arrived at the party?

3. _____ several members expressed concern about the new policies.

4. The bus was running late _____.

5. The greyhound darted _____ so fast he looked like a blur.

**B**  Rewrite each sentence so that it begins with an adverb phrase.

**Example:** We should be leaving for the airport within the next twenty minutes.

   <u>Within the next twenty minutes, we should be leaving for the airport.</u>

1. Dennis had finished polishing the silverware by midmorning.

   _____

2. A hearty meal suits me well after a long, strenuous hike.

   _____

3. A small figure slowly emerged from the darkened doorway.

   _____

4. Two playful chipmunks scampered up the tree trunk.

   _____

5. The bride had a long talk with her mother before the wedding.

   _____

© Pearson Education, Inc., publishing as Pearson Prentice Hall.

# Agreement and the Indefinite Pronouns *each* and *no one*

### Practice

The indefinite pronouns *each* and *no one* are always singular. Study the following examples of subject-verb and pronoun-antecedent agreement.

#### Subject-Verb Agreement

Finally, **each** of the children **has chosen** a color. [The singular verb *has chosen* agrees with the singular subject *each*.]
**No one** in the world **makes** tacos better than my dad does. [The singular verb *makes* agrees with the singular subject *No one*.]

#### Pronoun-Antecedent Agreement

Did **each** of the girls remember to bring **her** soccer uniform to the game? [The singular pronoun *her* agrees with its antecedent, *each*.]
**No one** misses debate practice unless **he or she** has a good excuse. [The pronoun pair *he or she* agrees with the singular antecedent *No one*.]

**A**  Underline the verb form in parentheses that agrees with the subject.

**1.** No one in any of the math classes ever (use, uses) a calculator.

**2.** Each of the boys (practice, practices) piano every evening.

**3.** In my opinion, no one (writes, write) more beautifully than Maya Angelou.

**4.** Each of the trees still (has, have) a few leaves that have not fallen off.

**5.** Each of the floats for the parade (were created, was created) in less than six months.

**B**  Underline the pronoun (or pronoun pair) in parentheses that agrees with the subject.

**1.** Then, each of the council members cast (his or her, their) vote.

**2.** No one can know for sure what the future holds for (them, him or her).

**3.** Each of the men did (his, their) best in the competition.

**4.** When the time came, no one was ready to give (their, his or her) speech.

**5.** No one on the girls' swim team has perfected (their, her) stroke yet.

© Pearson Education, Inc., publishing as Pearson Prentice Hall.

## Agreement and the Indefinite Pronouns *each* and *no one*

Assess

**A**   Underline the word or word pair in parentheses that completes the sentence correctly.

**1.** No one on stage (seem, seems) to know what is going on.

**2.** At the workshop, each of the poets shared (his or her, their) writing tips with the students.

**3.** Each of the dogs (eat, eats) a different kind of dog food.

**4.** No one who follows the league wants to miss seeing (their, his or her) favorite team in the playoffs.

**5.** Each of your textbooks should be right where you left (them, it).

**B**   Rewrite each sentence, correcting any errors in agreement. If a sentence does not contain an error, write *Correct.*

**1.** No one in our class was ever late unless they had a good reason.

_____

**2.** Remind each of the boys to bring his glove to baseball practice.

_____

**3.** Apparently no one in the park has seen the missing dog.

_____

**4.** Each of the job applicants left their résumé with the office manager.

_____

**5.** Luckily, each of us have brought enough money for the movie and a snack.

_____

© Pearson Education, Inc., publishing as Pearson Prentice Hall.

# Agreement in Inverted Sentences

## Practice

In most sentences, the subject precedes the verb, but in an **inverted sentence,** the verb comes first. Notice how the verb **agrees** in number with the verb in the following inverted sentences.

> **Singular:** Under the large chestnut tree *stands* a <u>memorial</u> to the war dead.
> **Plural:** Here *are* the <u>names</u> we read on the memorial.

---

**A**  Write the form of the verb needed to complete each sentence correctly.

1. _____ Within each one of us (lie, lies) the desire to explore frontiers.

2. _____ There (is, are) many different potential solutions to the problem.

3. _____ At the foot of the hill (run, runs) a small stream.

4. _____ Above our heads (is, are) a skylight.

5. _____ Here (is, are) the references you requested.

---

**B**  Underline the verb in parentheses that agrees with the subject of each sentence.

1. In the amphitheater (sit, sits) thousands of spectators.

2. Following the parade leader (was, were) six trumpeters.

3. Here (comes, come) the elephants! How exciting!

4. There (is, are) only two roads leading to town.

5. In the middle of the square (is, are) located a monument.

© Pearson Education, Inc., publishing as Pearson Prentice Hall.

# Agreement in Inverted Sentences

Assess

**A**  Write the form of the verb needed to complete each sentence correctly.

1. _____ Below the ship (was, were) the ocean depths, dark and mysterious.

2. _____ Reporting to the class (was, were) two students, Inez and Patrick.

3. _____ There (is, are) many reasons you should not take that risk, Enrique.

4. _____ On the table (is, are) several platters, loaded with sandwiches.

5. _____ "Here (is, are) the keys, Ms. Gustafson," replied Beth.

6. _____ Leading the field (was, were) two candidates, Ms. Paley and Mr. Hammock.

7. _____ Tremendously popular (has, have) been rayon and nylon, two synthetic fabrics.

8. _____ Hanging on the side of the warehouse (was, were) two signs, warning against trespassing.

**B**  Underline the verb in parentheses that agrees with the subject of each sentence.

1. Here (is, are) the instructions for installing the printer.

2. "On the table (is, are) two folders," Peter said. "Bring me the orange one."

3. Scribbled in the margin (was, were) the editor's comments.

4. There (is, are) only one brand of socks available at the store.

5. Rushing out of the building (was, were) two ladies, each with a shopping bag.

6. Near the shed (was, were) a barbecue grill, equipped with many handy features.

7. Hanging from the ceiling (was, were) two lanterns, which looked like valuable antiques.

© Pearson Education, Inc., publishing as Pearson Prentice Hall.

# Appositives and Appositive Phrases

An **appositive** is a noun or pronoun that is placed after another noun or pronoun to identify, rename, or explain it. In the example, the appositive is underlined.

Jeff, the <u>running back</u>, caught the ball and ran.

An **appositive phrase** is formed when an appositive is accompanied by its own modifiers.

Hogans, <u>traditional dwellings of the Navajos</u>, always face east.

If an appositive can be omitted from a sentence without altering its basic meaning, it must be set off by commas.

**A**  Underline the appositive or appositive phrase in each sentence. Then, draw an arrow to the word each one modifies.

1. Servette, who worked at the corner candy store, always gave samples.

2. Mr. Chang, the math teacher, was my homeroom teacher for the year.

3. James K. Polk, our eleventh president, was born in North Carolina.

4. Ms. Steffa, the school principal, canceled sports activities due to the storm.

5. Winnie the Pooh, a fictitious character, was a friend of Christopher Robin.

6. Mollie and Max, golden retrievers, were the winners of the dog show.

7. The Racing Rocket, a new thriller roller coaster, is now open at the park.

**B**  Combine the sentences using appositive phrases.

1. Monica Gonzales's painting was an oil and batik. The painting greatly impressed Vincent Goff.

_____

2. The aurora borealis appears at night in northern latitudes. It is sometimes called the northern lights.

_____

© Pearson Education, Inc., publishing as Pearson Prentice Hall.

# Appositives and Appositive Phrases

Assess

**A**  In each sentence, underline the appositive or appositive phrase. Then, circle the noun that the appositive phrase identifies or explains.

1. Norman Rockwell, a twentieth-century American painter, illustrated many covers of *The Saturday Evening Post.*

2. A large black cloud, a sign of a thunderstorm, appeared in the sky.

3. William Shakespeare, a playwright and poet, wrote during the fourteenth and fifteenth centuries.

4. Appomattox Court House, a National Historical Park, is where Robert E. Lee surrendered to Ulysses S. Grant.

5. Pete, my brother's friend, makes the best popcorn over a campfire.

**B**  Use each phrase in brackets as an appositive phrase in a sentence. Correctly punctuate each sentence.

1. [a treasure map]

_____

2. [a popular game]

_____

3. [my best friend]

_____

4. [an inspiration to all soccer players]

_____

5. [award-winning novel]

_____

© Pearson Education, Inc., publishing as Pearson Prentice Hall.

# Colons

A **colon** is a punctuation mark (**:**) that is used in the following places:

- before an extended quotation — The loudspeaker crackled: "The 5:30 flight to New York is now boarding."

- before an explanation — Caution: Keep this and all medications out of the reach of children.

- before an example — Two actors have refused Academy Awards: George C. Scott and Marlon Brando.

- before a series — Please bring the following items: a flashlight, a sleeping bag, and snack food.

- after a formal salutation — Dear Senator Robinson:

**A**  Insert colons where they are needed in the following sentences.

**1.** Danger This water is polluted.

**2.** Four states border Mexico California, Arizona, New Mexico, and Texas.

**3.** The box contained the following items rocks, marbles, shoes, and rope.

**4.** The process is somewhat involved It requires three separate stages.

**5.** This is what I have to do on Sunday clean my room, baby-sit for my brother, and finish my homework.

**6.** He excelled in one sport soccer.

**7.** Dear President Bush

**B**  Supply an appropriate list to complete each of these sentences. Insert colons and commas where they are needed.

**1.** I am taking the following subjects this year _____

_____.

**2.** You need these supplies for a picnic _____

_____.

**3.** We have seen the following birds this summer _____

_____.

© Pearson Education, Inc., publishing as Pearson Prentice Hall.

# Colons

**A**  Insert colons where they are needed in the following sentences.

1. Four team sports are popular in U.S. schools basketball, baseball, football, and soccer.

2. The day after Thanksgiving is a holiday in these states Florida, Maine, Minnesota, Nebraska, and Washington.

3. Caution Read this manual completely before using your chain saw.

4. Marianne chose three different poets to study Dickinson, Frost, and Poe.

5. The president banged the gavel "Let the meeting come to order."

6. Greetings, fellow club members

7. The salad contains three ingredients lettuce, tomatoes, and mushrooms.

8. My father grows a variety of vegetables carrots, squash, and cucumbers.

9. Warning This cabinet contains dangerous electrical equipment.

10. We have the following trees on our property maple, elm, and oak.

**B**  Write original sentences or examples according to the directions, using colons as needed.

1. a salutation for a business letter

_____

2. a sentence with an extended quotation

_____

3. a label with a warning or caution

_____

4. a sentence with a list of items, using the phrase "the following"

_____

5. an example

_____

© Pearson Education, Inc., publishing as Pearson Prentice Hall.

# Commas After Introductory Words

Practice

**Use commas to set off introductory words or phrases:**

I must say, the news about the peace treaty is hopeful.
Well, the parties worked hard at the negotiations.

---

**A**   Insert commas where needed in the following sentences.

1. By the way Kaplan's new book will be published on Monday.

2. Yes the researchers have discovered the cause of the new flu.

3. Tomorrow the governor will give the State of the State speech.

4. In the meantime you can practice your Spanish verbs.

5. No this is not a good time for a meeting.

6. Incidentally the cake will be delivered at 6:00.

---

**B**   Add the appropriate introductory word, with correct punctuation, to each sentence.

However     Unfortunately     Hey

1. _____ don't you want to come to the movie with us?

2. _____ I have too much to do today.

3. _____ I'll be happy to meet you for dinner later on.

**C**   Write sentences using the introductory words indicated.

1. Of course _____

2. Oh _____

3. Nevertheless _____

© Pearson Education, Inc., publishing as Pearson Prentice Hall.

Name _____ Date _____

# Commas After Introductory Words

Assess

**A** Insert commas where needed in the following sentences.

1. Of course you will need tickets for the show.

2. However the train is usually late.

3. First read the directions carefully.

4. Hey don't you think one helping is enough?

5. Oh there is the information I need.

6. Indeed the new sound system is a big improvement.

**B** Add the appropriate introductory word or phrase, with correct punctuation, to each sentence.

Nevertheless     At last     Fortunately     Well

1. _____ the flight has arrived.

2. _____ the snow is great for skiing.

3. _____ you need to be on the lookout for ice patches.

4. _____ let's get going.

**C** Write sentences using the introductory words indicated.

1. Yes _____

2. Well then _____

3. By the way _____

4. Good _____

© Pearson Education, Inc., publishing as Pearson Prentice Hall.

Reading Kit **255**

# Commas With Quotations

Use a comma after short introductory expressions that precede direct quotations. Do not use a comma when you are only quoting a word, phrase, or fragment of a complete sentence.

**Direct quotation:** The coach said, "Make sure to keep an eye on their quarterback."

**Partial quotation:** My opponent has dared to call this program a "frill"!

Rewrite the following sentences, adding or deleting commas where necessary. If the sentence is correct, write *Correct.*

1. Jared called his friend's scheme, "ridiculous" and refused to take part in it.

_____

2. The driver shouted, "This bus will not move until everyone sits down!"

_____

3. Major Morris warned "If you keep it, don't blame me for what happens."

_____

4. Louise Erdrich refers to her mother's movements as, "catlike."

_____

5. Achilles calls himself "the best of the Achaeans."

_____

6. Lita inquired, "Can you come over and show me how to put this table together?"

_____

7. The Blackfeet referred to horses as, "Elk Dogs."

_____

8. The appearance of the moon a few days before or after it is full is described as, "gibbous."

_____

© Pearson Education, Inc., publishing as Pearson Prentice Hall.

# Commas With Quotations

**A** Rewrite the following sentences, adding or deleting commas where necessary. If the sentence is correct, write *Correct.*

1. Venus angrily inquired "Am I then to be eclipsed by a mortal girl?"

_____

2. In the beginning of *The Phantom Tollbooth*, Milo holds the belief that learning is "the greatest waste of time of all."

_____

3. Wendy dismissed the play as "trite" and left during intermission.

_____

4. Mr. Darcy shocks Elizabeth by confessing "You must allow me to tell you how ardently I admire and love you."

_____

5. The name "Blackfoot" is a reference to the dark moccasins worn by early Blackfeet people.

_____

6. Roberto found the white-water challenge, "a wonderful wilderness experience."

_____

7. The doctor noted that the test results were, "promising" and vowed to do all that he could.

_____

8. The counselor advised "Grades are certainly an important factor in college admissions."

_____

**B** On a separate piece of paper, write a brief paragraph summarizing the action in a movie you have recently seen. Include at least two direct quotations and one partial quotation in your writing.

# Commonly Confused Words: *fewer, less; sit, set; in, into*

## Practice

Some **commonly confused words** have related meanings but different uses.

| Word | Function | Sample Sentence |
|------|----------|-----------------|
| *fewer*<br>*less* | used for items that can be counted<br>used for amounts or quantities that cannot be counted | The team has **fewer** *fans*.<br>There is **less** *interest* in the game this year. |
| *sit*<br>*set* | intransitive verb (no direct object)<br>transitive verb (with direct object) | We will **sit** in the last row.<br>**Set** your *books* on the desk.<br>[*books* = direct object] |
| *in*<br>*into* | refers to a place or position<br>suggests motion | The car is **in** the garage.<br>We *drove* the car **into** the garage. |

**A**  Underline the word in parentheses that correctly completes the sentence.

**1.** The club is (sitting, setting) new rules for membership.

**2.** The aroma of roasted turkey came (in, into) the living room.

**3.** Hollywood produced (fewer, less) comedies this year.

**B**  Write original sentences according to the instructions.

**1.** Use *fewer* in a sentence about clouds.

_____

**2.** Use *less* in a sentence about rain.

_____

**3.** Use *in* in a sentence about a forest.

_____

**4.** Use *into* in a sentence about a forest.

_____

**5.** Use *set* in a sentence about a baby.

_____

© Pearson Education, Inc., publishing as Pearson Prentice Hall.

# Commonly Confused Words: *fewer, less; sit, set; in, into*

Assess

**A** Underline the word in parentheses that correctly completes the sentence.

1. We have (fewer, less) problems with barking dogs than we used to.

2. There is much (fewer, less) noise in this neighborhood.

3. The statue (sits, sets) in the middle of the park.

4. The committee is (sitting, setting) the game schedule.

5. You will find biographies (in, into) the third set of shelves.

6. Sort the list of novels (in, into) alphabetical order by author.

**B** Cross out any word that is used incorrectly, and then write the correct form above it.

1. Remember to sit the plants near a sunny window.

2. Researchers found less head injuries among bike riders who wear helmets.

3. The celebrity left the red carpet and walked in the crowd, shaking hands with her fans.

**C** Write original sentences according to the instructions.

1. Use *fewer* in a sentence about cookies.

_____

2. Use *less* in a sentence about cookies.

_____

3. Use *in* in a sentence about a car.

_____

4. Use *into* in a sentence about a car.

_____

5. Use *set* in a sentence about a restaurant activity.

_____

© Pearson Education, Inc., publishing as Pearson Prentice Hall.

# Comparative and Superlative Adjectives and Adverbs

## Practice

The **comparative** form of an adjective or an adverb is used to compare two things or ideas. The **superlative** form compares more than two things or ideas. For most one-syllable words and some two-syllable words, form the comparative and superlative degrees by adding -*er* and -*est*.

| **Comparative** | **Superlative** |
|---|---|
| fast    Ron runs **faster** than Keith. | Of the four boys, Ron runs **fastest**. |
| angry    Jill was **angrier** than Evan. | Jill was the **angriest** of all the players. |

For some two-syllable words, as well as all words with three or more syllables, use the words *more* and *most* to form the comparative and superlative forms.

| **Comparative** | **Superlative** |
|---|---|
| cautious    Hank is **more cautious** than Rick. | Hank is the **most cautious** of the three brothers. |
| frequently    Ken jogs **more frequently** than Mary does. | Of all my friends, Ken jogs **most frequently**. |

Some adjectives and adverbs are **irregular.** They form their comparative and superlative degrees in unusual ways: *bad, worse, worst; good, better, best; well, better, best; little, less, least; many, more, most; much, more, most; far, farther, farthest.*

---

Complete each sentence by writing the form of the adjective or adverb indicated in parentheses.

**1.** The _____ hurricane of the year has hit the coast.
   (*bad*, superlative)

**2.** Do you think Phil is _____ than his brother?
   (*tall*, comparative)

**3.** Miss Perkins is the _____ person on our street.
   (*friendly*, superlative)

**4.** Carrots are _____ for you than potato chips.
   (*good*, comparative)

**5.** June approached the puzzle _____ than Gary did.
   (*patiently*, comparative)

© Pearson Education, Inc., publishing as Pearson Prentice Hall.

Name _____ Date _____

## Comparative and Superlative Adjectives and Adverbs

Assess

**A**    Underline the correct form of the adjective or adverb in parentheses.

1. Which test was (more difficult, most difficult), the science test or the math test?

2. The watch was (expensiver, more expensive) than the earrings.

3. Sarah sings well, but Michelle sings even (weller, better).

4. Dad says the market on the corner has the (fresher, freshest) produce.

5. The crowd cheered (more enthusiastically, most enthusiastically) for the second act than for the first one.

6. Hannah greeted me (cheerfullier, more cheerfully) than Pedro did.

7. My sister thinks (more optimistically, most optimistically) than I do.

8. Which of the two comedians did you think was (funnier, funniest)?

9. Of all my relatives, Aunt Kate drove the (most far, farthest) to get here.

10. The temperatures in Toronto are (colder, more cold) than those in Tampa.

**B**    Rewrite each sentence to correct any errors in the use of the comparative or superlative form. If a sentence does not contain an error, write *Correct*.

1. Which was hardest for you to learn, skiing or skating?

_____

2. Lilly is the most punctual person I know.

_____

3. Of the three pitchers on the team, Julio is the more accurate.

_____

4. I tried on all five pairs of shoes and then bought the pair I liked more.

_____

5. After the accident, Henry started to behave more responsibly than before.

_____

# Compound Adjectives

An **adjective** is a word that modifies, or gives a more specific meaning to, a noun or a pronoun.

> I admire Jody because she is an **efficient** worker. [The adjective *efficient* modifies the noun *worker*.]

A **compound adjective** is an adjective made up of two or more words. Some compound adjectives are open, or written as more than one word. Others are hyphenated, and still others are combined into one word with no hyphen.

### Open

Do you think the stadium is **well built**? [The compound adjective *well built* modifies the noun *stadium*.]

### Hyphenated

Fred's uncle is a **well-known** artist in this region. [*Well-known* is a compound adjective that modifies the noun *artist*.]

### One Word (No Hyphen)

At the medal ceremony, the winner took the **uppermost** position on the pedestal. [*Uppermost* is a compound adjective made up of the two words *upper* and *most*. It modifies the noun *position*.]

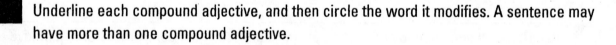

Underline each compound adjective, and then circle the word it modifies. A sentence may have more than one compound adjective.

1. Our visit to the animal shelter turned out to be an eye-opening experience.

2. The ten-year-old boy and the highly active puppy became fast friends.

3. I like the fabric with the crosshatched pattern.

4. According to my aunt, mixed-breed dogs are usually healthy.

5. David tried to avoid a face-to-face confrontation with the sales manager.

© Pearson Education, Inc., publishing as Pearson Prentice Hall.

# Compound Adjectives

**A** Underline each compound adjective, and then circle the word it modifies. A sentence may have more than one compound adjective.

1. The designer, well respected in his field, helped the couple fix up their out-of-date kitchen.

2. Hard-boiled eggs make a quick and nutritious snack.

3. After years of singing lessons, his voice had become a finely tuned instrument.

4. That country-and-western singer has recorded several crossover hits.

5. Dr. Hirsch has made a lifelong commitment to helping low-income families.

6. The family had no clue that they were moving into a mold-infested house.

7. Does the car have a five-speed transmission?

8. We conducted a brainstorming session to come up with project ideas.

**B** Rewrite each group of words by creating a compound adjective.

**Example:** a dragon that breathes fire _a fire-breathing dragon_

1. an athlete who is famous around the world _____

2. a cleaner for all purposes _____

3. a highway with six lanes _____

4. the computer, which is five years old _____

5. the floor, which is covered with dirt _____

6. a machine that is running smoothly _____

7. a storm that is moving fast _____

8. a vacation lasting one week _____

© Pearson Education, Inc., publishing as Pearson Prentice Hall.

# Compound Predicates

A **predicate** is the part of a sentence that tells what the subject does or is. The following example comes from the Book of Ruth:

Sentence: "But Ruth clung to her."
Subject (Who or What): Ruth
Predicate (Tells What Subject Is or Does): clung to her

A **compound predicate,** also called a **compound verb,** contains two or more verbs that share the same subject. Compound predicates are joined by conjunctions such as *and, but,* or *or.* In the following example from the Book of Ruth, the two verbs are underlined:

Sentence: "Meanwhile, Boaz had gone to the gate and sat down there."

| Subject | Predicate #1 | Conjunction | Predicate #2 |
| --- | --- | --- | --- |
| Boaz | had gone to the gate | and | sat down there |

Read the following sentences, which are based on sentences from the Book of Ruth or *A Doll House* by Henrik Ibsen. Then, circle the subject, underline the compound predicates, and place parentheses around the conjunction or conjunctions linking them.

**1.** Boaz ate and drank.

**2.** He came over and sat down.

**3.** He will renew your life and sustain your old age.

**4.** Naomi took the child and held it to her.

**5.** She prostrated herself with her face to the ground and spoke to him.

**6.** I locked myself in and sat writing every evening till late in the night.

**7.** He took over and decided what I should be and planned my costume.

**8.** I will stop by then and have a look at you all dressed up.

© Pearson Education, Inc., publishing as Pearson Prentice Hall.

## Compound Predicates

**A** Underline the two parts of each compound predicate. Then, write the subject of the sentence and the conjunction linking the predicates.

**1.** Long ago, a man journeyed to Moab and took his wife and two sons.

_____

**2.** Naomi returned from Moab and brought her daughter-in-law Ruth.

_____

**3.** Boaz talked to Ruth gently and showed her what to do.

_____

**4.** Ruth stayed close to the maidservants of Boaz and gleaned until the end of the harvests.

_____

**5.** Ruth went to the threshing floor and did what her mother-in-law said.

_____

**6.** The maid will show in Mrs. Linde or take care of the children.

_____

**7.** Nora breaks out into laughter but does not clap her hands.

_____

**B** Use the information given for each item to write a sentence with a compound predicate.

**1.** Subject: Ruth; Conjunction: and.

_____

**2.** Subject: Naomi; Predicate #1: welcomes her daughter-in-law.

_____

**3.** Subject: The doctor; Predicate #1: visits Nora. Conjunction: but.

_____

© Pearson Education, Inc., publishing as Pearson Prentice Hall.

# Compound-Complex Sentences

### Practice

A clause is a group of words with a subject and a verb. An independent clause can stand alone as a sentence; a subordinate clause cannot. A **compound-complex sentence** consists of two or more independent clauses and one or more subordinate clauses. The independent clauses are joined by a word such as *and, but,* or *or.* In the example, the subjects are underlined once, the verbs are underlined twice, and the subordinate clause is in **bold type.**

> Tim started riding only two years ago, but he has already been asked to ride in the exhibition horse show **that is scheduled** for next month.

---

**A**  Underline the independent clauses and circle the dependent clauses in each item.

**1.** David raked the leaves before he mowed the lawn, and Kenny helped him.

**2.** After the lawn was mowed and the gardens were weeded, Marla trimmed the hedge and painted the mailbox.

**3.** The dog was close to the road, and when I called him, he ran to me.

**4.** When the time came, we clipped on our microphones and went out onto the stage.

**5.** John suggested the show, and Rebecca and Megan were all for it when they heard his idea.

---

**B**  Add one more subordinate clause to each compound sentence to form a compound-complex sentence.

**1.** The book was long and dull, but I read it. _____

_____

**2.** The dancers were excellent, and the audience applauded loudly. _____

_____

**3.** Susan baked the bread, and Ron prepared the salad. _____

_____

© Pearson Education, Inc., publishing as Pearson Prentice Hall.

# Compound-Complex Sentences

**A**  Underline the independent clauses and circle the dependent clauses in each item.

**1.** We waited until the rain stopped, and then we went into the stadium where the baseball game would begin.

**2.** Because they were late, they missed the beginning of the movie that was being shown, but they still understood the plot.

**3.** Mary hoped that she could buy a new television set, but she did not purchase one because the sets were too expensive.

**4.** Because traffic was bad, we missed our morning flight, but we took an afternoon flight.

**5.** We unloaded the car, and the guide led us through the woods until we found a good campsite.

**B**  Add one more subordinate clause to each compound sentence to form a compound-complex sentence.

**1.** Last January was cold, but February was even colder. _____

_____

**2.** I understand your problems fully, and I sympathize with you. _____

_____

**3.** The wolves howled at the moon, and the campers cowered in their tents.

_____

**C**  Combine the sentences to form compound-complex sentences.

**1.** Julie went to Chicago. She took the train. When she goes to New York, she will fly.

_____

**2.** The storm increased in force. Ivan crawled under the bed. Hillary covered her head with a pillow.

_____

© Pearson Education, Inc., publishing as Pearson Prentice Hall.

# Concrete and Abstract Nouns

Practice

**Concrete nouns** name specific things that can be directly experienced or perceived by the senses. **Abstract nouns** name ideas or concepts that cannot be seen, heard, felt, tasted, smelled, or directly experienced. For example, *airplane* is a concrete noun because it names something you can see, feel, and hear. *Justice,* on the other hand, is a concept that cannot be directly perceived by the senses.

**A**  On the line, identify each noun as either *abstract* or *concrete*.

1. _____ cousin

2. _____ intelligence

3. _____ desk

4. _____ courage

5. _____ store

6. _____ sorrow

**B**  Write the concrete and abstract nouns in each sentence. You should find five concrete and four abstract nouns in all.

1. He drew his sketches from his thoughts.

   **concrete nouns** _____

   **abstract nouns** _____

2. Mr. Brett parked his car in his driveway.

   **concrete nouns** _____

   **abstract nouns** _____

3. America had a tradition of liberty and justice.

   **concrete nouns** _____

   **abstract nouns** _____

© Pearson Education, Inc., publishing as Pearson Prentice Hall.

# Concrete and Abstract Nouns

Assess

**A**  On the line, identify each noun as either *abstract* or *concrete*.

1. _____ newspaper

2. _____ respect

3. _____ continent

4. _____ umbrella

5. _____ truth

6. _____ strength

**B**  Write the concrete and abstract nouns in each sentence. You should find nine concrete and three abstract nouns in all.

1. The class held a discussion about the play.

    **concrete nouns** _____

    **abstract nouns** _____

2. The rainbow gave the children great pleasure to see.

    **concrete nouns** _____

    **abstract nouns** _____

3. My brother had a great idea of where to go on vacation.

    **concrete nouns** _____

    **abstract nouns** _____

4. All generations have their heroes and their ideals.

    **concrete nouns** _____

    **abstract nouns** _____

© Pearson Education, Inc., publishing as Pearson Prentice Hall.

# Direct Address

When a speaker in a literary work talks directly to someone or something, he or she uses **direct address.** When you use direct address, you put a comma after the name if it occurs first in the sentence. Put the comma before the name if it occurs last in the sentence, and on both sides of the name if it occurs in the middle of the sentence. In the following examples, the person being addressed is underlined.

**First in sentence:** <u>O genie</u>, grant my wish!
**Last in sentence:** Grant my wish, <u>O genie</u>!
**In the middle of sentence:** I beg you, <u>O genie</u>, grant my wish!

**A** Underline the words of direct address, and then add commas where necessary.

**Example:** I think Claire that your ride is here.
I think, <u>Claire</u>, that your ride is here.

**1.** Dr. Metz your next patient is ready.

**2.** Lovely sunshine you make me so happy today!

**3.** In another five minutes Ashley you may start the movie.

**4.** What did I tell you John about leaving the lights on?

**5.** I'll never trust you again you liar!

**6.** Fellow students today we celebrate our graduation.

**7.** Okay campers don't forget your sunscreen.

**B** Write sentences using direct address in the location indicated.

**1.** Uncle Earl (beginning of sentence)

_____

**2.** my friends (middle of sentence)

_____

**3.** waiter (end of sentence)

_____

© Pearson Education, Inc., publishing as Pearson Prentice Hall.

## Direct Address

Assess

**A** Underline the words of direct address, and then add commas where necessary.

**Example:** Tomorrow cast members we will have an early rehearsal.
Tomorrow, <u>cast members</u>, we will have an early rehearsal.

1. Mrs. Sanchez the book you ordered is in.

2. Your wish is my command Mother.

3. In that case Mr. Jackson I will give you my answer on Friday.

4. O mighty ocean what adventures do you hold?

5. Please take your seats ladies and gentlemen.

6. When you finish the hallway painters you may start on the bedroom.

7. Whoa there Nellie!

8. Mr. and Mrs. Kumar your table is ready for you.

9. Again today little bird your sweet song awakens me.

10. You are an exciting city Nashville!

**B** Write sentences using direct address in the location indicated.

1. my fellow Americans (middle of sentence)

   _____

2. ticket holders (end of sentence)

   _____

3. Beautiful elm tree (beginning of sentence)

   _____

4. Lita (middle of sentence)

   _____

5. those of you without reservations (end of sentence)

   _____

© Pearson Education, Inc., publishing as Pearson Prentice Hall.

# Elliptical Clauses

In an **elliptical clause,** one or more words are omitted because they are understood. (The word *ellipsis* means "omission.") In a sentence with an elliptical clause, the rest of the words must make the intended meaning clear. The reader can then mentally fill in the missing words.

In many elliptical clauses, the word *that* is missing. Another type of elliptical clause is used in comparisons. In such cases, words from the first part of the comparison are understood in the second part and do not need to be actually repeated.

## Sentences With Elliptical Clauses [*Understood Words*]

I realize [*that*] <u>you want to stay longer</u>.
Ted is quieter <u>than Maddie</u> [*is quiet*].
Dad likes lemon meringue pie better <u>than</u> [*he likes*] <u>any other dessert</u>.

In each sentence, underline the elliptical clause. Then, rewrite the sentence, including understood word(s).

**1.** I never felt happier than on that train ride to Seattle.

_____

**2.** President Kennedy told Americans they should find ways to serve their country.

_____

**3.** E-mail travels almost instantaneously, so much faster than so-called snail mail.

_____

**4.** I believe Jen read Momaday's story more eagerly than any other selection.

_____

**5.** My sister said we were never closer than when she was preparing to leave for college.

_____

**6.** Max told Ellen the secret he had promised to keep.

_____

© Pearson Education, Inc., publishing as Pearson Prentice Hall.

# Elliptical Clauses

Assess

**A** In each sentence, underline the elliptical clause. Then, rewrite the sentence, including understood word(s).

1. Wise people understand they cannot do everything they might want.

_____

2. It is vital to discover the one thing you want to do more than anything else.

_____

_____

3. There is no holiday I love better than Thanksgiving.

_____

4. Thanksgiving involves less work than some other holidays, and yet I feel it is more satisfying than most.

_____

_____

5. Of course, I also eat more on Thanksgiving than on any other holiday, too.

_____

_____

**B** Write four sentences describing your favorite activity, using at least three elliptical constructions.

_____

_____

_____

_____

_____

_____

_____

© Pearson Education, Inc., publishing as Pearson Prentice Hall.

# Gerunds and Gerund Phrases

Practice

A **gerund** is the present participle of a verb used as a noun. It can function as a subject, a direct object, a predicate noun, or the object of a preposition. A **gerund phrase** is a gerund and its modifiers, and it also acts as a noun.

| Function | Gerund | Gerund Phrase |
|---|---|---|
| Subject | *Waiting* bores me. | *Waiting for the bus* bores me. |
| Direct Object | I hate *waiting*. | I hate *waiting for the bus*. |
| Predicate Noun | Her talent is *painting*. | Her talent is *painting murals*. |
| Object of a Preposition | He wrote about *flying*. | He wrote about *flying 747s*. |

**A** Underline the gerund or gerund phrase in each sentence. Then, write whether it is used as a subject (S), a direct object (DO), a predicate noun (PN), or an object of a preposition (OP).

1. _____ Is this the line for buying tickets?

2. _____ Designing computer graphics is an excellent profession.

3. _____ My hobby is singing.

4. _____ The scientists continued looking for a cure.

5. _____ The negotiators worked at achieving a good settlement.

6. _____ This subject of the article was protecting the environment.

7. _____ The audience stopped paying attention to the speaker.

8. _____ Writing to persuade requires practice.

**B** Write sentences using gerunds or gerund phrases as indicated.

1. Use *watching television* as the subject of a sentence.

_____

2. Use *shoveling snow* as the object of a preposition.

_____

3. Use *traveling around the country* as a direct object.

_____

 © Pearson Education, Inc., publishing as Pearson Prentice Hall.

# Gerunds and Gerund Phrases

**A** Underline the gerunds or gerund phrases in each sentence. Then, write whether it is used as a subject (S), a direct object (DO), a predicate noun (PN), or an object of a preposition (OP).

1. _____ Our fall activities are raking leaves and planting bulbs.

2. _____ Singing and dancing raise a person's spirits.

3. _____ Before starting out on a trip, we highlight the route on a map.

4. _____ Alicia enjoyed getting a good night's sleep.

5. _____ An admirable activity is volunteering at an animal shelter.

6. _____ The article presented tips for protecting against identity theft.

7. _____ The chess players continued for four hours without stopping.

8. _____ Winning a scholarship was Tyler's goal.

9. _____ Would you mind keeping quiet?

10. _____ Learning a foreign language takes time and practice.

**B** Write sentences using gerunds or gerund phrases as indicated.

1. Use *running for town council* as the subject of a sentence.

_____

2. Use *Web surfing* as the object of a preposition.

_____

3. Use *watching tennis matches* as a predicate noun.

_____

4. Use *water skiing* as a direct object.

_____

© Pearson Education, Inc., publishing as Pearson Prentice Hall.

# Indefinite and Demonstrative Pronouns

An **indefinite pronoun** is used to refer to persons, places, or things without specifying which ones. Indefinite pronouns may be always singular, always plural, or either singular or plural. Notice in the following examples that verbs must always agree accordingly.

| | |
|---|---|
| **Always singular:** | another, anything, anyone, anybody, each, everything, everyone, everybody, some, someone, something |
| | *It seems that <u>everyone</u> <u>has</u> a cell phone these days.* |
| **Always plural:** | others, few, many, several |
| | *A <u>few</u> of the students <u>drive</u>, but <u>others</u> <u>take</u> the bus.* |
| **Singular or plural:** | all, most, none, some |
| **Singular:** | *<u>All</u> of the cake <u>is</u> gone.   <u>Some</u> of the cake <u>is</u> gone.* |
| **Plural:** | *<u>All</u> of the cookies <u>are</u> gone.   <u>Some</u> of the cookies <u>are</u> gone.* |

A **demonstrative pronoun** is used to point out a specific person, place, or thing. *This* and *that* refer to things nearby; *these* and *those* refer to things farther away.

| | | | |
|---|---|---|---|
| **Singular:** | this, that | *This <u>is</u> my book.* | *That <u>is</u> Simi's book.* |
| **Plural:** | these, those | *These <u>are</u> my books.* | *Those <u>are</u> Simi's books.* |

---

**A**   Underline each indefinite pronoun, and then circle the verb that agrees with it.

**1.** Most of the popular music today (is, are) available online.

**2.** All of my CDs (was, were) lost during our vacation.

**3.** Each of the CDs (has, have) special memories for me.

**4.** Several types of music (is, are) represented in the collection.

---

**B**   Underline each demonstrative pronoun, and then circle the verb that agrees with it.

**1.** The books on the table are mine; those on the shelf (belongs, belong) to Li.

**2.** Many novels tell adventure stories, but this (tells, tell) a love story.

**3.** She uses the atlas at the library, but that (is, are) from her homeroom.

© Pearson Education, Inc., publishing as Pearson Prentice Hall.

## Indefinite and Demonstrative Pronouns

Assess

**A**  Underline the pronoun in each sentence. Then, write *IP* if it is an indefinite pronoun or *DP* if it is a demonstrative pronoun.

1. _____ The committee hopes that everybody will want to help with the coat drive.

2. _____ Will someone please take charge of putting up the posters?

3. _____ Several bags of coats have already been donated.

4. _____ Carrie, will you take these to the Recreation Center?

5. _____ This is the last load for today.

6. _____ All of the volunteers will meet at the Center on Saturday.

7. _____ Please arrive at 9:00 A.M. That is the time the doors open.

8. _____ Check the coats to be sure all are in good shape.

9. _____ Do not keep any with bad stains or rips.

10. _____ Those should be returned to their owners or discarded.

**B**  Underline the indefinite or demonstrative pronoun in each sentence. Then, cross out any verb that does not agree with the pronoun, and write the correct form above. If the verb is correct, write *C* next to the sentence number.

has
**Example:** <u>Each</u> of the rooms ~~have~~ an air conditioner.

1. Blue paint can be pretty, but that is *too* bright.

2. The owner likes striped wallpaper, and some of it make the room look cheery.

3. Those is perfect pillows for the sofa.

4. Each of the rooms are being painted a different color.

5. In the redecorating of this house, everything is being done by professionals.

© Pearson Education, Inc., publishing as Pearson Prentice Hall.

# Infinitives and Infinitive Phrases

An **infinitive** is a verb form that acts as a noun, an adjective, or an adverb. An infinitive usually begins with the word *to*.

> Some cats like *to play*. (infinitive as a noun)
> Soccer is the game *to play*. (infinitive as an adjective modifying the noun *game*)
> Everyone waited *to hear*. (infinitive as an adverb modifying the verb *waited*)

An **infinitive phrase** is an infinitive plus its own modifiers or complements.

> Some cats like *to play all the time*. (phrase serving as object of the verb *like*)
> Soccer is the game *to play in the spring*. (phrase modifying the noun *spring*)
> Everyone waited *to hear the news*. (phrase modifying the verb *waited*)

---

**A** Read the following sentences. Then, underline the infinitives and circle any infinitive phrases.

**1.** Rudolf wants to play hockey this winter.

**2.** Beverly learned how to cook soufflé at the culinary institute.

**3.** To err is human, to forgive divine.

**4.** Practicing is important if you want to improve your swimming techniques.

**5.** To create a work of art, you first need to get an idea.

---

**B** Underline the infinitive phrase. On the line, indicate as what part of speech the infinitive phrase serves.

**1.** Jerry likes to play golf every day. _____

**2.** We went to listen to the opera. _____

**3.** I like to read stories to my brother. _____

**4.** Max left to join the Peace Corps. _____

© Pearson Education, Inc., publishing as Pearson Prentice Hall.

# Infinitives and Infinitive Phrases

Assess

**A** Underline the infinitive or infinitive phrase in each of the following sentences.

1. Her goal, to write a novel, was never realized.

2. The purpose of the class was to teach conservation skills.

3. To achieve the highest grade, the students created a multimedia presentation.

4. Alex and Anna wanted to ride their bikes to the beach.

5. Felix began to paint the house last summer.

**B** Underline the infinitive or infinitive phrase in each of the following sentences. On the line, indicate as what part of speech the infinitive phrase serves.

1. All the leaders wanted to sign the peace agreement. _____

2. The tailor made the dress to fit the actress. _____

3. The sound vibrations caused the table to shake. _____

4. Ethan was excited to fish in the lake. _____

5. The student artists began to paint watercolors. _____

**C** Use each of the following infinitives to create a complete sentence.

1. to eat

_____

_____

2. to anticipate

_____

_____

3. to lend

_____

_____

© Pearson Education, Inc., publishing as Pearson Prentice Hall.

# Interjections

### Practice

An **interjection** is a part of speech that expresses emotion and functions independently of a sentence. Some common interjections are *wow, oh, ouch, huh, whew, well, oops, hey, yuck,* and *hmm.* Use a comma to punctuate an interjection that expresses mild emotion. Use an exclamation point to punctuate an interjection that expresses strong emotion.

Ouch! I stubbed my toe.
Wow, she can run fast!

**A** In the blank, write an appropriate interjection for the feeling shown in parentheses.

**1.** (pain)! That really hurts.                _____

**2.** (joy)! That was a great game.             _____

**3.** (disgust)! That dinner was terrible.      _____

**4.** (fear)! I almost fell off the horse.      _____

**5.** (hesitation), I'm not sure of the answer.  _____

**6.** (relief)! I'm glad that is over!           _____

**B** Fill in each blank with an appropriate interjection. Use commas or exclamation marks as punctuation.

**1.** _____ We lost again.

**2.** _____ I am so happy to see you again.

**3.** _____ I just dropped the dumbbell on my foot.

**4.** _____ That was a close call.

**5.** _____ It isn't warm enough to go swimming.

**6.** _____ I wish I hadn't eaten that.

© Pearson Education, Inc., publishing as Pearson Prentice Hall.

# Interjections

**A**  Add an interjection to help express emotion in each sentence. Make sure to use proper punctuation after the interjection.

1. _____ That pianist plays well.

2. _____ This milk tastes spoiled.

3. _____ Ralph, you almost ran into that wall.

4. _____ What time is it?

5. _____ I left the tickets on top of my dresser.

**B**  Write an appropriate sentence for each interjection. Add the proper punctuation.

**1.** Yuck _____

_____

**2.** Hey _____

_____

**3.** Wow _____

_____

**4.** Hmm _____

_____

**5.** Oops _____

_____

© Pearson Education, Inc., publishing as Pearson Prentice Hall.

# Interrupting Phrases and Clauses

## Practice

Writers sometimes use phrases and clauses that break into a sentence and cause an abrupt change in thought. These **interrupting phrases and clauses** may imitate speech, provide explanations, or suggest intense emotion. When such interrupters break into the middle of a sentence, they are often set off with dashes. When they end a sentence, they are often preceded by a dash.

> What I meant to say—and I'm sorry if I confused you—was that I'll be on vacation with my family all next week.

> Carla's aunt has moved to Hollywood to pursue her lifelong dream —becoming a movie director.

Rewrite each sentence, adding dashes where needed to set off interrupting phrases and clauses.

1. I just finished reading *Romeo and Juliet* what a great work of literature!

   _____

2. The flight to Atlanta was extremely long about eight and a half hours for such a young child.

   _____

3. The gymnast what amazing balance and strength impressed everyone in the crowd.

   _____

4. Your examination someone should have already told you this has been rescheduled.

   _____

5. "May I please speak to oh, no, I've been put on hold," Phil said.

   _____

6. The wide receiver made an amazing circus catch I couldn't believe how high he leapt!

   _____

7. The day of my trip to China a lifelong dream of mine finally arrived.

   _____

© Pearson Education, Inc., publishing as Pearson Prentice Hall.

# Interrupting Phrases and Clauses

Assess

**A**   Circle the letter of the sentence that is punctuated correctly.

**1. A.** Dad sometimes refers to our pets a cat, two dogs, and three ferrets as "the zoo."

    **B.** Dad sometimes refers to our pets—a cat, two dogs, and three ferrets—as "the zoo."

**2. A.** "Hand me that bucket—no, wait a second," Julia stuttered.

    **B.** "Hand—me that bucket no, wait a second," Julia stuttered.

**3. A.** We won by two points in double overtime—what an incredible game!

    **B.** We won by two points in double overtime, what an incredible game!

**4. A.** My friend Kevin he wants to be a professional chef—is making a stew.

    **B.** My friend Kevin—he wants to be a professional chef—is making a stew.

**5. A.** Mr. Polk's travels—trips to France, Spain, and Italy—took four weeks.

    **B.** Mr. Polk's travels—trips to France, Spain, and Italy, took four weeks.

**B**   Rewrite each sentence, adding dashes to set off any interrupting phrase or clause.

**1.** Wild rabbits look! there's one now often come to this field to graze.

_____

**2.** The items in the wheelbarrow some rocks, a mallet, and two pieces of rope had spilled onto the ground.

_____

**3.** I think Derrick will reach his goal getting an academic scholarship for college.

_____

**4.** Then my sister showed me watch out for that car! the way to the bus station.

_____

**5.** What I'm trying to say please try to focus is that you need to study more.

_____

© Pearson Education, Inc., publishing as Pearson Prentice Hall.

# Noun Clauses

A subordinate clause (or dependent clause) cannot stand alone as a full sentence and functions as a noun, an adjective, or an adverb within a sentence. A **noun clause** is a subordinate clause used as a noun. It can be used as a subject, a predicate nominative, a direct object, an indirect object, or the object of a preposition. Noun clauses are commonly introduced by words such as *that, which, where, what, who, whatever, whoever,* and *why.*

| USES OF NOUN CLAUSES | |
|---|---|
| **Use** | **Example** |
| Subject | *Whomever you choose* will be our representative. |
| Direct Object | I wonder *how they plan to go.* |
| Indirect Object | She will give *whoever asks* directions to the stadium. |
| Object of a Preposition | Fortunately, he usually talks about *what he knows best.* |
| Predicate Nominative | A good film with lots of action is *what my father prefers.* |

Underline the noun clause in each sentence, and then tell how it is used.

**Example:** I know <u>what they can do</u>. _____ *direct object* _____

**1.** This news is just about what I expected. _____

**2.** Whatever price they ask is probably too much. _____

**3.** Do you like what they suggest? _____

**4.** She gave whoever called both messages. _____

**5.** A rigid diet is what Lester needs. _____

**6.** What most surprised Rita was how little the repairs cost. _____

© Pearson Education, Inc., publishing as Pearson Prentice Hall.

# Noun Clauses

**A** Circle the letter of the correct answer.

**1.** A noun clause is what type of clause?

   **A.** subordinate          **B.** main          **C.** relative

**2.** Which statement about subordinate clauses is true?

   **A.** Subordinate clauses contain a subject and a verb and can stand alone as a sentence.

   **B.** Subordinate clauses cannot stand alone as a sentence and can function as a noun, an adjective, or an adverb within a sentence.

   **C.** Subordinate clauses are introduced by a relative pronoun.

**B** Underline the noun clause in each sentence. Then, write whether it is used as a subject (S), a direct object (DO), an indirect object (IO), an object of a preposition (OP), or a predicate nominative (PN).

**1.** _____ How this business manages to survive is anyone's guess.

**2.** _____ I can't imagine how they can go.

**3.** _____ The speaker will arrive at whatever time you say.

**4.** _____ She will give whoever asks directions to the stadium.

**5.** _____ A good film with lots of action is what my father prefers.

**C** Add a noun clause to complete each sentence.

**1.** I wonder _____.

**2.** We told them about _____.

**3.** I will give _____ two tickets to the concert.

**4.** A well-organized chairperson is _____.

**5.** My father cannot decide _____.

© Pearson Education, Inc., publishing as Pearson Prentice Hall.

# Parallel Structure

**Parallelism** is the repetition of words, phrases, clauses, or sentences that are similar in structure or meaning.

Example: I came, I saw, I conquered.

**Parallel structure** is the expression of similar ideas using similar grammatical form. Parallel structures can include the use of adjectives, verbs, phrases, or entire sentences.

Example: . . . government of the people, by the people, and for the people . . .

**Parallel coordinate elements** are elements linked by coordinating conjunctions such as *and, but, or, nor,* or *so.* Parallel coordinate elements may be nouns, adjectives, adverbs, clauses, or phrases. To make elements that are linked with coordinating conjunctions parallel, put them in the same grammatical form.

Example: She knew neither how to phrase her inquiry nor where to address it.

**A**   In each sentence, underline the parallel structure.

1. He went to the department store, to the library, and to the town hall.

2. Twisting and turning, she managed to avoid the obstacles on the road.

3. Eddie decided to wash his truck, to change the oil, and to fix the radio.

4. Karl, Brandy, and I all agreed to work an extra shift at the restaurant.

5. He knew that one of his cousins liked rock and that the other preferred jazz.

**B**   Rewrite each sentence to correct errors in parallel structure.

1. Penelope would rather visit a new restaurant than going to an old favorite.

_____

2. Nick knows how to plan, how to take notes, and using different sources.

_____

3. Brad likes jogging, playing tennis, and to go on hikes.

_____

4. The mayoral candidate is intelligent, compassionate, and we can trust her.

_____

   © Pearson Education, Inc., publishing as Pearson Prentice Hall.

# Parallel Structure

Assess

**A** In each of the following sentences, underline the parallel structure.

1. Marco washed the dishes, did the laundry, and waxed the floors.

2. The children were busy wrapping presents and tying ribbons.

3. Ronda typed her report, printed it out, and bound it.

4. Shouting and splashing, the youngsters frolicked in the ocean surf.

5. That short story had neither a credible plot nor effective characterization.

6. The goal of epic heroes is to accept a difficult challenge and to succeed on their quest.

7. The orchestra played a march, an overture, and a full-length symphony.

8. Tracy will purchase the ingredients, bake the cookies, and prepare the pies.

9. The cat moved around the room, explored the house, and then jumped on the table.

**B** Rewrite each of the following sentences to correct errors in parallel structure.

1. Barb likes visiting new places and to explore foreign countries.

_____

2. Ms. Harlan loves to bake, to sew, and watching television.

_____

3. Herb bought the car because it was stylish and that it was well priced.

_____

4. The candidate endorsed the sale of state bonds, the establishment of a new state park, and to have the state cut property taxes.

_____

_____

© Pearson Education, Inc., publishing as Pearson Prentice Hall.

# Participial Phrases

## Practice

**Participles** are forms of verbs that can act as adjectives. Present participles end in *-ing*. The past participles of regular verbs end in *-ed*. A **participial phrase** is a participle that is modified by an adverb or adverb phrase or accompanied by a complement.

Present Participle:   my *throbbing* headache
Past Participle:      *exhausted* runner
Participial Phrase:   *Feeling fatigued,* I immediately went to bed.

**A**  Underline the participial phrase in each sentence. Then, circle the noun each participial phrase modifies.

**1.** Has anyone kept a record of all the money spent on this project?

**2.** Saving money from each paycheck, Cheryl was able to put a down payment on a house.

**3.** Henry is dancing with the woman wearing a turquoise bonnet.

**4.** Any car parked illegally in an alley will be towed immediately.

**5.** Last month the troops were invited to a special concert held in their honor.

**B**  Rewrite each pair of sentences as a single sentence with a participial phrase.

**Example:** The money was stolen from First Bank. It was later recovered.
        *The money stolen from First Bank was later recovered.*

**1.** The small boy sits at the end of the pier. He has caught nothing all day.

_____

**2.** The sun sets behind the mountains. It is a beautiful sight.

_____

**3.** Many books have been written by that author. Many of them have been bestsellers.

_____

© Pearson Education, Inc., publishing as Pearson Prentice Hall.

# Participial Phrases

**A** Circle the letter of the correct answer.

1. A participle is a _____ form that is used as a(n) _____.

   **A.** noun, verb                    **C.** adjective, noun
   **B.** verb, adjective              **D.** adverb, verb

2. A participial phrase is a group of words that functions as a(n) _____ in the sentence and contains a _____.

   **A.** participle, phrase            **C.** verb, noun
   **B.** direct object, noun          **D.** adjective, participle

**B** Underline the participial phrase in each sentence. Then, circle the noun each participial phrase modifies.

1. Fractured in the accident, my arm will take several weeks to heal.

2. Crossing the finish line, Jerry threw up his arms in glee.

3. The letter announcing my prize in the contest arrived today.

**C** Rewrite each pair of sentences as a single sentence with a participial phrase.

1. The speaker appeared somewhat nervous. The speaker approached the microphone.

   _____

2. The players sat on the bench. They cheered for their teammates.

   _____

3. The children played in the park. They built sand castles in the sandbox.

   _____

4. My mom noticed that the laundry was dry. My mom immediately removed the clothes from the dryer.

   _____

© Pearson Education, Inc., publishing as Pearson Prentice Hall.

# Participles as Adjectives

### Practice

A **participle** is a verb form that can act as an adjective. A participle used as an adjective modifies a noun or a pronoun and answers the question *What kind?* or *Which one?* about the term it modifies. **Present participles** end in *-ing (quivering)*. **Past participles** may end in *-ed (humbled)*, *-d (heard)*, *-t (lost)*, or *-en (mistaken)*.

past participle                         present participle

I bowed my humbled head and managed a quivering smile.

           modifies                                    modifies

**A**  Underline the participles in these sentences, and then circle the words they modify.

**1.** Our fencing class featured exciting duels between the most experienced students.

**2.** We peered around us for any familiar sights or identifying marks.

**3.** The rain-soaked grass glittered against the gleaming marble wall.

**4.** The fatigued travelers sank happily into their inviting, newly made beds.

**5.** The wandering cat mewed hungrily at the locked door.

**B**  For the following verbs, write the present and past participle forms.

**1.** make    *present participle:* _____

            *past participle:* _____

**2.** break    *present participle:* _____

            *past participle:* _____

**3.** forget    *present participle:* _____

            *past participle:* _____

**4.** lose    *present participle:* _____

            *past participle:* _____

© Pearson Education, Inc., publishing as Pearson Prentice Hall.

# Participles as Adjectives

**A**   Complete each sentence by writing the correct participle form of the verb in parentheses.

**1.** The _____ *(break)* bathroom window was not repaired until

some _____ *(chatter)* birds flew in.

**2.** We found the _____ *(miss)* watch in a _____
*(forget)* cabinet.

**3.** "Who is that?" I cried out in a _____ *(quaver)* voice, since I

felt more like a _____ *(terrify)* child than a

_____ *(poise)* adult.

**4.** Ahab's _____ *(doom)* hunt for the White Whale had a certain

_____ *(hypnotize)* appeal.

**5.** The _____ *(drive)*, _____ *(haunt)* genius Edgar

Allan Poe wrote _____ *(stun)* poems and _____

*(intrigue)* stories, created from a _____ *(teem)* mind and a

_____ *(shatter)* heart.

**B**   Write a few sentences describing a busy street. Use at least three participles as
adjectives. Then, underline the participles you used, and circle the nouns or pronouns
these participles modify.

_____

_____

_____

_____

_____

_____

_____

© Pearson Education, Inc., publishing as Pearson Prentice Hall.

# Past Perfect Verb Tense

The **past perfect verb tense** expresses an action that was completed before a specific moment in the past. Use the past perfect tense to show a connection between past actions or conditions. Study the examples to see how the past perfect tense is used. Notice that the past perfect tense is formed by using the helping verb *had.*

Although he **had seen** the movie before, Ben did not tell us the ending. [Both of Ben's actions—seeing the movie before and not telling the ending— happened in the past. First, he saw the movie, and then, later, he did not tell the ending.]

Finally a rescue team arrived. The baby elephant **had been trapped** in the ditch for hours. [The baby elephant's condition of being trapped took place before the rescue team arrived.]

Underline the past perfect verb in each sentence. Then, explain the connection between the two past actions or conditions.

By the end of the school day, Robert had become feverish.
Robert's fever started sometime before the school day ended.

**1.** By noon, the hikers had reached a sparkling lake.

_____

**2.** The players had run at least ten laps before the coach let them rest.

_____

**3.** Ken had traveled to twenty different cities, all before the age of thirty.

_____

**4.** By the time the firefighters arrived, most of the building had been destroyed.

_____

**5.** During her college years, Tina had expected to become a biologist.

_____

© Pearson Education, Inc., publishing as Pearson Prentice Hall.

# Past Perfect Verb Tense

Assess

**A** Underline each past perfect verb in this passage. Not every sentence contains a past perfect verb.

[1] On the day of the nature walk, we students gathered in the school parking lot and got on the bus. [2] We had looked forward to the field trip for weeks, and spirits were high as we rode the bus to the state park. [3] Although the forecast had called for rain, the day was pleasant. [4] We were well prepared because Mr. Chang had reminded us to bring our sketchbooks and pencils. [5] He pointed out many species of plants, several insects, and a few mammals for us to sketch. [6] We had learned about many of these species in class. [7] After we had thanked Mr. Chang for organizing the walk, we carpooled home. [8] The next day in class we discussed what we had seen on the walk.

**B** Complete each sentence by writing the past perfect tense of the verb in parentheses.

1. The attorney _____ to get his client a change of venue. (hope)

2. Bill _____ a master cellist before he even finished high school. (become)

3. City workers _____ off the street in preparation for the festival. (block)

4. By the age of thirty she _____ three novels. (write)

5. No one _____ that the other team would be so highly skilled. (anticipate)

6. After two years as team captain, Cindy _____ a reputation as a strong leader. (gain)

7. If you _____ earlier, I might have been able to go with you to the mall. (call)

8. It did start raining, but fortunately we _____ our umbrellas. (remember)

9. Most of my friends _____ before I got there. (arrive)

10. Because she _____ her clarinet, Debra was not able to practice with the rest of the band. (forget)

© Pearson Education, Inc., publishing as Pearson Prentice Hall.

# Predicate Adjectives

## Practice

**Linking verbs** connect the subject with a word in the predicate. A **predicate adjective** is an adjective that follows a linking verb and describes the subject of the sentence. Common linking verbs include forms of the verb *be* (*am, is, are, was, were*), *appear, become, feel, look, seem, smell,* and *taste.*

S     LV     PA

Predicate adjective: The <u>house</u> **seemed** lonely.

---

**A** Each subject is underlined. Circle each predicate adjective.

**1.** <u>Jan</u> is very intelligent.

**2.** An atomic <u>reactor</u> is very powerful.

**3.** My <u>glasses</u> are dirty.

**4.** <u>She</u> is highly susceptible to colds.

**5.** The <u>girls</u> were hoarse from cheering.

**6.** That <u>pitcher</u> of lemonade tasted sour.

---

**B** Complete each sentence with a predicate adjective.

**1.** The roast at dinner tasted _____.

**2.** My brother is _____.

**3.** I like foods that taste _____.

**4.** After their long race, Molly and Sam appeared _____.

**5.** The inside of the cave was _____.

© Pearson Education, Inc., publishing as Pearson Prentice Hall.

## Predicate Adjectives

Assess

**A**   Underline the subject of each sentence, and then circle the predicate adjective.

1. The mayor's policy is important to the city.

2. Through hard work Jennie became famous.

3. These curved roads are dangerous after a snow.

4. Susie is unusually tall for her age.

5. The senator often appears tired.

6. Suddenly, the sky seems threatening.

7. English and science seem to be the most difficult for her.

8. The crowd grew restless because of the long delay.

9. Adam remained loyal to his friends.

10. The singer's albums are as popular now as ever.

**B**   Complete each sentence with a predicate adjective.

1. The sky became _____ toward evening.

2. The winner of the race will be _____.

3. The weather remained _____ all week.

4. The price of the car is much too _____.

5. Your new boots smell _____.

6. Anita's suggest was tactful and _____.

# Prepositional Phrases

A **preposition** is a word that shows the relationship between a noun or pronoun—called the object of the preposition—and another word in the sentence. A **prepositional phrase** is a group of words that includes a preposition and the object of the preposition.

> The mouse scurried <u>under the table</u>.
> In this sentence, *table* is the object of the preposition *under*, which relates to *scurried*.

When a prepositional phrase modifies a noun or pronoun, it is called an adjective phrase; when it modifies a verb, an adjective, or an adverb, it is called an adverb phrase.

> **Adjective phrase:** The soprano *with red hair* is my sister.
> **Adverb phrase:** The contestant answered the question *with skill*.

**A** Underline the prepositional phrase in each sentence. Then, circle the object of the preposition.

**1.** The ballplayer hit the ball over the fence.

**2.** The crowd grew silent when the officer walked into the room.

**3.** The editors gathered for an urgent meeting about the newspaper.

**4.** Did you check behind the couch?

**5.** The shelter was found deep within the cave.

**B** Underline the prepositional phrase in each sentence. Then, write whether the phrase serves as an adjective (ADJ) or an adverb (ADV).

**1.** _____ A monorail runs around the entire nature preserve.

**2.** _____ An English team under Robert Falcon Scott reached the South Pole.

**3.** _____ Kit bought the diary with the green silk cover.

**4.** _____ The mansion on the proposed highway route is a landmark.

**5.** _____ The Azores Islands were settled before Columbus's birth.

**6.** _____ That critic's opinion of modern music is prejudiced.

© Pearson Education, Inc., publishing as Pearson Prentice Hall.

# Prepositional Phrases

**A** Underline the prepositional phrases in each sentence. The figures in parentheses tell how many each sentence contains.

1. The train for Calgary left an hour behind schedule. (2)

2. The quarrel among the actors started during rehearsal. (2)

3. As a child the trumpeter had discovered a battered bugle underneath some old clothes piled inside a musty closet. (3)

4. Under the pen name A. M. Barnard, Louisa May Alcott wrote stories of mystery and horror. (2)

5. Every day from the end of school until dusk, the child practiced tennis against a playground wall. (4)

**B** Underline the prepositional phrase in each sentence. Then, write whether the phrase serves as an adjective (ADJ) or an adverb (ADV).

1. _____ Famous authors may hide minor works behind pen names.

2. _____ Boneshakers were early bicycles with huge front wheels.

3. _____ Geoffrey Chaucer is buried in Westminster Abbey.

4. _____ The Atlantic hurricane season begins in early June.

5. _____ Mount Everest is the tallest mountain on Earth.

**C** Use each of the given prepositional phrases in an original sentence.

1. into the cup _____

_____

2. at the restaurant _____

_____

3. behind the curtain _____

_____

# Present Perfect Verb Tense

## Practice

Verb tenses express time in three general categories: present, past, and future. One of the most frequently used tenses for indicating past action is the present perfect tense. The **present perfect tense** shows that an action or a condition occurred at some indefinite time in the past or began in the past and continues into the present. Present perfect tense is formed by adding *has* or *have* to the past participle form of the verb *(has spoken, has been, have entered)*.

> **Present perfect tense:** "A Dream Deferred" has moved many readers.
> (The action continues into the present.)

---

**A** Underline each verb in the present perfect tense. If the sentence does not contain a verb in the present perfect tense, write *N* next to the number.

**1.** We studied the Harlem Renaissance in class this week.

**2.** I have decided to write my paper about Zora Neale Thurston.

**3.** Have you ever been to Hawaii?

**4.** My family went to Oahu six years ago.

**5.** The power of the individual will has remained a major theme in American literature.

**6.** Melville explored that issue in his great novel *Moby-Dick*.

**7.** How long have you ever gone without watching television?

**8.** Several U.S. universities have existed for centuries.

**9.** For instance, Harvard first opened its doors in the 1630s.

**10.** My sister's e-mails have given me a close-up view of college life.

---

**B** Change the verb in each sentence to the present perfect tense.

**1.** I studied _____ French for two years.

**2.** The classes were _____ difficult.

**3.** The French teacher assigned _____ a poem by Victor Hugo.

**4.** We also read _____ news articles from *Paris Match* magazine.

© Pearson Education, Inc., publishing as Pearson Prentice Hall.

## Present Perfect Verb Tense

Assess

**A**   Underline each verb in the present perfect tense. If the sentence does not contain a verb in the present perfect tense, write *N* next to the number.

**1.** I realized my mistake just an hour ago.

**2.** I have been wrong many times, but this mistake has been spectacular.

**3.** Both Emerson and Thoreau knew the family of Louisa May Alcott.

**4.** Emerson lent money to Bronson Alcott, who was Louisa May's father.

**5.** Readers have enjoyed Alcott's novels for more than 150 years.

**6.** At least three film versions of *Little Women* have appeared.

**7.** Have you seen the latest one?

**8.** It came out in 1994.

**B**   Fill in the blank with the present perfect tense of the verb indicated.

**1.** Over the years Hollywood _____ (produce) three versions of *King Kong.*

**2.** The theme _____ (continue) to thrill audiences for many decades.

**3.** Other monster movies, such as *Godzilla,* _____ (be) popular.

**4.** We _____ (watch) some of these movies many times on television.

**C**   Write sentences using the present perfect tense of the verbs indicated.

**1.** think _____

**2.** read _____

**3.** forget _____

**4.** win _____

**5.** meet _____

© Pearson Education, Inc., publishing as Pearson Prentice Hall.

# Pronouns and Antecedents

A **pronoun** takes the place of one or more nouns. An **antecedent** is the word or words to which a pronoun refers. An antecedent may appear before or after the pronoun. Sometimes the antecedent is not in the same sentence as the pronoun.

A pronoun must agree with its antecedent in the following ways:

- in number—singular or plural
- in gender—masculine or feminine

  *Jennifer* was in such a hurry that *she* forgot to turn off the lights.
  (feminine, singular)

**A**  Circle the antecedent of the underlined pronoun.

**1.** Vermont and <u>its</u> climate attract many visitors throughout the year.

**2.** The mountains with <u>their</u> natural beauty also attract visitors.

**3.** During the winter, visitors often go skiing, so <u>they</u> bring their equipment.

**4.** Many Vermonters work in the tourist industry; <u>they</u> support the state.

**5.** "<u>I</u> enjoy visiting during autumn," one woman told the tourist board.

**B**  For each item, circle the correct pronoun. Then, underline its antecedent.

**1.** "(It, He) has a wonderful history," said one man about the state.

**2.** The British fought hard to keep Vermont as (its, their) colony.

**3.** Ethan Allen led (his, their) Green Mountain Boys against British soldiers.

**4.** Vermonters were few in number, but (it, they) helped win the Revolutionary War.

**5.** Vermont joined the Union in 1791; (it, its) became the fourteenth state.

**6.** The tallest monument is 406 feet high; (it, they) honors colonial soldiers.

**7.** Calvin Coolidge and Chester A. Arthur were born in Vermont. (He, They) later became U.S. presidents.

© Pearson Education, Inc., publishing as Pearson Prentice Hall.

## Pronouns and Antecedents

**A** Underline the pronoun that refers to the circled antecedent in each of the following sentences.

**1.** (Mr. Garcia) had spent all winter planning his garden.

**2.** He had studied seed (catalogues) and had ordered seeds from them.

**3.** Mrs. Suzuki's (children) were curious. They wondered what he would plant.

**4.** The (neighbors) all took their turns glancing over Mr. Garcia's fence.

**5.** His polished and sharpened tools were (Mr. Garcia's) particular pride and joy.

**B** Circle the antecedent to which each underlined pronoun refers.

**1.** Mr. Garcia turned the soil with <u>his</u> shovel.

**2.** Then, he took seeds from a packet and scattered <u>them</u> in rows.

**3.** As soon as <u>they</u> saw the seeds, birds flocked over the garden.

**4.** Mrs. Suzuki waved <u>her</u> arms to frighten away the birds.

**5.** Mr. Garcia nodded gratefully. Mrs. Suzuki smiled at <u>him</u>.

**C** Write the correct pronoun for each circled antecedent.

**1.** Mrs. Suzuki said that _____ would be a beautiful (garden).

**2.** (Mr. Garcia) stopped and wiped _____ forehead.

**3.** Then, Mr. Garcia turned on the (hose) and drank water from

_____.

**4.** When _____ was finished, (Mr. Garcia) invited Mrs. Suzuki to visit.

**5.** The two (neighbors) had _____ first good opportunity to chat.

# Punctuating Dialogue

## Practice

Dialogue—the exact words of speakers in a story—is one of the most effective tools in a writer's toolkit. To **punctuate dialogue** correctly, put quotation marks around the speaker's exact words. Place periods and commas inside the quotation marks. A question mark or exclamation point goes inside only if it is the end punctuation of the quotation itself; otherwise, it goes outside. Use a new paragraph for each new speaker.

**Example:** Mom asked, "Are you taking your rain boots to school, Helen?"

**A**  The punctuation marks in the following pieces of dialogue have been misplaced or omitted. Rewrite each item, using correct punctuation.

**1.** Harry complained, This flight is always late

_____

**2.** "I'll be there in ten minutes", Josh replied.

_____

**3.** Is the Internet connection working Paula asked.

_____

**4.** We are almost out of gas, Eddie warned, so we had better get some.

_____

**5.** "How old are you, Grandpa"? Jenna inquired.

_____

**B**  Write a few lines of original dialogue. Use two different characters and include a few lines of description. Enclose the lines of dialogue in quotation marks. Include enough conversation tags (such as "Sarah replied") to avoid confusion about who is speaking.

_____

_____

_____

_____

© Pearson Education, Inc., publishing as Pearson Prentice Hall.

## Punctuating Dialogue

Assess

**A** The punctuation marks in the following pieces of dialogue have been misplaced or omitted. Rewrite each item using correct punctuation.

**1.** David replied, "I think I'd prefer to visit the mountains rather than the beach".

_____

**2.** "What happened to my new slippers"? Dad inquired.

_____

**3.** "The shed needs a coat of paint" Sally observed, but the job shouldn't take too long.

_____

**4.** "What an extraordinary work of art"! Timothy exclaimed.

_____

**5.** "Swimmers going to the meet must board the bus by 10:00 o'clock" Coach Johnson announced.

_____

**B** Imagine that you and a friend have just returned from volunteering at a local charitable organization. Write a few lines of original dialogue to describe the conversation that might take place between the two of you. Make sure to use correct punctuation and include conversation tags.

_____

_____

_____

_____

_____

_____

© Pearson Education, Inc., publishing as Pearson Prentice Hall.

# Restrictive and Nonrestrictive Adjective Clauses

## Practice

**Adjective clauses** contain both a subject and a verb. These clauses add information about nouns in the main part of a sentence. They often begin with the words *that, which, who, whom,* or *whose.*

A **restrictive adjective clause** is necessary to complete the meaning of the noun or pronoun it modifies.

> Restrictive: The book *that is lying on the table* belongs to Randy.
> (essential: tells which *book*)

A **nonrestrictive adjective clause** provides additional but nonessential information and must be set off by commas.

> Nonrestrictive: Mark, *whom I saw last week,* is learning to speak Japanese.
> (nonessential: modifies *Mark*)

---

**A** Underline the adjective clause in each sentence, and then circle the noun or pronoun it modifies.

**1.** This is a day that we will all remember.

**2.** This is the statue that he wrote about.

**3.** Professor Johnson, who was recently appointed by the university, will teach the course in advanced biology.

**4.** The jackets, which were on sale, were very stylish.

**5.** Len is the one whose mother is the district attorney.

---

**B** Identify each adjective clause as restrictive or nonrestrictive.

**1.** _____ Where is the box in which I keep my change?

**2.** _____ The potato bread, which he baked himself, was a little dry.

**3.** _____ Emily Dickinson is a poet whose work was once ignored.

**4.** _____ The harp, which was played in ancient Egypt, is a stringed musical instrument.

© Pearson Education, Inc., publishing as Pearson Prentice Hall.

# Restrictive and Nonrestrictive Adjective Clauses

Assess

**A**   Underline the adjective clause in each sentence, and then circle the noun or pronoun it modifies.

1. I tried to match the color that she had described to me.

2. She is the woman who works at the bank.

3. The piano, whose strings are hit by hammers to produce sound, can be made louder or softer by foot pedals.

4. The political issue on which the argument centered seemed trivial.

5. My bicycle, which I bought two years ago, needs new brakes.

**B**   For each item, write a sentence that uses the adjective clause in parentheses. If the clause is nonrestrictive, remember to use commas.

1. (who live on that street)

_____

_____

2. (to whom I owe money)

_____

_____

3. (that you asked for)

_____

_____

4. (whom Peter told you about)

_____

_____

5. (whose house is filled with valuable antiques)

_____

_____

© Pearson Education, Inc., publishing as Pearson Prentice Hall.

## Transitions and Transitional Phrases

**Transitions** are words that show relationships between ideas. Groups of words that serve as transitions are called **transitional phrases.**

| Transitions or Transitional Phrases | Type of Relationship They Show | Example |
|---|---|---|
| above; behind; in front of; next to; on top of | Position in space (spatial) | *In front of Socrates* sat those who would judge him. |
| afterward; before; in a while; recently; then; when | Order in time (chronological) | *When* my sons have grown up, I would ask you . . . |
| although; however; in contrast; like; similarly; yet | Comparison and contrast | You will not believe me, *yet* I say what is true. |
| as a result; because; consequently; therefore; wherefore | Cause and effect | I have no property, and *therefore* I must ask you to make my fine smaller. |
| above all; least important; less important; more important; most important | Order of importance | *Most important* to Socrates was to speak the truth. |
| also; further; in addition to | Addition | *In addition to visiting* the poets, Socrates went to the artisans. |

Underline the transitional word in each numbered item. Then, on the line, write the type of relationship it shows.

1. _____ And although some of you may think that I am joking, I declare that I will tell you the entire truth.

2. _____ Why do I mention this? Because I am going to explain to you why I have such an evil name.

3. _____ When I began to talk with him, I could not help thinking that he was not really wise . . .

4. _____ You will not easily find another like me, and therefore I would advise you to spare me.

   © Pearson Education, Inc., publishing as Pearson Prentice Hall.

# Transitions and Transitional Phrases

**A** Rewrite each of the following pairs, adding a transition or transitional phrase to indicate a relationship between the items in the pair.

**1. A.** Socrates explained his actions to the citizens of Athens.
   **B.** He went to the place where the sentence was to be carried out.

_____

_____

**2. A.** Socrates was a wise and good man.
   **B.** The judges condemned him to death anyway.

_____

_____

**3. A.** Plato's "Apology" is still read today.
   **B.** The words of Socrates are eloquent.

_____

_____

**4. A.** Socrates thought about the statement that he was the wisest of men.
   **B.** He decided to test the statement by looking for a man wiser than himself.

_____

_____

**B** On a separate sheet of paper, rewrite the paragraph, adding transitions or transitional phrases.

Rock 'n' roll exploded onto the scene in the 1950s. Some people claimed it was immoral. They argued that it should be banned. A similar debate about the morality of music took place more than 2,000 years ago in ancient Greece. This debate focused on Greek musical scales, called modes. Each Greek mode had seven notes. The names of modes were associated with groups and regions. Lydia was viewed as a corrupt place. Songs in the Lydian mode were suitable for feasts. Plato banned songs in the Lydian mode from his ideal republic. These songs made men "soft." He favored the Dorian mode, which was "warlike."

© Pearson Education, Inc., publishing as Pearson Prentice Hall.

# The Understood *You* in Imperative Sentences

An **imperative sentence** states a request or gives an order. The subject of the sentence, *you,* is implied, or understood, rather than stated. In the following examples, the subjects are underlined once and the verbs twice.

> Question: <u>Will</u> <u>you</u> <u>return</u> that book to the library?
> Declarative sentence: <u>I</u> <u>want</u> you to return that book to the library.
> Imperative sentence: <u>Return</u> that book to the library. (*You* is implied.)

---

**A**   Write *I* if the sentence is imperative, *Q* if it is a question, or *D* if it is declarative.

1. _____ **A.** Would you please feed the cat?

_____ **B.** Feed the cat.

_____ **C.** I would like you to feed the cat.

2. _____ **A.** You should reserve the book today.

_____ **B.** Will you reserve the book today?

_____ **C.** Reserve the book today.

3. _____ **A.** Arrive early if you want to get a good seat.

_____ **B.** Will you arrive early to get a good seat?

_____ **C.** You had better arrive early to get a good seat.

---

**B**   Rewrite each declarative sentence or question as an imperative sentence.

1. You do not have to think about this problem anymore.

_____

2. Will you close the door and lock it?

_____

3. You can use this brush to paint the trim.

_____

4. Would you slice the apples while I roll out the dough?

_____

© Pearson Education, Inc., publishing as Pearson Prentice Hall.

# The Understood *You* in Imperative Sentences

Assess

**A**   Write *I* if the sentence is imperative, *Q* if it is a question, or *D* if it is declarative.

**1.** ____ Please wait for me by the car.

**2.** ____ Don't forget to pack your camera.

**3.** ____ Will you help me carry the suitcases?

**4.** ____ Take these tickets, and put them in a safe place.

**5.** ____ I would prefer that you keep the maps in that plastic envelope.

**6.** ____ Make sure that our address tags are attached securely.

**7.** ____ Would you find the suntan lotion and gather the beach towels?

**8.** ____ Remember that we need to get to the airport early.

**B**   Rewrite each declarative sentence or question as an imperative sentence.

**1.** I wish you would not look at me with those sad eyes.

_____

**2.** Will you pay at the counter and then come back with the receipt?

_____

**3.** You should do twenty laps every day if you want to stay in shape.

_____

**4.** Would you memorize this poem, please, and recite it for the class?

_____

**5.** I would not skate on that ice; it's not frozen through.

_____

© Pearson Education, Inc., publishing as Pearson Prentice Hall.

# Usage: who and whom

Practice

Learn to use the pronouns **who** and **whom** correctly in sentences. **Who,** like *he* or *she*, is used as a subject or subject complement. **Whom,** like *him* or *her*, is used as a direct object or the object of the preposition.

>**Subject:** *Who* will bring the dessert?
>**Object:** *Whom* have you told?

It is especially important to examine the pronoun's use in a complex sentence. Reword the clause that the pronoun is in to check whether you have used it correctly.

>This waiter is an unpleasant fellow *whom* I dislike.
>**Subordinate clause:** whom I dislike
>**Reworded clause:** I dislike *him*. (not *he*)
>**Use of pronoun:** direct object of *dislike*

---

**A**  Identify the function of *who* or *whom* in the following sentences. In the blank, write *subject, subject complement, direct object,* or *object of the preposition.*

1. _____ Who knows the answer?

2. _____ Whom have you invited so far?

3. _____ To whom did you give the message?

4. _____ Joe had to introduce a woman whom he did not like.

---

**B**  Complete each sentence by correctly inserting *who* or *whom.*

1. _____ was elected president in 1968?

2. To _____ did you report the accident?

3. _____ did the teacher appoint as class monitor?

4. A good babysitter must be someone _____ likes children.

5. Anyone _____ witnessed the accident should contact the police.

© Pearson Education, Inc., publishing as Pearson Prentice Hall.

# Usage: *who* and *whom*

Assess

**A** Determine the function of *who* or *whom* in the following sentences by identifying and rewording the subordinate clause, as in the example.

There are still a few actors whom the director has not auditioned.
**Clause:** whom the director has not auditioned
**Rewording of clause:** the director has not auditioned *them*
**Function of pronoun:** direct object of *auditioned*

1. He is the one who will get the job.

   Clause: _____

   Rewording of clause: _____

   Function of pronoun: _____

2. Laurie is a person who knows what she wants.

   Clause: _____

   Rewording of clause: _____

   Function of pronoun: _____

3. Do you know for whom the judges voted?

   Clause: _____

   Rewording of clause: _____

   Function of pronoun: _____

**B** Complete each sentence by correctly inserting *who* or *whom*.

1. I want to know _____ wrote this.

2. From _____ did you receive this excellent résumé?

3. Lenny Jacobs is a coach _____ gets results.

4. The job is open to anyone _____ can speak German.

5. _____ can I contact to find out more about the job?

6. That band director is the one to _____ she gave lessons.

© Pearson Education, Inc., publishing as Pearson Prentice Hall.

# Using Dashes

**Practice**

**Dashes** (—) are a form of punctuation that create a longer, more emphatic pause than commas. They signal information that interrupts the flow of text. Dashes can indicate an abrupt change of thought, a dramatic interrupting idea, or a summary statement.

| Uses of the Dash | |
|---|---|
| **Change of Thought** | I'm almost finished—oh, no, someone is at the door! |
| **Dramatic Interruption** | Kevin's party—it's sure to be a huge, noisy one—is on Saturday night. |
| **Summary Statement** | La Maison, Chez Pierre, and L'Etoile—all are excellent French restaurants in town. |
| **Nonessential Element** | That red sweater—you know, the one with the reindeer knitted in—was a gift from my aunt. That bright object—you saw it too, didn't you?—may have been a UFO. |

■ Insert a caret (^) where a dash is needed in the following sentences.

**Example:** Judy's essay she wrote it in only a half an hour won first prize.
       ^                                                      ^

1. That circus act the one with the aerialist walking on a wire high above the ground always makes me uneasy.

2. The meeting didn't you say it was at Tom's house? begins at 8:00.

3. The players, the coaches, and the grounds crew all were given a bonus.

4. The new corporate president he worked his way up from stock boy, you know is sure to make some changes.

5. I hope that Ellen will not be oh, here she is now.

© Pearson Education, Inc., publishing as Pearson Prentice Hall.

## Using Dashes

Assess

Rewrite the following sentences, adding dashes where needed. If no dashes are needed, write *No dashes*.

**1.** Our team is winning the game no, the other team just scored a touchdown.

_____

**2.** Stacey used a small notebook to write down her homework assignments.

_____

**3.** Bruce Springsteen, Mick Jagger, and Roger Daltry are famous rock stars.

_____

**4.** This Sunday's game it should be the best one this season starts at 1:00.

_____

**5.** Once the storm passes if it ever does the weather should be beautiful.

_____

**6.** Morton that very gentle old man who feeds the geese at the park is friends with my grandmother.

_____

_____

**7.** I can't find my ah, there they are!

_____

**8.** Washington, Jefferson, Lincoln, and Teddy Roosevelt these are the presidents whose faces are carved in the granite of Mount Rushmore.

_____

_____

**9.** Stephen Spielberg's new movie have you seen it yet? is sure to be a great success.

_____

_____

© Pearson Education, Inc., publishing as Pearson Prentice Hall.

# Varying Sentences

By **varying sentence beginnings,** you can avoid a repetitive rhythm and enliven your writing. In addition to beginning a sentence with a subject followed by a verb, use one of these types of sentence openers:

**Prepositional Phrase:** With a deafening clap of thunder, the storm broke.
**Participial Phrase:** Cheering loudly, the fans celebrated the team's victory.
**Subordinate Clause:** As the turkey browned in the oven, we felt even hungrier.
**Adverb:** Now, she became excited by what the future would bring.

**A** Rewrite each sentence to make it begin with a prepositional phrase, a participial phrase, a subordinate clause, or an adverbial phrase.

**1.** Tim consulted his Yellow Pages and found the location of a nearby hardware store.

_____

_____

**2.** Lori replied enthusiastically with a broad smile on her face.

_____

**3.** The assistant submitted his resignation; the president accepted it with regret.

_____

_____

**4.** Darren analyzed the problem and then devised an ingenious solution.

_____

**B** On a separate sheet of paper, rewrite the following paragraph, using a variety of different sentence openers. You may combine sentences or rearrange ideas.

A fire extinguisher is a device for putting out fires. Hardware stores stock several different types of extinguisher. The customer's choice depends on the type of flammable material he or she wants to protect. The kind of fires an extinguisher will put out are listed on the nameplate. The nameplate is attached to the front of the device. Home fire extinguishers are useful. They have a short discharge time. This lasts from 8 to 24 seconds. The user must direct the spray at the base of the fire.

© Pearson Education, Inc., publishing as Pearson Prentice Hall.

## Varying Sentences

**A** Rewrite each sentence to make it begin with a prepositional phrase, a participial phrase, a subordinate clause, or an adverbial phrase.

**1.** We outfitted ourselves carefully, and then we began to climb the mountain.

_____

**2.** A crumbling old house stood at the edge of the road.

_____

**3.** The lifeguard swam steadily and succeeded in reaching the child in distress.

_____

_____

**4.** The prosecutor probed relentlessly, asking the witness question after question.

_____

_____

**5.** The project had been poorly designed and ran way over budget.

_____

**6.** Tito was painfully shy and did not attend the party.

_____

**7.** We returned from baseball practice and found that our food was cold.

_____

**B** On a separate sheet of paper, rewrite the following paragraph, using a variety of different sentence openers. You may combine sentences or rearrange ideas.

I was on my own for about an hour. I walked along the beach. I began my walk near a rocky outcropping. I stopped every once in a while to examine unusual shells at the water's edge. At that time, they seemed unique and intriguing. At other times, they might be judged drab and dull. I lost interest in the shells. They were all along the beach. I moved on. Farther on, the sand was almost pure white. There was no litter or debris on the beach. I could not hold myself back. I ran splashing into the water.

© Pearson Education, Inc., publishing as Pearson Prentice Hall.

# Autobiographical Narrative

**Autobiographical narratives** describe real events in the writer's life and share the wisdom the writer gained from the experience. A well-written autobiographical narrative should feature the following elements:

- well-established characters, including the writer as the main character
- an organized sequence of events with a significance that is clearly communicated
- action that incorporates shifts in time and mood
- conflict or tension between characters or between a character and another force
- insights that the writer has gained from the experience

Use the word web below to choose a topic for an autobiographical narrative. In the center oval, write either an experience that shaped your life or an insight that you have gained. In the outer ovals, write events related to that experience or insight. Then, respond to the item that follows.

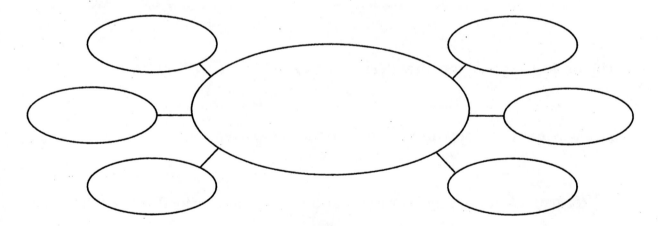

Now, choose an event from the word web that was most significant to your experience or insight. Describe the scene in which the event took place by writing about the specific actions and feelings of the characters involved.

_____

_____

_____

_____

_____

© Pearson Education, Inc., publishing as Pearson Prentice Hall.

# Autobiographical Narrative

**A**   Circle the letter of the correct answer.

1. Which element is essential to a well-written autobiographical narrative?

    **A.** a really fascinating ending
    **B.** insights that the writer has gained from experience

2. Autobiographical narratives describe ____ events in the writer's life.

    **A.** real                              **B.** made-up

**B**   Use the word web below to choose a topic for an autobiographical narrative. In the center oval, write either an experience that shaped your life or an insight that you have gained. In the outer ovals, write events related to that experience or insight. Then, respond to the item that follows.

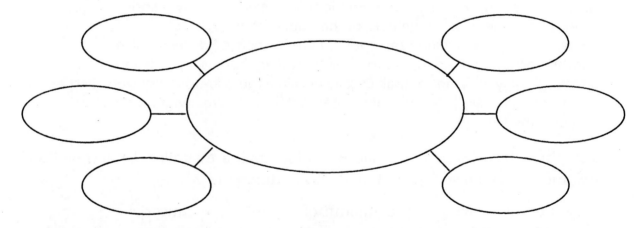

Now, choose an event from the word web that was most significant to your experience or insight. Describe the scene in which the event took place by writing about the specific actions and feelings of the characters involved.

_____

_____

_____

_____

_____

_____

© Pearson Education, Inc., publishing as Pearson Prentice Hall.

# Comparison-and-Contrast Essay

## Practice

A **comparison-and-contrast essay** describes the similarities and differences between two or more related subjects. A good comparison-and-contrast essay has the following features:

- a topic that includes two or more things that are neither nearly identical nor extremely different
- details that illustrate the similarities and details that illustrate the differences
- an organization that highlights the points of comparison

**A** Read the following passage. Then, complete the activities below.

Soccer and football are two popular sports. The two sports are similar in many ways. In both sports, two teams try to move a ball down the field to their opponent's goal. Players in each sport need to be able keep up a fast pace, and teamwork plays a vital role in the success of the two sports. A goal cannot be made without the help of the entire team.

While I enjoy watching both sports, I prefer soccer. Soccer involves constant action and motion. In football, however, there is a pause in action after each play. Plays in football usually end in large pile-ups of players, and a spectator can easily lose sight of the ball. While both are invigorating sports, soccer is my favorite.

1. Circle the categories in which soccer and football are similar. Underline the categories in which soccer and football are different.

the goal of the game        the amount of action        teamwork
the need for speed and stamina        the ease in following the game

2. List at least one other similarity between soccer and football. _____

_____

3. List at least one other difference between soccer and football. _____

_____

**B** Choose two of your favorite sports figures or movie stars. Decide which is your favorite. Then, list below three categories that you would use to compare and contrast them. Choose categories that will show why you prefer one to the other.

_____

© Pearson Education, Inc., publishing as Pearson Prentice Hall.

# Comparison-and-Contrast Essay

Assess

**A** Choose one of the following topics or a topic of your own for a comparison-and-contrast essay. Then, complete the activities below.

dogs or cats as pets                    the seasons of summer or winter
two books you have read            playing computer games or board games

1. List the topic and the three categories you will use to explain the similarities and differences. Choose categories that will help explain why you prefer one of the two items being compared.

_____

_____

2. Fill in the headings of this chart with each category you have listed in item 1, and then list supporting details in each column.

|  |  |  |
|---|---|---|
|  |  |  |

3. Write the opening paragraph of a comparison-and-contrast essay. Include what is being compared. Explain which of the two items you prefer. Then, write the second paragraph, comparing the two using the first category.

_____

_____

_____

_____

_____

_____

_____

© Pearson Education, Inc., publishing as Pearson Prentice Hall.

# Job Portfolio and Résumé

## Practice

A **job portfolio** includes a résumé. In a **résumé**, you tell about the experience and skills that make you a good candidate for a job. Your résumé should have these elements:

- your name and contact information prominently presented
- accounts of jobs, education, and other experiences that highlight your strengths
- an emphasis on experiences that make you suited to the job
- a clear, consistent organization and format that allows readers to find information easily
- formal, active language and a consistent style. Usually, the first-person pronoun *I* is not used on a résumé.

---

**A** Read this portion of a résumé. Then, answer the questions that follow.

(A) Ben Sinclair
10 Smith St., Tacoma, WA

(B) WORK EXPERIENCE
(C) 10/05–Present
Assistant Manager          Ernie's Hot Dog Hut, Main Street, Tacoma
(part time)                Supervise cooks and counter personnel. Close out
                           registers and run daily tallies. Responsible for opening
                           restaurant.

(D) 6/04–10/05
Counterperson              I waited on the customers who came to eat at Ernie's.
(part time)                I set tables and helped clean up at the end of a shift.
                    (E) *Education*
2003–Present               Horace Mann High School

**1.** Which information is missing from part A of the résumé?

   **A.** the writer's phone number      **B.** the writer's school

**2.** Which parts of this résumé show an inconsistency in format?

   **A.** C and D              **B.** B and E

---

**B** On a separate sheet of paper, list three experiences of your own that you might include on a résumé, such as volunteer experience, awards you have received, and any special talents or skills you have. Include approximate starting and ending dates where relevant.

© Pearson Education, Inc., publishing as Pearson Prentice Hall.

# Job Portfolio and Résumé

Assess

**A**   Circle the letter of the best answer to each question.

1. Ashley has worked at a bookstore. She is applying for a job as a programmer. Which aspect of her bookstore work should she be sure to include on her résumé?

   **A.** her experience working the cash register
   **B.** the computer database she designed to track special orders
   **C.** the compliments she received from customers for her help

2. Which description uses the most active language?

   **A.** Managed a team of counselors; led problem-solving sessions.
   **B.** Was the head counselor; tried to help campers by talking to them.
   **C.** Served as leader of team of counselors; was responsible for problem-solving sessions.

**B**   Begin to create a résumé by filling in the blanks below. Use formal, active language in your descriptions. In the "Other Experience" section, list any experiences that show your ability to take responsibility, including extracurricular activities such as sports. You may also include special skills, such as knowledge of a foreign language.

[Name and contact information]

_____

_____

_____

## WORK EXPERIENCE

[Dates] _____

[Title] _____     [Employer] _____

[Description of responsibilities and accomplishments]

_____

_____

_____

## OTHER EXPERIENCE, SKILLS, AND AWARDS

[Description of responsibilities and accomplishments]

_____

_____

_____

© Pearson Education, Inc., publishing as Pearson Prentice Hall.

# Multimedia Report

A **multimedia report** is a special kind of research report. It presents information in many forms, including a variety of media such as slides, video, music, maps, charts, artwork, and text. Your library is a good source for audio and video clips, as well as documentaries, music, and art resources. The Internet can also be a good source.

## Elements of a Successful Multimedia Report

| An interesting *topic*, narrow enough to be covered in the allotted time | A *clear and logical organization* | Varied use of *relevant audio and visual features* | Good *pacing*, including smooth transitions | A *strong introduction and a memorable conclusion* |
|---|---|---|---|---|

Read this description of a plan for a multimedia report, and then respond to each item.

John wanted to do a multimedia report on the entire history of the Civil War. He wanted to share the excitement of the more than three hundred battles that took place. He went to the library and looked in an encyclopedia and five books. He did some online research. He figured he would write scripts and have other students act out several of the battles. Then, he planned to videotape each battle. He planned to find some old clothes at a thrift store.

1. Explain the problem with John's topic. _____

_____

2. Explain how John could improve his topic. _____

_____

3. Give at least two examples of how John might change the way in which he is planning to present information on his topic.

_____

_____

4. What other audio and visual features might John use? Give at least two suggestions of other relevant media.

_____

_____

© Pearson Education, Inc., publishing as Pearson Prentice Hall.

## Multimedia Report

Assess

**A**  Read this description of a plan for a multimedia report, and then respond to each item.

Kate is creating a multimedia report on the great artists of the twentieth century. She wants to arrange a slide show. She also plans to play some music to make the slide show more interesting. She is not sure where to find information on her subject, but her grandmother has some old paintings in the attic. Kate also knows a local artist, and she could go watch him work to get a better understanding of the process involved in bringing art to life.

1. Explain the problem with Kate's topic and how you would solve it. _____

_____

2. Explain where Kate can go for research help on her topic. _____

_____

3. Give at least two examples of how Kate might change her presentation.

_____

_____

_____

**B**  Suppose that you are planning a multimedia report about a form of art, music, or film. Fill in the information below. Then, write a description of your planned multimedia report.

1. My topic: _____

2. Two examples of media I can use to support my topic: _____

_____

3. How I will do my research: _____

_____

4. Brief description of my multimedia report: _____

_____

_____

_____

© Pearson Education, Inc., publishing as Pearson Prentice Hall.

# Persuasive Essay

## Practice

When you use words to try to get others to think a certain way or to do something, you are using persuasion. A **persuasive essay** is a brief work in which a writer tries to convince readers to agree or disagree with a particular position. A persuasive essay should feature the following elements:

- a clear statement of your position on an issue with more than one side
- evidence and reasons that support your position and persuade readers to agree
- statements that identify and address readers' possible arguments against your position
- effective rhetorical devices such as charged language, vivid images, and dramatic analogies

**Read the following part of a student's persuasive essay. Then, respond to each item.**

> I feel very strongly that homework for high-school students should take no longer than two hours a night. More than two hours of homework makes it very hard for students to participate in after-school activities like sports or clubs. It also makes it almost impossible for students to have a part-time job, which many students rely on for money.

**1.** What issue is addressed in this essay? _____

**2.** What is the writer's position? _____

**3.** What reasons does the writer give for his or her position? _____

_____

_____

**4.** What is one argument a reader might make against this position? How

might the writer address this argument? _____

_____

_____

**5.** On the lines below, write the next two sentences in this essay.

_____

_____

© Pearson Education, Inc., publishing as Pearson Prentice Hall.

## Persuasive Essay

**Complete the following activities.**

**1.** List three issues about which you could argue persuasively.

_____

_____

_____

**2.** Choose and circle one of the three issues you listed. Write three facts or reasons why someone should agree with your opinion on this issue.

_____

_____

_____

**3.** Write two arguments someone might make against your position. Then, write your responses to these arguments.

Argument against your position: _____

_____

Your response: _____

_____

Argument against your position: _____

_____

Your response: _____

_____

**4.** On the following lines, write the first paragraph of your persuasive essay.

_____

_____

_____

© Pearson Education, Inc., publishing as Pearson Prentice Hall.

# Problem-and-Solution Essay

A **problem-and-solution essay** identifies a problem and presents one or more solutions. The author's purpose in a problem-and-solution essay is to inform and explain. A problem-and-solution essay should contain a statement describing the problem, details that develop the problem and show its significance, and a description of one or more solutions to the problem.

Prepare to write a brief essay about the amount of litter in your town. Use the following chart to help you list the problems and identify the solutions.

| Town | Problem Faced | Solution |
|------|---------------|----------|
| Ball fields | | |
| Community park | | |
| Roads | | |

**1.** Clearly state the problems below.

_____

_____

_____

**2.** How will you solve the problems step by step? List the steps below.

_____

_____

_____

**3.** Support each solution with examples. List the examples below.

_____

_____

_____

**4.** What is the conclusion? Write it below.

_____

© Pearson Education, Inc., publishing as Pearson Prentice Hall.

# Problem-and-Solution Essay

## Assess

**A** Answer these questions to prepare a problem-and-solution essay about the importance of using public transportation to reduce pollution.

1. Write your statement of the problem. _____

_____

_____

2. How will you solve your problems step by step? List your steps. _____

_____

_____

_____

_____

3. Support each solution with examples. List your examples. _____

_____

_____

_____

_____

4. Summarize the solution in a concluding statement. Write your statement.

_____

_____

_____

**B** Use your answers to write a brief problem-and-solution essay.

_____

_____

_____

_____

_____

© Pearson Education, Inc., publishing as Pearson Prentice Hall.

# Reflective Essay

A **reflective essay** shares the writer's thoughts about a personal experience, an event, or an idea. A strong reflective essay includes these elements:

- It features the writer as the main character.
- It includes the writer's personal feelings and ideas.
- It shows a connection between events and ideas.
- It shares the writer's insights.

**Read the example. Then, answer the questions that follow.**

> When my parents first told me I would soon have a little brother or sister, I thought they were joking. After all, I had been an only child for eleven years. I was used to having all my parents' time and attention. To be honest, I was afraid that when the baby came, I would be ignored and neglected. That was five years ago. What I didn't realize at the time was how much I would enjoy being a big sister.

**1.** Who is the focus of this reflective essay? _____

**2.** What event does the writer describe? _____

_____

**3.** How does the writer feel about the event? _____

_____

**4.** What insight does the writer gain as a result of the event? _____

_____

**5.** What event from your life could you use as the focus for a reflective essay?

_____

**6.** What insight did you gain as a result of the event? _____

_____

_____

© Pearson Education, Inc., publishing as Pearson Prentice Hall.

# Reflective Essay

Assess

**Read the following prompts. Then, respond to each one on the lines below.**

**1.** What event or experience from your life could you use as the focus for a reflective essay?

_____

**2.** List three details about the event or experience. _____

_____

_____

_____

**3.** Describe your thoughts and feelings about the event. _____

_____

_____

_____

**4.** What insight did you gain as a result of the event? _____

_____

_____

**5.** Write the first paragraph of your reflective essay.

_____

_____

_____

_____

_____

_____

_____

_____

© Pearson Education, Inc., publishing as Pearson Prentice Hall.

# Research Paper

A **research paper** analyzes information gathered from reference materials, observations, interviews, or other sources to present a clear and accurate picture of a topic or to answer a question. A research paper should include a clear thesis statement, factual information from a variety of sources, a consistent organization, and a list of works consulted.

**A**  Narrow each topic to one that could be covered in a research paper of six to eight paragraphs.

**1.** South America _____

_____

**2.** Great Inventors _____

_____

**3.** Jungle Animals _____

_____

**4.** Weather _____

_____

**5.** Athletics _____

_____

**6.** Careers in Medicine _____

_____

**B**  Choose three of the following topics. Write one good question to use in researching each of the chosen topics.

Martin Luther King, Jr.     Marie Curie          Japanese Poetry
The Civil War               African Art          Careers in Law Enforcement

_____

_____

_____

_____

© Pearson Education, Inc., publishing as Pearson Prentice Hall.

# Research Paper

## Assess

**A**  Read one student's plan for a research paper. Then, answer the questions that follow.

José is very interested in reality television shows. He has decided to write a research paper that examines why reality shows are so popular. He will be videotaping some shows and asking his class to vote on their favorite show. He is also preparing a list of survey questions to give to students to find out whether they prefer a contest-type of reality show or a show about the lives of famous people.

As part of his report, José is also going to trace the history of certain periods in television, such as the 1950s. He will look at the popularity of certain comedy shows during the 1950s and compare their popularity to that of today's comedy shows.

**1.** What is José's thesis? _____

_____

**2.** What are some questions José might ask as part of his research? _____

_____

**3.** What is a problem with the focus of José's research report, and what would

you suggest as a solution? _____

_____

_____

**B**  Think of a time period in American history that interests you. Then, fill in the blanks.

A topic that is narrow enough to cover in a short paper: _____

_____

A thesis that states my main idea: _____

_____

Where I could find information: _____

_____

How I plan to organize the information: _____

_____

# Response to Literature

When you write a **response to literature,** you state your overall opinion of the work and support that opinion using aspects of the text. For example, you might have liked a work because the characters were well developed and interesting. A response to literature should include the following:

- **thesis statement**—a short expression of your overall response to the work

- **a definite focus,** either on a single aspect of the work (for example, the setting of a story) or on two to three aspects of the work that were important in forming your opinion

- **specific evidence** from the work (including quotations) that support the opinions you have stated

Here is an example of an introduction to a response to literature:

> (Thesis statement:) "The Weary Blues" by Langston Hughes is an excellent poem. (Focus:) The sounds and rhythm in the poem echo the sounds and rhythm of blues songs. (Evidence:) The sounds of these lines make their own rhythm and music: "Down on Lenox Avenue the other night / By the pale dull pallor of an old gas light."

## A  Respond to each item below.

1. Songs are poems set to music. Think of one of your favorite songs. Write a thesis statement for a response to the words of this song.

   _____

   _____

2. What focus would you use to prove your thesis?

   _____

## B  In the left column are two elements found in "Metaphor," a poem by Eve Merriam. In the right column are excerpts from the poem. Match each element with the extract that best illustrates it.

1. _____ extended metaphor

2. _____ simple, ordinary words

A. "all day, / until night"

B. "Morning is / a new sheet of paper / for you to write on."

© Pearson Education, Inc., publishing as Pearson Prentice Hall.

## Response to Literature

**A**  Read the following haiku by Matsuo Bashō, translated by Daniel C. Buchanan. Then, answer the questions.

> Has spring come indeed?
> On that nameless mountain lie
> Thin layers of mist.

**1.** If you were writing a response to this poem focusing on its imagery, or the word-pictures it presents, what words would you quote? _____

_____

**2.** If your written response to this poem were to focus on the poem's emotion, what would your thesis statement be? _____

_____

**3.** This poem is a haiku, which means that its first line has five syllables, its second line has seven syllables, and its third line has five syllables. Haikus usually present a single, strong image from nature that invites readers to imagine and think. If your written response were to focus on the appeal of this particular form of poetry, what would your thesis statement be?

_____

_____

_____

_____

**B**  Write three brief paragraphs responding to the poem above. The first paragraph is the introduction and should contain the thesis and the focus you are using. The second paragraph should restate the focus and give details and quotations that demonstrate your point. The last paragraph is the conclusion. Use a separate sheet of paper if needed.

_____

_____

_____

_____

© Pearson Education, Inc., publishing as Pearson Prentice Hall.

# Everyday Reading Strategies

# Predictogram Relating Words

## About the Strategy

Predictograms ask students to use what they know about words and phrases from a selection to make predictions about its content and structure. Prediction activities involve students in the text, engage their attention, and give them a stake in the outcome of a story.

A sample predictogram is provided using the story "Seventh Grade."

*A relating words predictogram works well with any fictional piece in which the words, phrases, and quotations selected can show associations between characters and concepts.*

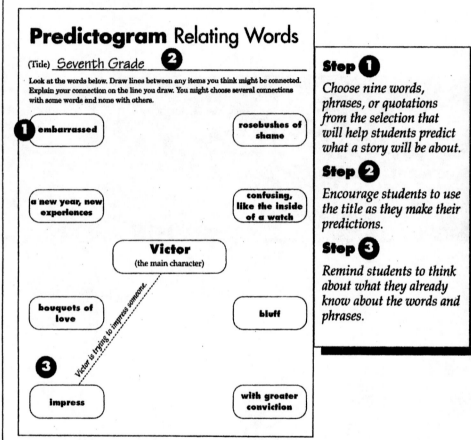

### Predictogram Relating Words

(Title) **Seventh Grade** ❷

Look at the words below. Draw lines between any items you think might be connected. Explain your connection on the line you draw. You might choose several connections with some words and none with others.

❶ embarrassed

rosebushes of shame

a new year, new experiences

confusing, like the inside of a watch

**Victor** (the main character)

*Victor is trying to impress someone.*

bouquets of love

bluff

❸ impress

with greater conviction

**Step ❶**
*Choose nine words, phrases, or quotations from the selection that will help students predict what a story will be about.*

**Step ❷**
*Encourage students to use the title as they make their predictions.*

**Step ❸**
*Remind students to think about what they already know about the words and phrases.*

**Skills and Strategies:** *predict outcomes, activate prior knowledge, draw conclusions*

**Idea Exchange**

### Keep in Mind
• Choose appropriate words, phrases, quotations, and topical cues, such as titles or key words, to help students make associations.
• Model one prediction before individuals begin.
• Be sure students return to their predictograms after reading to confirm their predictions.

### All Together Now
You might use the relating words predictogram to begin a class discussion. Students could state their predictions rather than writing them down.

© Pearson Education, Inc., publishing as Pearson Prentice Hall.

# **Predictogram** Relating Words

(Title) _____

Look at the words below. Draw lines between any items you think might be connected. Explain your connection on the line you draw. You might choose several connections with some words and none with others.

# Predictogram Literary Features

## About the Strategy

Predictograms ask students to use what they know about words and phrases from a selection to make predictions about its content and structure. Prediction activities involve students in the text, engage their attention, and give them a stake in the outcome of a story.

The following model is based on "All Summer in a Day."

*A literary features predictogram works well with any fictional piece in which the words or phrases selected can help students identify specific features of a story.*

### Predictogram Literary Features

(Title) __All Summer in a Day__ ❷

Look at the selection title above and this list of words and phrases to write sentences that predict who and what this story might be about.

| | | |
|---|---|---|
| teacher | silence was so immense | jungle |
| solemn and pale | remembered a warmness | Margot |
| ❶ muffled cries | turning their faces up | Venus |
| 9 years old | rocket men and women | a closet |
| then looked away | raining for seven years | soon |
| It's stopping. | very frail | running |

Characters: _____

_____

Setting: _____

_____

❸

Problem: _____

_____

Events: _____

_____

_____

Outcome: _____

_____

Mystery Words or Phrases: _____

_____

**Step ❶**

*Choose five to ten words or phrases from the selection that will help students predict what the story will be about.*

**Step ❷**

*Encourage students to use the title as they make their predictions.*

**Step ❸**

*Remind students to think about what they already know about the words and phrases.*

**Skills and Strategies:** *predict outcomes, activate prior knowledge, draw conclusions*

## Keep in Mind

• Choose appropriate words, phrases, and topical cues, such as titles or key words, to help students make associations.

• Model one prediction before individuals begin.

• Be sure students return to their predictograms after reading to confirm their predictions.

## Solo Exploration

Encourage students to use this predictogram to plan their own writing. They can collect their ideas in the box and sort them according to literary feature as a prewriting strategy. **(writing)**

© Pearson Education, Inc., publishing as Pearson Prentice Hall.

# **Predictogram** Literary Features

(Title) _____

Look at the selection title above and this list of words and phrases to write
sentences that predict who and what this story might be about.

[ ]

**Characters:** _____

_____

**Setting:** _____

_____

**Problem:** _____

_____

**Events:** _____

_____

_____

**Outcome:** _____

_____

**Mystery Words or Phrases:** _____

_____

# Predictogram Asking Questions

## About the Strategy

Predictograms ask students to use what they know about words and phrases from a selection to make predictions about its content and structure. Prediction activities involve students in the text, engage their attention, and give them a stake in the outcome of a story.

Look at the following example.

*An asking questions predictogram works well with any fictional piece in which the words and phrases selected suggest questions to the reader.*

### Predictogram Asking Questions

(Title) __A Ribbon for Baldy__ ②

Look at the title of the selection above and the words or phrases below. Can you think of any questions to ask about this selection?

**①**

| | |
|---|---|
| project | Why is a project important in this story? |
| posture | |
| Little Baldy | |
| cone-shaped | |
| broom-sedge | |
| fire | |
| corn row | |
| corkscrew | |

Choose one of your questions and write a paragraph answering it.

**③**

Question: _____

_____

Answer: _____

_____

_____

_____

_____

_____

_____

#### Step ❶

*Choose eight words or phrases from the selection that will help students write questions to predict what a story will be about.*

#### Step ❷

*Encourage students to use the title as they make their predictions.*

#### Step ❸

*Remind students to think about what they already know about the words and phrases as they answer the question.*

**Skills and Strategies:** *predict outcomes, activate prior knowledge, draw conclusions*

**Idea Exchange**

### Keep in Mind
• Choose appropriate words, phrases, and topical cues, such as titles or key words, to help students write their questions.
• Model one prediction before individuals begin.
• Be sure students return to their predictograms after reading to confirm their predictions.

### Buddywork
Suggest to students that they use the glossary at the end of a chapter in their social studies book to create an asking questions predictogram. They can use their predictograms to help them set purposes for reading the chapter. **(cross-curricular connection)**

© Pearson Education, Inc., publishing as Pearson Prentice Hall.

# Predictogram Asking Questions

(Title) _____

Look at the title of the selection above and the words or phrases below. Can
you think of any questions to ask about this selection?

|  |  |
|---|---|
|  |  |
|  |  |
|  |  |
|  |  |
|  |  |
|  |  |
|  |  |

Choose one of your questions and write a paragraph answering it.

**Question:** _____

_____

**Answer:** _____

_____

_____

_____

_____

_____

© Pearson Education, Inc., publishing as Pearson Prentice Hall.

# Predictogram Using Quotations

## About the Strategy

Predictograms ask students to use what they know about words and phrases from a selection to make predictions about its content and structure. Prediction activities involve students in the text, engage their attention, and give them a stake in the outcome of a story.

Look at the following example.

*A using quotations predictogram works well with any fictional piece in which characters can be identified by their words.*

---

### Predictogram Using Quotations

(Title) Becky and the Wheels-and-Brake Boys

Look at the title above and the descriptions of each character below. Can you predict who might have said each of the following? Write the quotation next to the character who might have said it.

**1**

"D'you think you're a boy?"

"I can't get rid of it, mam.

"What am I going to do?"

**2**

| Character | Quotation |
|---|---|
| **Becky:** a young girl who wants a bike | **3** |
| **Mum:** Becky's mother | |

Now write a paragraph about one of the characters using the quotations above.

_____

_____

_____

_____

### Step **1**

*Choose three to ten quotations from the selection that will help students predict what a story will be about.*

### Step **2**

*Choose two main characters and write a brief description of each.*

### Step **3**

*Ask students to match the quotations with the characters who might say them.*

---

**Skills and Strategies:** *predict outcomes, activate prior knowledge, draw conclusions*

Idea Exchange

## Keep in Mind
• Choose identifying quotations and topical cues, such as titles or key words, to help students make associations.
• Model one prediction before individuals begin.
• Be sure students return to their predictograms after reading to confirm their predictions.

## All Together Now
Students could take turns reading the quotations with differing inflections. The class could predict how each sentence might be said in the context of the story. While reading they can check their predictions.

© Pearson Education, Inc., publishing as Pearson Prentice Hall.

# **Predictogram** Using Quotations

(Title) _____

Look at the title above and the descriptions of each character below. Can you predict who might have said each of the following? Write the quotation next to the character who might have said it.

| Character | Quotation |
|---|---|
|  |  |
|  |  |

Now write a paragraph about one of the characters using the quotations above.

_____

_____

_____

_____

© Pearson Education, Inc., publishing as Pearson Prentice Hall.

# K-W-L Chart

## About the Strategy

K-W-L is a strategy for reading expository text that helps students use their prior knowledge to generate interest in a selection. K-W-L also helps students set purposes for reading by encouraging them to express their curiosity for the topic they will be reading about. K-W-L encourages group members to share and discuss what they know, what they want to know, and what they learn about a topic.

*List selections for which you would like to use a K-W-L chart.*

**Step 1**
*Students brainstorm what they know or think they know about the topic.*

**Step 2**
*Students list questions they hope to have answered as they read.*

**Step 3**
*Students list what they learn as they read.*

## K-W-L Chart

Topic: Abraham Lincoln

| What We **K**now | What We **W**ant to Know | What We **L**earned |
|---|---|---|
| Lincoln was president of the United States. | What was Lincoln's childhood like? | Lincoln was born in a log cabin and was poor as a child. |
| Lincoln grew up poor. | How was Lincoln educated? | Lincoln went to school when he could and read everything he could find. |
| | What kind of person was Lincoln? | Lincoln was a good wrestler and runner and loved to tell jokes and stories. |
| **1** | **2** | **3** |

**Skills and Strategies:** *activate prior knowledge, generate questions, set purpose, summarize facts*

**Idea Exchange**

### Keep in Mind
• If students are unsure of a fact they listed in column one, they can turn it into a question in column two.
• Encourage students to find out the answers to any unanswered questions.

### Solo Exploration
Students can use a K-W-L chart to set purposes for reading a daily newspaper. Before reading, students should think about what they know (e.g., the weather forecast from listening to the radio) and what they want to know. **(cross-curricular connection)**

© Pearson Education, Inc., publishing as Pearson Prentice Hall.

# K-W-L Chart

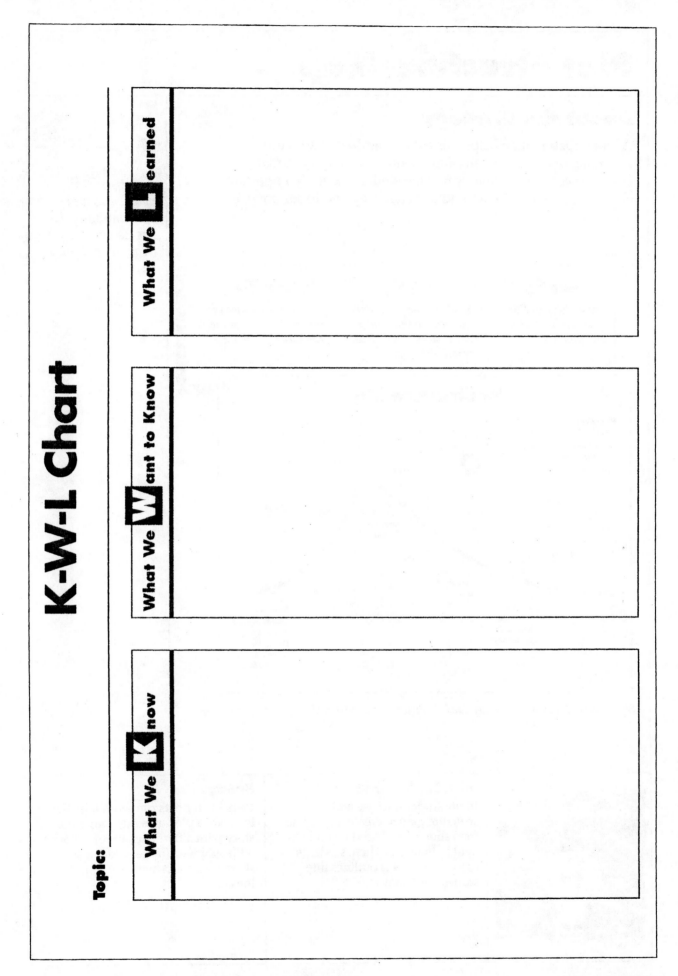

Topic: _____

**What We Know**

**What We Want to Know**

**What We Learned**

© Pearson Education, Inc., publishing as Pearson Prentice Hall.

# Plot Structure Map

## About the Strategy

A plot structure map helps students recognize the structure, or grammar, of a fictional selection. Identifying story grammar enhances comprehension by helping students identify important characters, predict events, and be better prepared to summarize a selection.

*A plot structure map works well with any story that has rising action, a clear climax, and a resolution.*

**Step 1**
*Students record the setting, characters, and problem.*

**Step 2**
*Students list the events that lead to the climax of the story before they record the climax.*

**Step 3**
*The events that lead to the resolution and the resolution itself are recorded.*

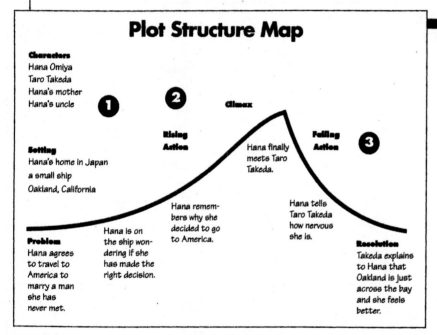

### Plot Structure Map

**Characters**
Hana Omiya
Taro Takeda
Hana's mother
Hana's uncle

**Setting**
Hana's home in Japan
a small ship
Oakland, California

**Problem**
Hana agrees to travel to America to marry a man she has never met.

**Rising Action**

**Climax**

**Falling Action**

Hana is on the ship wondering if she has made the right decision.

Hana remembers why she decided to go to America.

Hana finally meets Taro Takeda.

Hana tells Taro Takeda how nervous she is.

**Resolution**
Takeda explains to Hana that Oakland is just across the bay and she feels better.

**Skills and Strategies:** *understand characters, note setting, identify plot, summarize*

**Idea Exchange**

### Solo Exploration

Invite students to use a plot structure map to create an outline for a short story based on an incident in their life. Then, students can develop their outlines into stories. **(writing)**

### Buddywork

Pairs of students can work together to create a plot structure map for a story with a flashback or for a story with subplots. Invite students to share their maps with the rest of the class.

© Pearson Education, Inc., publishing as Pearson Prentice Hall.

# Plot Structure Map

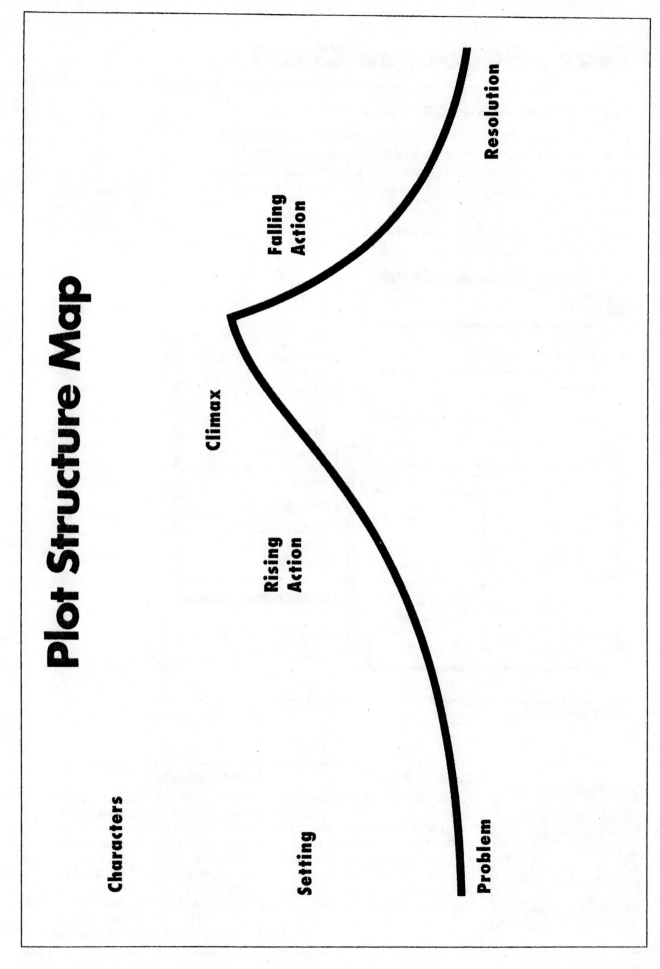

Characters

Climax

Falling
Action

Rising
Action

Resolution

Setting

Problem

© Pearson Education, Inc., publishing as Pearson Prentice Hall.

# Story Sequence Chart

## About the Strategy

A story sequence chart helps students recognize the sequence of events in a selection. Keeping track of the sequence of events is a simple way to give students a sense of story. In addition, understanding sequence prepares students for more complex types of story structures.

Modify the chart to fit the specifics of a story.

*A story sequence chart works well with any story that has a clear sequence of events.*

### Story Sequence Chart

**1**

**Title:**
Zlateh the Goat

**Setting:**
a village and the road to town

**Characters:**
Aaron, a boy; Reuven, his father; Zlateh, their goat

**Problem:**
The family needs money and Reuven decides to sell the goat.

**Events**

**2**

The butcher offers money for the goat.

Aaron and Zlateh leave for the butcher.

On their way, a huge snowstorm develops and they get lost.

Zlateh and Aaron take shelter in a haystack, where Zlateh provides warmth and milk.

**3**

**Solution:**
The family is grateful to Zlateh and decides never to sell the goat.

### Step **1**
*Students record the title, setting, characters, and problem.*

### Step **2**
*Students list the events that take place before the problem is resolved.*

### Step **3**
*Students record the solution to the central problem.*

**Skills and Strategies:** *understand characters, note setting, sequence events, identify plot, summarize*

**Idea Exchange**

### Keep in Mind
• Remind students that dates, time of day, and words like *first*, *next*, and *last* are clues to the sequence of events in a story.
• Encourage students to look for clue words like *while* and *during* that indicate two or more events happening at the same time.

### All Together Now
Discuss with students the relative importance of events as well as the time order by asking questions like "Would the story have turned out differently if things hadn't happened in this order?" or "Would it matter if 'such and such' hadn't happened at all?" Students can adjust their charts to show what changes would occur. **(discussion)**

© Pearson Education, Inc., publishing as Pearson Prentice Hall.

# Story Sequence Chart

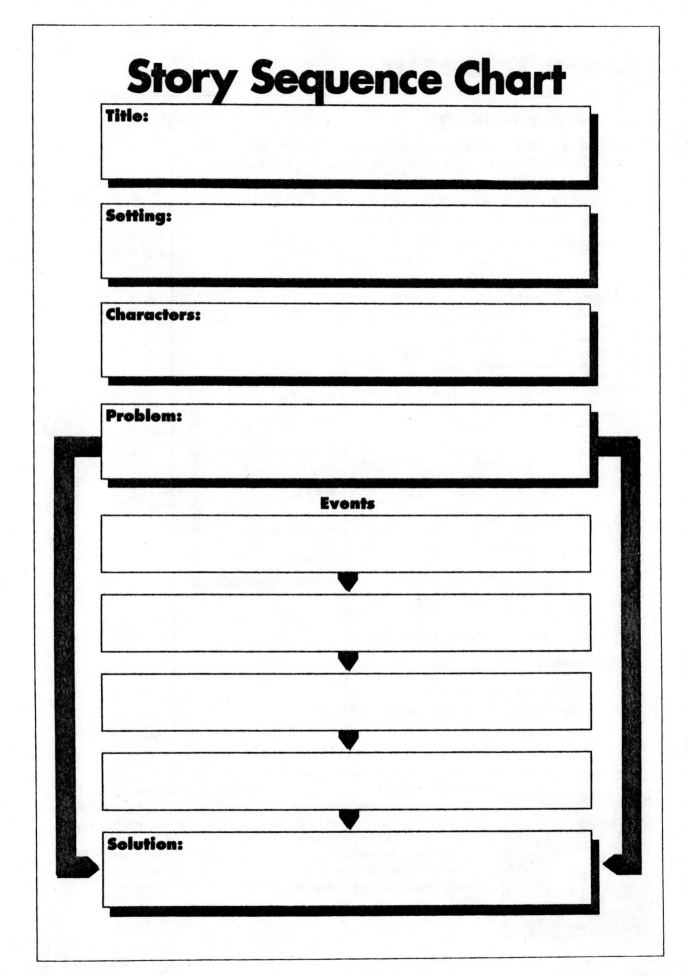

**Title:**

**Setting:**

**Characters:**

**Problem:**

**Events**

**Solution:**

© Pearson Education, Inc., publishing as Pearson Prentice Hall.

# Story Triangle

## About the Strategy

A story triangle is a creative way to think about and summarize a story. Like a traditional story map, the story triangle helps students recognize story elements. However, a story triangle allows students to respond personally to a story since students must describe rather than just list characters, events, and problems.

The following model is based on the story "Seventh Grade."

*Story triangles work well with all types of fiction, including realistic and historical fiction.*

### Story Triangle

1. Name of main character
2. Two words describing main character
3. Three words describing setting
4. Four words stating main problem
5. Five words relating one event
6. Six words relating second event
7. Seven words relating third event
8. Eight words reporting solution

**1**

1.    Victor

2.    friendly    shy

**2**

3.    Fresno    school    warm

4.    Victor's    shyness    with    Theresa

5.    Victor    tries    talking    to    Theresa.

6.    Victor    looks    for    Theresa    during    lunch.

7.    Victor    fakes    knowing    French    and    embarrasses    himself.

8. Theresa,    impressed    by    Victor's "French,"    requests    his    help.

### Step **1**
*Students follow the directions at the top of the page to fill in the story triangle.*

### Step **2**
*Encourage students to be creative as they choose words, phrases, and sentences.*

**Skills and Strategies:** *understand characters, note setting, identify plot, summarize*

### Idea Exchange

### Keep in Mind
• If students get stuck in the middle, encourage them to start with the last line and work backward.
• When using a story triangle with another story, be sure to change the guidelines to match the story.

### Solo Exploration
After students complete their story triangles, they can circle any vague words they used. Encourage students to choose synonyms that are more interesting and specific to replace the vague words.

© Pearson Education, Inc., publishing as Pearson Prentice Hall.

# Story Triangle

1. Name of main character
2. Two words describing main character
3. Three words describing setting
4. Four words stating main problem
5. Five words relating one event
6. Six words relating second event
7. Seven words relating third event
8. Eight words reporting solution

1. _____

2. _____ _____

3. _____ _____ _____

4. _____ _____ _____ _____

5. _____ _____ _____ _____ _____

6. _____ _____ _____ _____ _____ _____

7. _____ _____ _____ _____ _____ _____ _____

8. _____ _____ _____ _____ _____ _____ _____ _____

© Pearson Education, Inc., publishing as Pearson Prentice Hall.

# Story-Within-a-Story Map

## About the Strategy

A story-within-a-story map helps students identify the plot events of this complex text structure. Keeping track of plot events enhances comprehension by helping students recognize the change in narrative that is part of this structure.

*Story-within-a-story maps work well with fiction in which the plot includes a story within the story.*

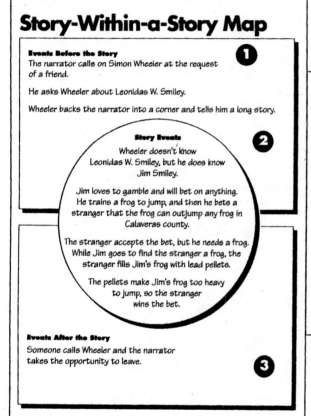

### Story-Within-a-Story Map

**Events Before the Story** ❶
The narrator calls on Simon Wheeler at the request of a friend.

He asks Wheeler about Leonidas W. Smiley.

Wheeler backs the narrator into a corner and tells him a long story.

**Story Events** ❷
Wheeler doesn't know Leonidas W. Smiley, but he does know Jim Smiley.

Jim loves to gamble and will bet on anything. He trains a frog to jump, and then he bets a stranger that the frog can outjump any frog in Calaveras county.

The stranger accepts the bet, but he needs a frog. While Jim goes to find the stranger a frog, the stranger fills Jim's frog with lead pellets.

The pellets make Jim's frog too heavy to jump, so the stranger wins the bet.

**Events After the Story** ❸
Someone calls Wheeler and the narrator takes the opportunity to leave.

**Step ❶**

*At the top, students write the plot events that take place before the story is told.*

**Step ❷**

*In the inner circle, students list the plot events of the story.*

**Step ❸**

*At the bottom, students write the events that happen after the story is told.*

**Skills and Strategies:** *use story elements, use text structure/genre, sequence*

**Idea Exchange**

### Keep in Mind

If students are having difficulty recognizing this text structure, have them reread to look for the point in the story when the narrative shifts.

### Solo Exploration

Suggest that students do a story-comparison map for the story and the story within the story to look for similarities and differences between them.

© Pearson Education, Inc., publishing as Pearson Prentice Hall.

# Story-Within-a-Story Map

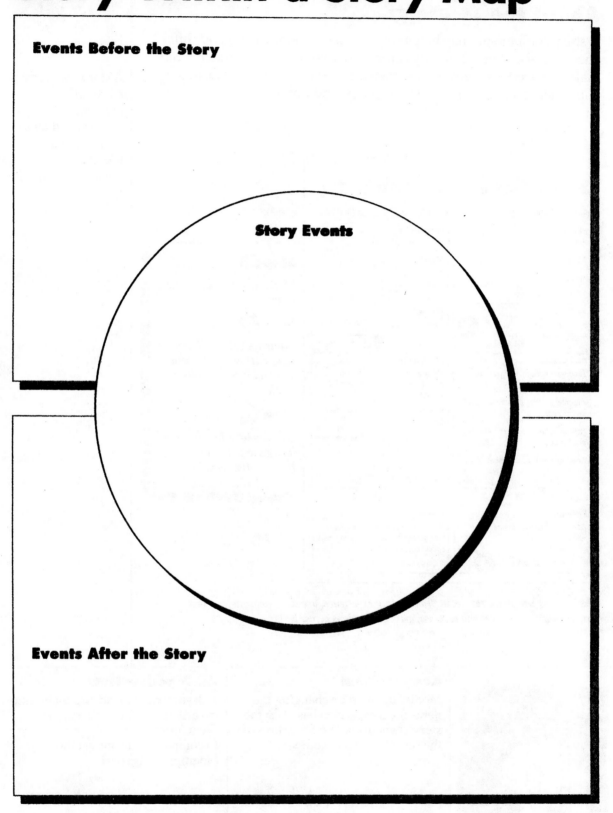

**Events Before the Story**

**Story Events**

**Events After the Story**

© Pearson Education, Inc., publishing as Pearson Prentice Hall.

# Story-Comparison Map

## About the Strategy

A story-comparison map helps students see the similarities and differences between two stories. By comparing two selections, students can make connections across texts—between text structures, characters and other story elements, authors' styles, and points of view.

*A story-comparison map works well with selections by the same author or selections that have unique story elements but similar text structures.*

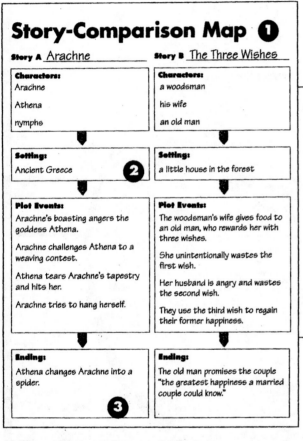

**Story-Comparison Map ❶**

**Story A** Arachne     **Story B** The Three Wishes

**Characters:**
Arachne
Athena
nymphs

**Characters:**
a woodsman
his wife
an old man

**Setting:** ❷
Ancient Greece

**Setting:**
a little house in the forest

**Plot Events:**
Arachne's boasting angers the goddess Athena.

Arachne challenges Athena to a weaving contest.

Athena tears Arachne's tapestry and hits her.

Arachne tries to hang herself.

**Plot Events:**
The woodsman's wife gives food to an old man, who rewards her with three wishes.

She unintentionally wastes the first wish.

Her husband is angry and wastes the second wish.

They use the third wish to regain their former happiness.

**Ending:**
Athena changes Arachne into a spider.

**Ending:**
The old man promises the couple "the greatest happiness a married couple could know."

❸

**Step ❶**
*Students write down the titles.*

**Step ❷**
*Students list the characters, settings, plot events, and endings for both stories.*

**Step ❸**
*Discuss together the similarities and differences between the selections.*

**Skills and Strategies:** *recall prior reading experience, use story elements, use text structure/genre, compare and contrast, make connections across texts*

**Idea Exchange**

### Keep in Mind
Modify the map by changing the items for comparison based on the story elements or text structures of the selections being compared.

### All Together Now
Ask students to read two biographical articles on the same person. Then, use a story-comparison map to compare and contrast the two biographies. **(genre)**

© Pearson Education, Inc., publishing as Pearson Prentice Hall.

# Story-Comparison Map

**Story A** _____     **Story B** _____

**Characters:**

**Characters:**

**Setting:**

**Setting:**

**Plot Events:**

**Plot Events:**

**Ending:**

**Ending:**

© Pearson Education, Inc., publishing as Pearson Prentice Hall.

# Cause-Effect Frame

## About the Strategy

A cause-effect frame helps students identify what happened and why it happened in both fictional and nonfictional texts. When students can see that there are causal relationships between events or ideas in text, they can make generalizations about other causal relationships in new texts and in life situations.

*Cause-effect frames work well with any selection that has clear cause-and-effect relationships.*

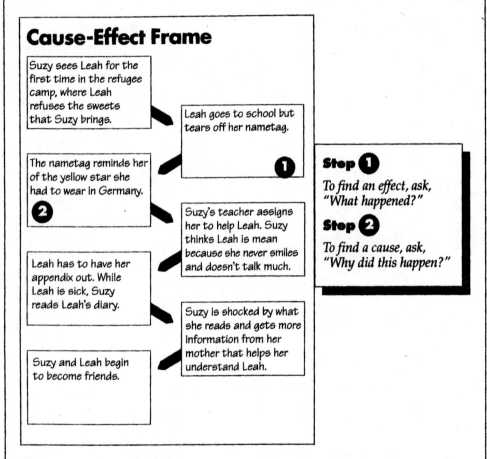

### Cause-Effect Frame

Suzy sees Leah for the first time in the refugee camp, where Leah refuses the sweets that Suzy brings.

Leah goes to school but tears off her nametag. **1**

The nametag reminds her of the yellow star she had to wear in Germany. **2**

Suzy's teacher assigns her to help Leah. Suzy thinks Leah is mean because she never smiles and doesn't talk much.

Leah has to have her appendix out. While Leah is sick, Suzy reads Leah's diary.

Suzy is shocked by what she reads and gets more information from her mother that helps her understand Leah.

Suzy and Leah begin to become friends.

**Step 1**
*To find an effect, ask, "What happened?"*

**Step 2**
*To find a cause, ask, "Why did this happen?"*

**Skills and Strategies:** *summarize, sequence, cause-effect, make inferences*

---

**Idea Exchange**

### Keep in Mind
• Suggest that students look for clue words, such as *since*, *as a result*, *consequently*, *therefore*, and *thus*.
• Remind students that some causes are not stated in the text. Students will have to figure out the cause by looking at what happened and asking themselves, "Why might this have happened?"

### Solo Exploration
Help students see that they can use cause-effect frames as a way to organize their writing. Students can choose an important school issue and use a cause-effect frame to outline the main point. Ask students to place the outlines in their portfolios to use for future writing. **(portfolio)**

© Pearson Education, Inc., publishing as Pearson Prentice Hall.

# Cause-Effect Frame

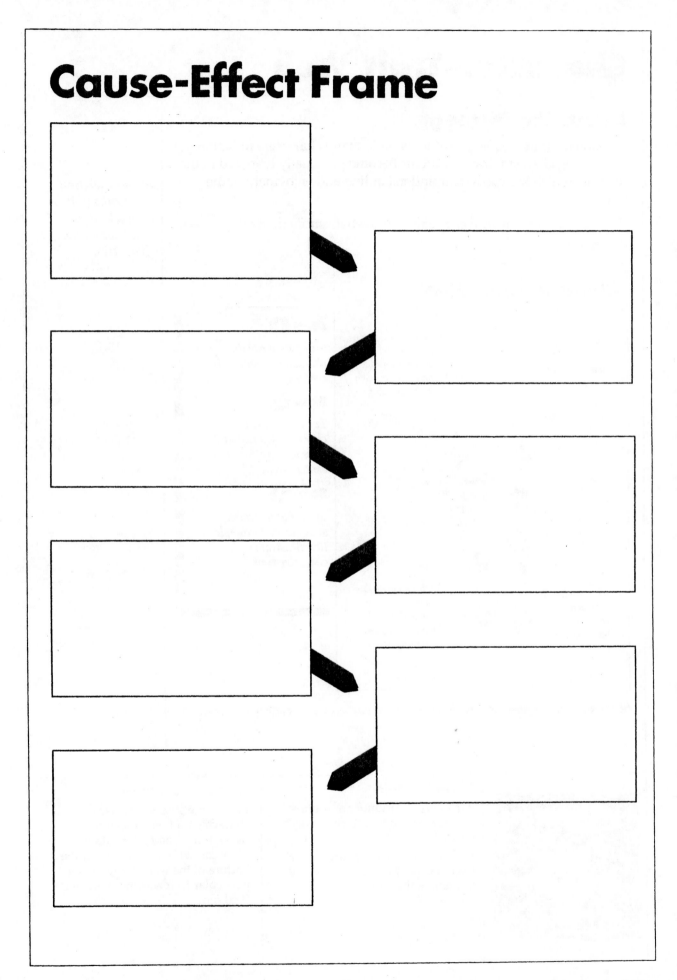

© Pearson Education, Inc., publishing as Pearson Prentice Hall.

# Character-Trait Web

## About the Strategy

A character-trait web helps students understand characters in fiction. By identifying character traits, students become personally involved in their reading, which increases their understanding and enjoyment of the selection.

You may want to create a character-trait web for more than one character in a selection.

*A character-trait web works well with selections that have strong characters.*

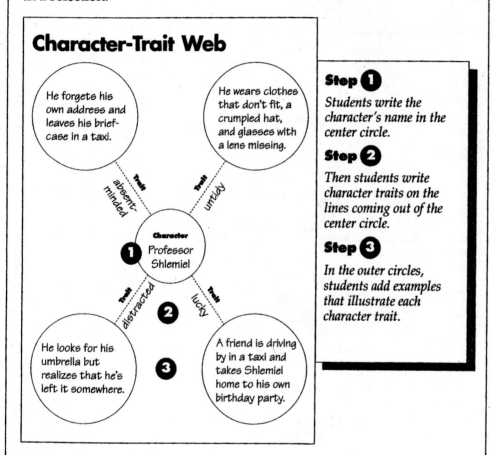

## Character-Trait Web

He forgets his own address and leaves his brief-case in a taxi.

He wears clothes that don't fit, a crumpled hat, and glasses with a lens missing.

**Trait** absent-minded

**Trait** untidy

**Character** 1 Professor Shlemiel

**Trait** distracted

2

**Trait** lucky

3

He looks for his umbrella but realizes that he's left it somewhere.

A friend is driving by in a taxi and takes Shlemiel home to his own birthday party.

### Step ❶
Students write the character's name in the center circle.

### Step ❷
Then students write character traits on the lines coming out of the center circle.

### Step ❸
In the outer circles, students add examples that illustrate each character trait.

**Skills and Strategies:** *understand characters, draw conclusions, make inferences*

**Idea Exchange**

### Keep in Mind
- Modify the number of traits as necessary to fit a selection or character.
- Examples can come directly from the story or can be based on inferences that students make.

### All Together Now
Encourage students to use a character-trait web to determine if a character had a fatal flaw. They can write a statement at the bottom of the web telling why a particular trait was the character's fatal flaw.

© Pearson Education, Inc., publishing as Pearson Prentice Hall.

# Character-Trait Web

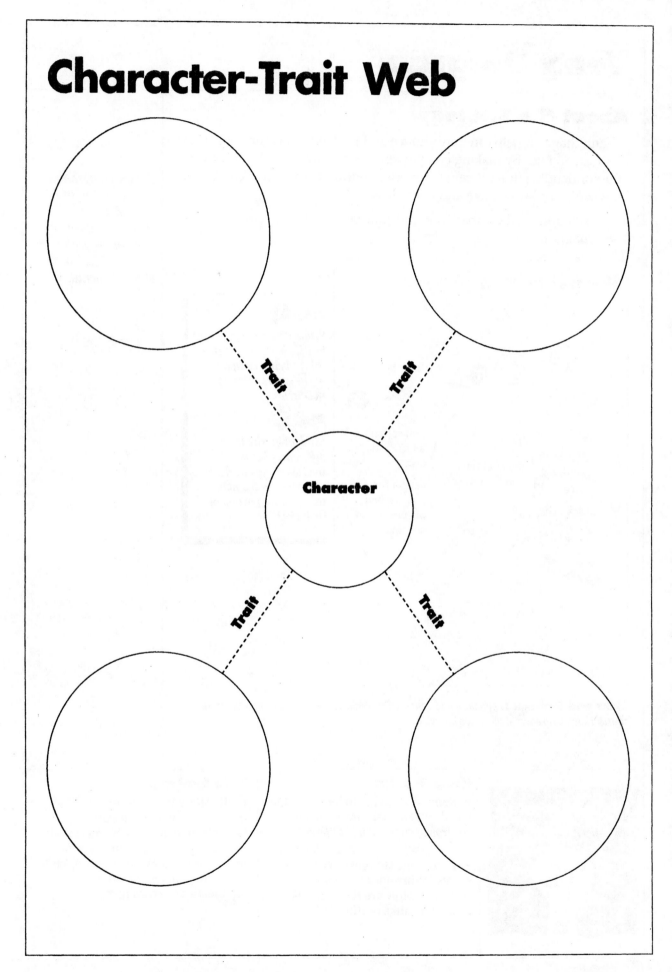

# Venn Diagram

## About the Strategy

A Venn diagram helps students notice and understand comparisons and contrasts in text. By making comparisons and contrasts in both fiction and nonfiction, students can clarify ideas within a text, across texts, and between prior knowledge and new ideas.

To make additional comparisons and contrasts, add more circles to the Venn diagram.

*A Venn diagram works well with any selection that lends itself to a comparison between ideas or story elements.*

### Venn Diagram

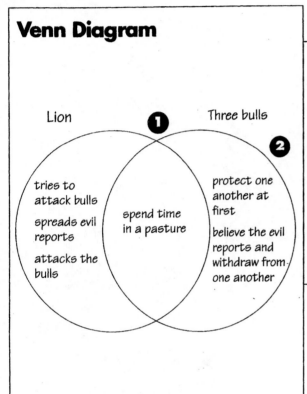

Lion

Three bulls

**1**

**2**

tries to attack bulls

spreads evil reports

attacks the bulls

spend time in a pasture

protect one another at first

believe the evil reports and withdraw from one another

**Step 1**

*Students write any similarities between the two things being compared in the intersection of the circles.*

**Step 2**

*Students write the differences between the two things being compared in the non-intersecting portion of each circle.*

**Skills and Strategies:** *compare and contrast, summarize, use story elements, make connections across texts, use prior knowledge*

**Idea Exchange**

### Keep in Mind

• Remind students to look for clue words that signal comparisons and contrasts, such as *like*, *different*, and *however*.

• Encourage students to ask themselves "What does this remind me of?" and "How are these things or characters alike or different?"

### Solo Exploration

Invite students to create Venn diagrams to make comparisons between two authors. Suggest that they compare where the authors live, how old they are, the subjects they write about, and so on. **(connections across texts)**

© Pearson Education, Inc., publishing as Pearson Prentice Hall.

# Venn Diagram

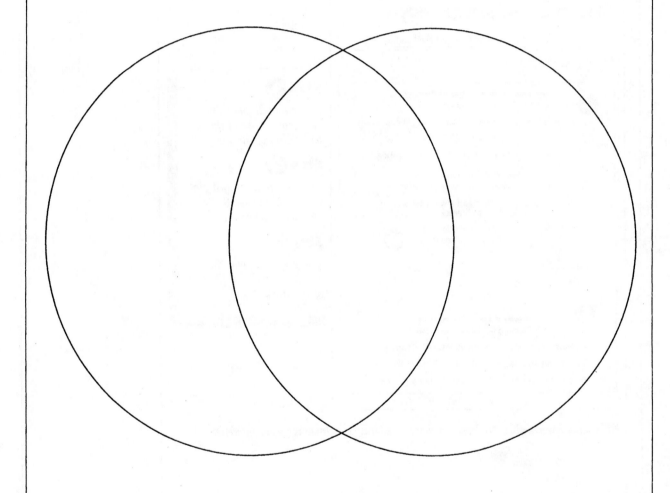

© Pearson Education, Inc., publishing as Pearson Prentice Hall.

# Character-Change Map

## About the Strategy

A character-change map helps students understand characters in fiction. By analyzing a character over the course of a story, students can see how a character changes in response to plot events.

The following character-change map is modeled using an excerpt from *I Know Why the Caged Bird Sings*.

*A character-change map works well with selections that have dynamic characters.*

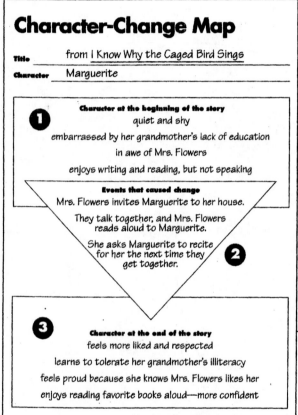

### Character-Change Map

**Title**  from I Know Why the Caged Bird Sings

**Character**  Marguerite

**1** Character at the beginning of the story
quiet and shy
embarrassed by her grandmother's lack of education
in awe of Mrs. Flowers
enjoys writing and reading, but not speaking

**Events that caused change**
Mrs. Flowers invites Marguerite to her house.
They talk together, and Mrs. Flowers reads aloud to Marguerite.
She asks Marguerite to recite for her the next time they get together. **2**

**3** Character at the end of the story
feels more liked and respected
learns to tolerate her grandmother's illiteracy
feels proud because she knows Mrs. Flowers likes her
enjoys reading favorite books aloud—more confident

**Step ①**
Students tell what the character is like at the beginning of the story.

**Step ②**
Then students record plot events that cause the character to change.

**Step ③**
Students tell what the character is like at the end of the story.

**Skills and Strategies:** *understand characters, draw conclusions, make inferences*

**Idea Exchange**

### Keep in Mind
You may want to ask students to map the changes in more than one character in a selection.

### Solo Exploration
To help students see that cause-and-effect relationships are often a part of change, suggest that they create a cause-and-effect map for the changes a character goes through in a story.

© Pearson Education, Inc., publishing as Pearson Prentice Hall.

# Character-Change Map

**Title** _____

**Character** _____

**Character at the beginning of the story**

**Events that caused change**

**Character at the end of the story**

© Pearson Education, Inc., publishing as Pearson Prentice Hall.

# Details Web

## About the Strategy

A details web helps students organize information in fictional or non-fictional text when many details are centered around one key or main idea. By completing the web, students see the relationship between the key or main idea and the details that support it.

*A details web works well with informational selections.*

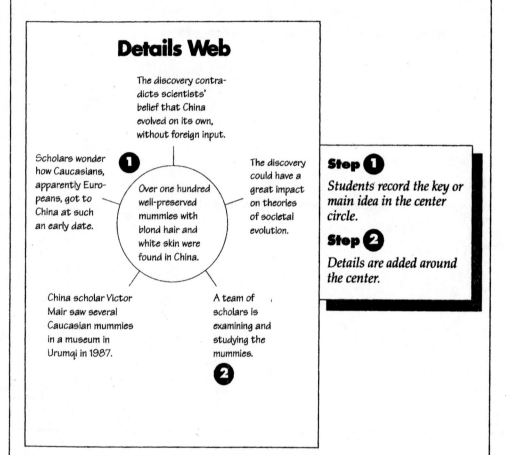

**Details Web**

The discovery contradicts scientists' belief that China evolved on its own, without foreign input.

Scholars wonder how Caucasians, apparently Europeans, got to China at such an early date.

**1**

Over one hundred well-preserved mummies with blond hair and white skin were found in China.

The discovery could have a great impact on theories of societal evolution.

China scholar Victor Mair saw several Caucasian mummies in a museum in Urumqi in 1987.

A team of scholars is examining and studying the mummies.

**2**

**Step 1**
*Students record the key or main idea in the center circle.*

**Step 2**
*Details are added around the center.*

**Skills and Strategies:** *main idea/supporting details, summarize*

**Idea Exchange**

### Keep in Mind
• If there is more than one key or main idea in a selection, create a separate details web for each idea.
• Help students identify the main idea of a nonfictional selection by asking "What is the most important idea in the selection?"

### Solo Exploration
Encourage students to create details webs to help organize their thoughts for a panel discussion or debate. Students can write the discussion/debate topic in the center of the web and brainstorm ideas in support or opposition. **(discussion)**

© Pearson Education, Inc., publishing as Pearson Prentice Hall.

# Details Web

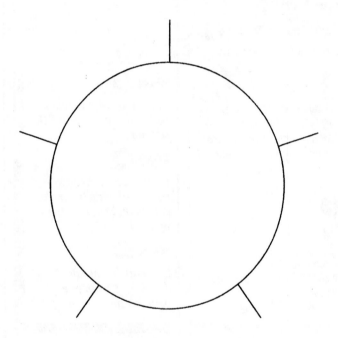

# Main Idea Map

## About the Strategy

A main idea map helps students recognize the main idea of a nonfictional selection and distinguish between the main idea and supporting details. Students determine the relative importance of what they read by organizing and reorganizing information from the text.

*Main idea maps work well with any nonfictional selection that is organized around one main idea supported by major and minor details.*

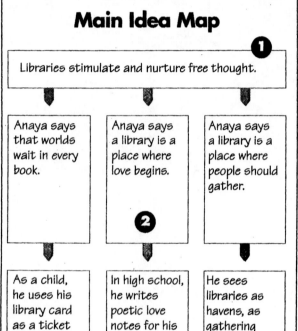

## Main Idea Map

**1** Libraries stimulate and nurture free thought.

Anaya says that worlds wait in every book.

Anaya says a library is a place where love begins.

Anaya says a library is a place where people should gather. **2**

As a child, he uses his library card as a ticket to magical worlds that feed his imagination.

In high school, he writes poetic love notes for his classmates. **3**

He sees libraries as havens, as gathering places, and as storehouses of knowledge.

**Step 1**
*In the top box, students record the main idea of the selection.*

**Step 2**
*In this second row of boxes, students list major details that support the main idea.*

**Step 3**
*Students list minor details or examples in the bottom row.*

**Skills and Strategies:** *main idea/supporting details, summarize, analyze information*

## Idea Exchange

### Keep in Mind

- Encourage students to think about the most important idea in the selection to figure out the main idea.
- Remind students that the main idea is not always stated in the text. Sometimes students will have to state the main idea in their own words.
- Sometimes it's easier to see a main idea *after* listing the details.

### Solo Exploration

Invite students to use the information in a main idea map to create a pie chart showing the importance of the details. Each detail becomes a slice of the pie, with more important details making up the larger slices. **(cross-curricular connection)**

© Pearson Education, Inc., publishing as Pearson Prentice Hall.

# Main Idea Map

# Time Line

## About the Strategy

A time line helps students organize both fictional and nonfictional events in sequential order along a continuum. Not only do students see the events in order, but they are also exposed to the overall time frame in which the events occurred.

*Time lines work well with any fictional or non-fictional selection in which understanding the order of events would help comprehension.*

### Step ❶
*Students record the first event.*

### Step ❷
*Students add the remaining events, placing them on the time line relative to the other events.*

## Time Line

| After church, Pepys goes to a meeting to talk about ways to keep the plague from growing. ❶ | Alderman Hooker tells the story of a man and his wife who took their last surviving child from an infected house in London. | Pepys mentions the good news that there has been a decrease of over five hundred in the number of new cases of the plague. | Pepys is very sad to hear of the people he knows who have lost someone to the plague or are sick themselves. | Jane, one of Pepys' maids, wakes him and his wife in the middle of the night to tell them about a great fire in the city. ❷ | Pepys goes out to track the progress of the fire, then goes to Whitehall to make a report. | As the fire continues to burn, Pepys and his family are forced to pack up their belongings and evacuate their home. |
|---|---|---|---|---|---|---|
| Sept. 3, 1665 | | Sept. 14, 1665 | | Sept. 2, 1666 | | |

**Skills and Strategies:** *summarize, sequence*

**Idea Exchange**

### Buddywork
Invite pairs of students to create time lines into the future. They can list events that they imagine will occur before people live on the moon. Students might place their time lines in their portfolios to use for future writing. **(portfolio)**

### All Together Now
As a class, make a list of the clue words in a selection organized by chronological, or time, order. You can add to the list as you read other selections organized by time order. Remind students to include clue words that indicate simultaneous order (*meanwhile, during,* etc.).

© Pearson Education, Inc., publishing as Pearson Prentice Hall.

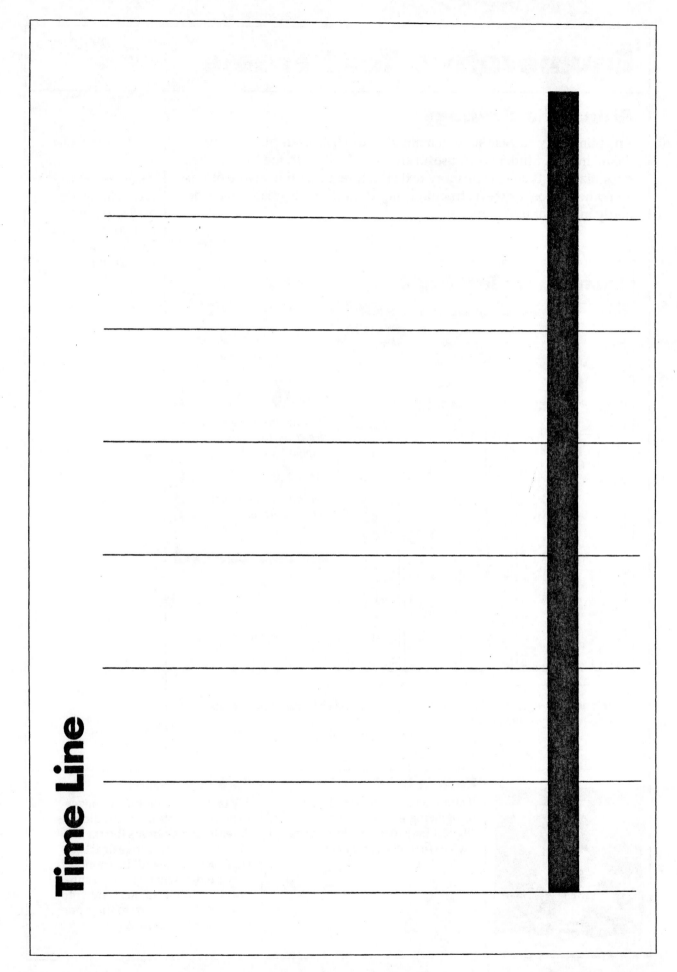

# Time Line

# Enumerative Text Frame

## About the Strategy

An enumerative article states a main idea and lists examples to support the main idea. Students can use an enumerative text frame to help them recognize this type of expository text structure. Becoming aware of this and other expository text structures improves students' reading, particularly in the content areas.

*An enumerative text frame works with selections that are organized according to this text structure.*

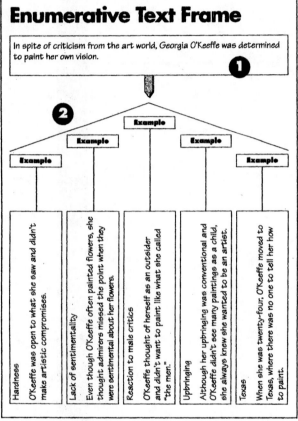

### Enumerative Text Frame

In spite of criticism from the art world, Georgia O'Keeffe was determined to paint her own vision. **1**

**2**

Example

Example

Example

Example

Example

**Hardness**
O'Keeffe was open to what she saw and didn't make artistic compromises.

**Lack of sentimentality**
Even though O'Keeffe often painted flowers, she thought admirers missed the point when they were sentimental about her flowers.

**Reaction to male critics**
O'Keeffe thought of herself as an outsider and didn't want to paint like what she called "the men."

**Upbringing**
Although her upbringing was conventional and O'Keeffe didn't see many paintings as a child, she always knew she wanted to be an artist.

**Texas**
When she was twenty-four, O'Keeffe moved to Texas, where there was no one to tell her how to paint.

### Step ❶

*Students fill in the main idea at the top of the graphic organizer.*

### Step ❷

*Students list examples that support the main idea.*

**Skills and Strategies:** *main idea/supporting details, use text structure/genre, use text features, analyze information*

---

Idea Exchange

### Keep in Mind

If students are having difficulty recognizing this text structure, suggest they look for clue words such as *first*, *next*, and *finally*.

### Solo Exploration

Try using this graphic organizer to help students make predictions. After telling students the main idea of an enumerative article, suggest that they fill in examples they predict will be used to support the main idea. Remember to have students return to their predictions after reading.

© Pearson Education, Inc., publishing as Pearson Prentice Hall.

# Enumerative Text Frame

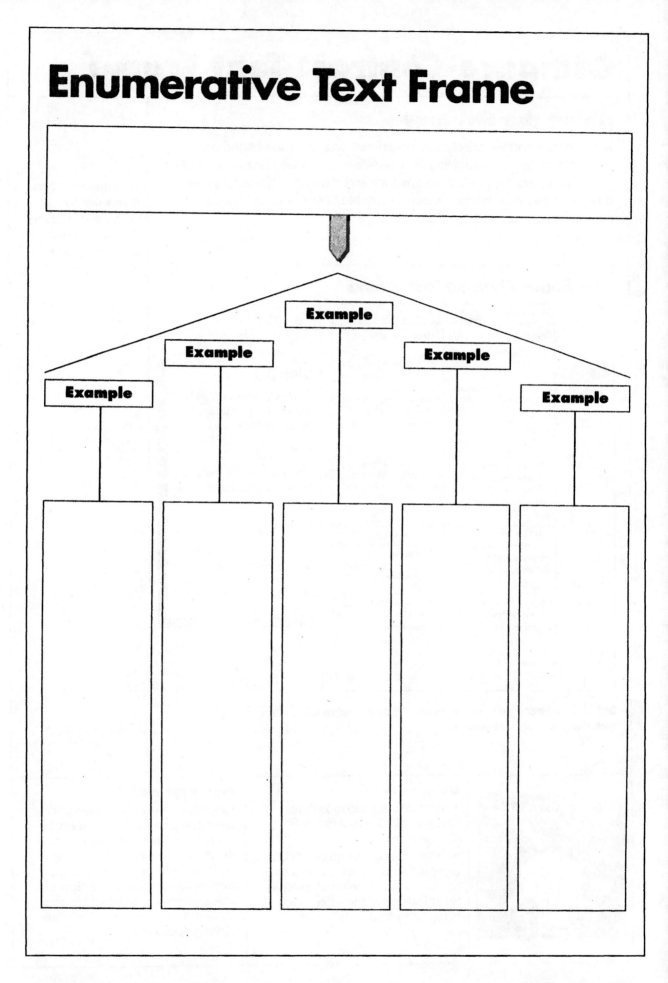

# Compare-Contrast Text Frame

## About the Strategy

A compare-contrast selection is organized on the basis of similarities and differences of its subjects. A compare-contrast text frame helps students recognize this type of expository text structure. Knowledge of this and other expository text structures helps students comprehend content-area texts and compare texts.

*A compare-contrast text frame works well with selections that have clear similarities and differences.*

### Compare-Contrast Text Frame

|  | "A Problem" ❶ | "Luck" |
|---|---|---|
| Main Character ❷ | Sasha Uskov | Arthur Scoresby |
| Setting | The study of the Uskov home | A military academy and a battle in the Crimean War ❸ |
| Conflict | Sasha has disgraced his family by getting into debt and cashing a false promissory note at the bank. | Scoresby is really a blundering soldier, but every military situation works in his favor and he becomes famous and highly decorated. |
| Denouement | After his family has forgiven him, Sasha demands money from his uncle. | Scoresby wins a great victory because he makes a mistake and moves his regiment left instead of right and forward instead of back. |
| Theme | Forgiveness does not always lead to responsibility. | Those who create heroes, like the clergyman, can be held responsible for the false heroes' actions. |

### Step ❶
Students record the subjects or the two texts at the top of the frame.

### Step ❷
Students list the features being compared and contrasted.

### Step ❸
Students fill in the supporting details telling how the subjects or texts are alike and/or different.

**Skills and Strategies:** *compare-contrast, draw conclusions, use text structure/genre, use text features*

**Idea Exchange**

### Keep in Mind
• Remind students to look for clue words, such as *different from, alike,* and *resemble.*
• If students are having difficulty recognizing comparisons and contrasts, encourage them to consider what features of the subjects are being compared.

### Solo Exploration
Help students see how they can use a compare-contrast text frame to organize ideas for writing. Students can choose two time periods such as the Middle Ages and the present to compare and contrast. Students can place the text frames in their portfolios to use for future writing. **(portfolio)**

© Pearson Education, Inc., publishing as Pearson Prentice Hall.

# Compare-Contrast Text Frame

| | | |
|---|---|---|
| | | |
| | | |
| | | |
| | | |
| | | |

© Pearson Education, Inc., publishing as Pearson Prentice Hall.

# Cause-Effect Frame  Multiple Causes

## About the Strategy

This type of cause-effect frame helps students identify what happened and multiple reasons why it happened in both fictional and nonfictional texts. When students can see that there are causal relationships between events or ideas in text, they can make generalizations about other causal relationships in new texts and in life situations.

*This cause-effect frame works well with any selection that has clear cause-and-effect relationships with multiple causes.*

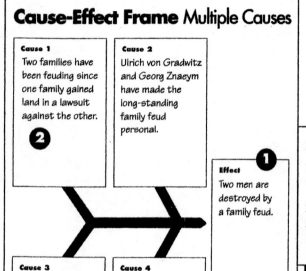

**Cause-Effect Frame Multiple Causes**

**Cause 1**
Two families have been feuding since one family gained land in a lawsuit against the other.
**2**

**Cause 2**
Ulrich von Gradwitz and Georg Znaeym have made the long-standing family feud personal.

**Effect** **1**
Two men are destroyed by a family feud.

**Cause 3**
The two men meet in the woods intending to destroy one another, but they are trapped together under the branches of a fallen beech tree.

**Cause 4**
As they wait helplessly for someone to find and free them, they reconcile. But the sounds of rescuers turn out to be the sounds of wolves.

**Step 1**
*To find the effect, ask, "What happened?"*

**Step 2**
*To find the causes, ask, "Why did this happen?"*

**Skills and Strategies:** *summarize, sequence, cause-effect, make inferences*

**Idea Exchange**

### Keep in Mind
• If students have trouble identifying cause-and-effect relationships, suggest they look for clue words, such as *since, as a result, consequently, therefore,* and *thus.*
• Remind them that not all causes are stated directly in the text.

### All Together Now
Try posing a question for students, such as "What would life be like if freedom of the press were not guaranteed under the First Amendment?" Ask students to suggest possible effects.
**(cross-curricular connection)**

© Pearson Education, Inc., publishing as Pearson Prentice Hall.

# Cause-Effect Frame Multiple Causes

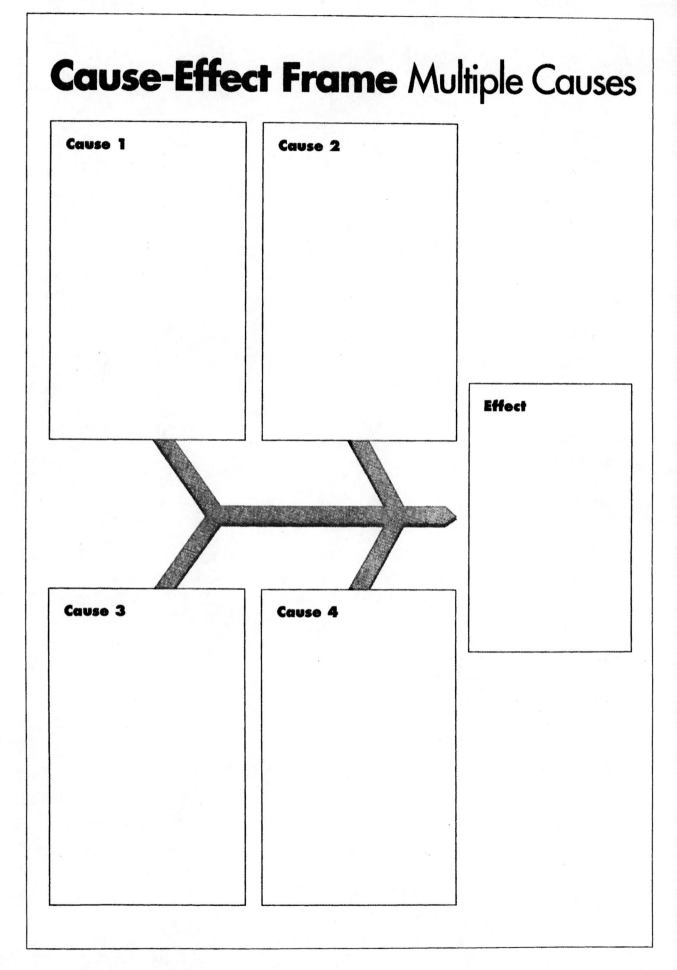

**Cause 1**

**Cause 2**

**Effect**

**Cause 3**

**Cause 4**

© Pearson Education, Inc., publishing as Pearson Prentice Hall.

# Classroom Management for Differentiated Instruction

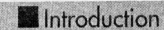
## The Challenge of Academic Text Reading

Most students enter classrooms woefully underprepared to independently navigate their reading assignments across the subject areas. While they may be able to tackle recreational reading of teen novels and magazines with relative ease, they often lack the academic language and strategic knowledge necessary for comprehending and studying concept and data rich texts. The challenging narrative and non-fiction selections students will be assigned in the course of an academic year are meant to be approached as learning tasks, not recreational activities. As such, these texts must be read multiple times with a clear learning purpose in mind.

Such an approach to reading is far from typical of adolescents engaging today's standards-driven Language Arts curricula. It is absolutely essential for teachers to assume an active instructional role, responsibly preparing students with the linguistic and strategic tools necessary for this potentially daunting task.

## Strategies for Structuring Reading

The worksheets that follow offer strategies a teacher can draw on in taking this active role. The following worksheets give concrete formats for structuring students reading:

- Choral Reading
- Oral Cloze
- Silent Independent Rereading
- Structured Partner Reading

Sophisticated texts require rereading, and scaffolding the types of reading students do on each pass is essential to bringing them into a more sophisticated engagement with the text. Here is one recommended way of using these strategies to scaffold readings:

**First Reading**—Oral Cloze with broad task
**Second Reading**—Silent rereading with detailed task
**Conclude**—Class discussion/debriefing

## Strategic Questioning

In traditional content-area reading instruction, the teacher assigns independent reading followed by an end-of-text question and answer session, in which the teacher and a handful of students dominate the discussion, leaving struggling readers disengaged and confused. Research suggests that struggling readers need explicit guidance in emulating the behaviors of competent readers.

This guidance must include breaking the reading into manageable chunks, approaching each section of text with a concrete question or purpose, and rereading sections for different levels of details. Teachers should pose increasingly complex questions while modeling a more active and strategic approach to reading.

The following worksheets give strategies to assist struggling readers in formulating appropriate reading questions and in connecting their guide questions to concrete tasks.

- Preparing-to-Read Questions
- Reading Guide Questions
- A Range of Appropriate Questions
- Question Frames

© Pearson Education, Inc., publishing as Pearson Prentice Hall.

# Choral Reading

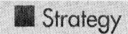 

A common primary-grade practice, choral reading can also work very well with older readers. Choral reading is effective because it requires that each student, regardless of level or proficiency in English, actively engage in attending to the text while it provides a nonthreatening atmosphere in which to practice. Many teachers find it helpful to use choral reading one row or group at a time. This modification tends to be less demanding and more manageable for diverse learners.

**Tips to ensure success with choral reading:**

- Request students to "Keep your voice with mine" to discourage them from racing ahead.
- Choose relatively short passages (e.g., 300–500 words).
- Follow with a silent rereading. Now that all students have basic access to the text, a second reading can elicit deeper understanding, supply an opportunity to apply previously taught strategies, answer inductive questions, and so on, while reinforcing the message that "constructing meaning is your job. I am here to help, not to do it for you."

© Pearson Education, Inc., publishing as Pearson Prentice Hall.

# Oral Cloze

The oral cloze is a choral reading adaptation of a commonly used reading-comprehension assessment process, in which words are selectively deleted from a brief passage, and students are prompted to fill-in reasonable word choices. In the oral cloze, the teacher reads aloud while students follow along silently. The teacher occasionally omits selected words, which the students chime in and read aloud together. The oral cloze is useful in guiding students in an initial read of a difficult passage, thereby insuring that struggling readers will have access to the text. Often during teacher read-alouds, students listen passively, read ahead, or remain off-task. This strategy keeps students on their "reading toes" by giving them a concrete job while allowing teachers to check participation.

## Tips to ensure success with cloze reading:

- To begin, demonstrate the oral cloze by contrasting it with a traditional read-aloud. Read a few sentences aloud without assigning students a role or task. Clarify the importance of being an active, thoughtful reader when the goal is accountable reading to learn, often with an assessment (e.g., quiz or paper). Explain that you will be reading aloud, and their job is to follow along, reading at the same pace and chorally chiming in when a word is occasionally omitted. Then reread the same sentences leaving out 2–3 words so that students see the contrast and grasp their active role.

- Choose to leave out meaningful words (e.g., nouns, verbs, adjectives) that most students can easily pronounce (prepositions and other connecting words do not work well).

- Take care to not distract students by leaving out too many words, not more than one per sentence (e.g., in a 50-word paragraph, delete 2–3 words).

- Pick words that come at a natural pause.

- Pick words (if any) that you have pretaught, providing students with a meaningful context for the new word.

- Provide students with an additional concrete active-reading task or question directing their attention to the content of the passage. On the first read, this task should be fairly broad and easy (e.g., Circle two adjectives describing how the character felt).

- In a mixed-ability class with many struggling readers, consider guiding students' reading with two rounds of the oral cloze before assigning a silent reading task. On the second reading, omit different words and pick up the pace a bit while providing an additional focus question or task.

© Pearson Education, Inc., publishing as Pearson Prentice Hall.

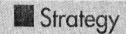

■ Strategy

After facilitating students in their first reading of a challenging passage using the oral cloze, prepare them for an active independent rereading of the passage.

The essential element here, as with both choral and cloze reading, is to make sure the students have a job, a task during reading that increases their attentiveness, cognitive focus, and accountability. Rereading silently to answer a question previously posed to the class as a whole efficiently meets this goal. Teachers may pose useful questions that the class reads silently to answer. Over time, students are taught to construct a range of questions themselves before such class reading (moving from literal to inferential).

After each section is read, engage students in a brief discussion to clarify questions and vocabulary and to ensure common understanding of essential big ideas in the text. You may choose to guide students in mapping or note-taking from the text at this point as well.

## Tips to Get the Most From Structured Silent Rereading

- Chunk the text into 1–4 paragraph sections within which students silently reread and actively identify information necessary to respond to the teacher's focus question.

- Request that anyone who finishes before you convene the discussion go back and reread the section to look for additional details in the text.

- The first few times, model how one thinks while reading to find answers to a question. Think aloud to give students a "window" on this sophisticated cognitive task.

- Encourage students to discuss their thinking, as well as their answers, during whole-class discussion. For example, focus on such issues as *"How did you know?"* or *"Why did you think that?"*

© Pearson Education, Inc., publishing as Pearson Prentice Hall.

# Structured Partner Reading

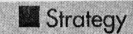 

Research has consistently pointed to partner reading as a potent strategy to increase the amount of actual reading students engage in, while providing access for all students to key ideas in the text. Partner reading is an excellent way to ensure that all students are actively engaged in the text and accountable for doing their jobs.

**Tips to get the most from structured partner reading:**

- Rank-order students by overall literacy and proficiency in English. In a group of 30 students, for example, students #1 and #15 are the first readers and #16 and #30 are the first coaches.
- Ensure that activities are fully reciprocal—students should spend equal time in the roles of reader and coach.
- Provide specific directions and demonstrate the roles of reader and coach (e.g., "First reader: Whisper-read the first paragraph, coaches follow along, fix mistakes, and ask the comprehension questions.").

## The Reader

The reader reads a paragraph or a page or reads for a given amount of time. Touching under the words may be helpful if the students have extremely limited literacy.

## The Coach

The coach encourages and supports the reader.

**1.** If the reader asks for a word, the coach will say the word.

**2.** If the reader makes a mistake, the coach will correct the error using the following steps:

    **a.** Point to the word and say, *"Can you figure out this word?"*
    **b.** If the reader cannot figure out the word in five seconds, say *"This word is __."*
    **c.** Have the reader repeat the word and then reread the sentence.

    Why reread the entire sentence?

- Improve comprehension.
- Practice the word again—read it fluently in context.
- Hold students accountable for reading more carefully.

After students have mastered the basic sequence, add various comprehension strategies, such as retelling main ideas after each page or section.

**Summarize/paraphrase.** State the main idea in ten words or less. (Using only ten words prompts students to use their own words.)

**Predict and monitor.** Reader predicts what will happen next, reads a paragraph/section and then determines if the prediction was accurate, revises as needed, summarizes, and predicts again, continuing for a set amount of time.

 © Pearson Education, Inc., publishing as Pearson Prentice Hall.

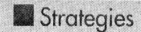

## Provide focused questions to guide students before reading.

If students have background knowledge regarding the subject, it is very helpful to pose a few open-ended questions to elicit a lively brainstorming session prior to reading. Cueing students to examine any related visual support, as well as the title, can assist students in focusing their thinking more productively.

> What are the possible effects of eating too much junk food?
> Take a look at this school lunch menu in the photograph and identify with your partner two healthy and two unhealthy foods.

***Instructional Tip:*** *Guide students to share answers with a teacher-selected partner; take care to designate roles (1s and 2s) to insure ALL are active participants.*

When students lack critical background knowledge related to a topic, brainstorming alone is often insufficient. Students will benefit from carefully formulated questions before and during each reading segment to focus their attention on the most important information. Without a concrete purpose when tackling each segment of a text, less proficient readers are apt to get mired in confusing details and distracted by unfamiliar yet non-essential vocabulary. Thus, it is essential to provide students a very specific question to guide their initial reading.

> What are the three most important reasons cited by the author in favor of recycling? How can recycling actually save money?

## Provide questions during the reading process.

It is critical that teachers guide less proficient students in reading each segment of text at least twice, providing a clear task each time. Posing a thoughtful question before students read challenging text will help them understand the active and focused approach necessary for reading to learn. Global questions are most appropriate for initial reading, followed by questions that require more careful analysis and attention to detail in subsequent reading.

> **1st read:** What is this section in our article on teen health mainly about?
> **Task:** Identify a word or phrase that names our topic (e.g., *teen diet*).
>
> **2nd read:** Why is the author so concerned about adolescent diet?
> **Task:** Identify two reasons stated by the author.
>
> **3rd read:** Since the snack foods provided at school are a major cause of poor adolescent health, why do you think schools continue to sell them?
> **Task:** Write down a specific reason you think schools still make candy, sodas, and chips so easily available in vending machines.

***Instructional Tip:*** *Complement the guide question with a concrete task to increase student accountability and increase focus and attention.*

© Pearson Education, Inc., publishing as Pearson Prentice Hall.

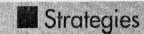
There are common text elements that teachers can utilize to frame reading guide questions and model an alert and strategic reading process for students.

## Use headings and topic sentences to generate reading guide questions.

Model for students how to turn a heading into a reading guide question for the initial reading of a passage. Be sure to prompt them to translate the question into a concrete task for which they will be held accountable in subsequent class discussion.

> **Subheading:** Recycling Saves Money
>
> **Guide question:** How does recycling save money?
>
> **Task:** "I need to identify two ways that recycling helps people save money."

Students need to approach each paragraph within a section of text with a clear sense of what they need to attend to in and extract from their reading. While a heading often provides the overall topic for a section of text, topic sentences provide a more specific focus for developing reading guide questions for discrete paragraphs.

> **Subheading:** Recycling Saves Money
>
> **Topic sentence, paragraph one:** "Because of the recent downturn in the auto industry, Smithville has come up with a creative recycling program to support their cash-strapped schools."
>
> **Guide Question:** What is Smithville's recycling program?
>
> **Task:** I need to identify the key features of Smithville's recycling program.

Helping struggling students develop genuine competence in formulating and applying reading guide questions is rather labor intensive. Students who are accustomed to approach all forms of reading material in a generic, unfocused manner will require considerable hand-holding through a gradual release process that moves systematically from "I'll do it" (teacher modeling) to "We'll do it" (unified class with teacher guidance) to "You'll do it" (partner practice) to "You do it on your own" (independent practice).

## Provide questions after reading a passage.

After students have navigated a demanding text and achieved basic comprehension, they are well positioned to extend their thinking by responding to higher-order questions requiring greater reflection and application. These questions are the interesting and provocative ones that teachers long to pose but that fall flat unless students have been prepared.

> How could we set up a viable recycling program in our school community?
>
> If you had two minutes to address the school board, what are the three best arguments you would provide to support the development of a district wide recycling program?

© Pearson Education, Inc., publishing as Pearson Prentice Hall.

# A Range of Appropriate Questions

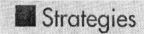 

**Begin with "on the surface" questions.**

**Why?** Struggling readers must be able to identify the most essential information in the reading *before* they are guided in grappling with more abstract analysis/interpretation. Otherwise, many students will not have the cognitive tools to benefit from the discussion.

**What?** Ask questions that require literal, factual recall and text-based answers that students can point to, underline, or circle.

> What is an endangered species? What are two examples of endangered species mentioned in this article? How are environmentalists working with oil companies to protect the red-tailed hawk?

**Include "under the surface" questions.**

**Why?** To comprehend challenging reading material, students must go beyond the factual basics of the text. Getting the gist certainly is no small feat for many struggling readers. However, it is important to help less proficient students acquire a more in-depth understanding and the strategic know-how required for mature comprehension.

**What?** Ask questions that require students to make inferences from or to analyze and synthesize text-based information, as well as to make inferences connecting new ideas from the text with prior knowledge.

> Why has it been difficult for environmentalist and oil companies to work together in protecting the red-tailed hawk? What environmental factors are placing some animal species in danger in your community?

**Teach students the questions for reading to learn.**

**Why?** Less proficient readers have often spent their early literacy development with relatively undemanding stories. In the classroom, they have largely responded to the "who, where, and when" questions appropriate for stories, leaving them ill equipped to reply to the "why, how, and what" demands of information text comprehension.

**What?** Teachers need to teach specific tasks involved in responding to questions associated with informational texts. Students need to understand that when asked a "why question" (e.g., Why have many schools outlawed soft drink sales?), they need to read, looking for specific reasons. It is not enough simply to model the questions; students must understand what prompted you to ask that specific question and the kind of information the question suggests.

> Why? = For what reasons? What are the reasons?
> How? = What was the process? What was the sequence?
> What? = Definition (What is _____?)
> What? + signal word   What are the <u>benefits</u> of _____?
>                        What was the <u>reaction</u> to _____?

© Pearson Education, Inc., publishing as Pearson Prentice Hall.

# Question Frames

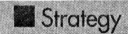 

Teaching students how to generate their own questions is an important comprehension-enhancing element of structured silent reading. Underprepared readers are often overly dependent on teachers and have not learned to self-question as they read. According to the research of Taffy Raphael,[1] students who understand how questions are written are more capable of analyzing and answering them than students who lack this understanding. One useful model, derived from Bloom's *Taxonomy*,[2] was developed by Stiggins[3] using Question Frames for different levels of questions to provide initial support for students during self-questioning:

---

**Recall (Literal)** ("I can put my finger on the answer in the text.")
  What is the name of _____?
  Define _____.
  Identify the _____.
  Who did _____?
**Analysis (Inferential)** ("I combine my knowledge with the author's information to understand.")
  What is the main idea?
  The most important part of _____ is _____ because _____.
  The essential parts are _____.
**Compare/Contrast** ("I analyze similarities and differences.")
  Compare the motives of _____ to those of _____.
  What are the most important differences/similarities between _____ and _____?
**Prediction** ("I predict based on the evidence so far.")
  What do you think will happen in the next _____?
  Predict what you think _____ will do. Why?
  What would happen if _____?
**Evaluation** ("I make and defend judgments.")
  What is your opinion of _____?
  What is the best solution to the problem of _____?
  Defend why _____ is a better solution than _____.

---

Question Frames are helpful when teaching diverse learners to ask questions beyond simple recall/literal questions. Teacher modeling and well-supported initial practice are key to assisting all students in generating different types of questions.

---

1. Raphael, T. "Teaching Learners About Sources of Information for Answering Questions." *Journal of Reading* (1984), vol. 28(4), 303–311.
2. Bloom, B. *Taxonomy of Educational Objectives.* New York: Longmans, Green, 1956.
3. Stiggins, R. "Improving Assessment Where It Means the Most: In the Classroom." *Educational Leadership* (1985), 43, 69–74.

   © Pearson Education, Inc., publishing as Pearson Prentice Hall.

## Vocabulary

To succeed in narrowing the language divide, a school-wide comprehensive academic vocabulary program must include the following four components:

1. **Fluent, wide reading.** Vocabulary for academic purposes grows as a consequence of independent reading of a variety of texts (in particular, informational texts) and increasing reading volume.

2. **Direct scaffolded teaching of critical words.** Students learn new words via various explicit, teacher-directed instructional strategies.

3. **Teaching word-learning strategies.** When taught the tools to exploit context, analyze prefixes, and various other strategies, students can independently learn new word meanings while reading independently.

4. **Daily participation in structured, accountable contexts for daily speaking and writing.** Academic language develops when students are engaged in rigorous and meaningful application of newly acquired vocabulary and syntax in structured speaking and writing tasks.

The following group of worksheets, marked with the triangle icon, provide concrete strategies for addressing many of these objectives for vocabulary development:

- Preteaching Vocabulary: Convey Meaning
- Preteaching Vocabulary: Check Understanding
- Vocabulary Development
- Choosing Vocabulary Words
- Possible Sentences
- Word Analysis/Teaching Word Parts
- Assessing Vocabulary Mastery

Concept development goes hand in hand with vocabulary enrichment. The following worksheets, also labeled with the triangle icon, provide strategies for concept development:

- List-Group-Label
- Concept Mapping/Clarifying Routine
- Using Concept Maps

The remaining worksheets in Part 3, marked with the circle icon, offer strategies for structuring academic discussion and writing.

© Pearson Education, Inc., publishing as Pearson Prentice Hall.

- If your goal is simply to familiarize students with a word to help them recognize and comprehend it in a reading, follow steps 1–4.

  **1.** Pronounce the word (and give the part of speech).

  This article focuses on an *ecstatic* moment in a high school student's life.

  **2.** Ask students to all repeat the word.

  Say the word *ecstatic* after me. (ec stat' ic)

  **3.** Provide an accessible synonym and/or a brief explanation.

  *Ecstatic* means "extremely happy."

  **4.** Rephrase the simple definition/explanation, asking students to complete the statement by substituting aloud the new word.

  If you are extremely happy about something, you are ____ (students say *ecstatic*).

- If your goal is to familiarize students with a word that is central to comprehending the reading and that you also want them to learn, continue with step 5, then check for understanding.

  **5.** Provide a visual "nonlinguistic representation" of the word (if possible) and/or an illustrative "showing" sentence.

  Showing image: a picture of a man happily in love.
  Showing sentence: Julio was *ecstatic* when Melissa agreed to marry him.

  Have students fill out a vocabulary worksheet as you preteach the words; doing so involves them more directly and provides them with a focused word list for later study and practice.

## Sample Vocabulary Note-Taking

| Term | Synonym | Definition/Example | Image |
|------|---------|--------------------|-------|
| **ecstatic,** *adj.* | extremely happy | feeling very happy, excited, or joyful<br><br>*Julio was ecstatic when Melissa agreed to marry him.* | |
| **distraught,** *adj.* | extremely worried and upset | feeling very worried, unhappy, or distressed<br><br>*Mark was distraught to learn that the camp bus had left without him.* | |

© Pearson Education, Inc., publishing as Pearson Prentice Hall.

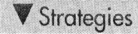

## 1. Focused Questions

Ask focused questions to see if students seem to grasp the word's meaning (as opposed to questions such as *Any questions? Do you understand?* or *Is that clear?*). Questions may be initially directed to the unified group for a thumbs-up or thumbs-down response; to teams using Numbered Heads; or to pairs using Think-Pair-Share, followed by questions to individuals.

> - Would you be ecstatic if you won the lottery?
> - Would you be ecstatic if you were assigned a 20-page report to complete over the Spring break?
> - Would you be ecstatic if you won two front-row tickets to a concert given by your favorite band?
> - Would you be ecstatic if your mother bought your favorite brand of breakfast cereal?

## 2. Images

If the word is crucial (for the lesson and their academic vocabulary tool kit), consider asking students to generate their own relevant images or examples.

> - Turn to your partner and ask what has happened recently that made him/her ecstatic. Or ask what would make him/her ecstatic. Be prepared to share one example with the class.
> - What other images might we associate with *ecstatic?* Think of one or two, turn to your partner and discuss, and then be prepared to share one of your images with the class.

© Pearson Education, Inc., publishing as Pearson Prentice Hall.

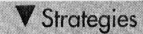
Words that are new to students but that represent familiar concepts can be addressed using a number of relatively quick instructional tactics. Many of these (e.g., synonyms, antonyms, examples) are optimal for prereading and oral reading, which call for more expedient approaches.

## Brief Strategies for Vocabulary Development (Stahl[4])

- **Teach synonyms.** Provide a synonym that students know (e.g., link *stringent* to the known word *strict*).

- **Teach antonyms.** Not all words have antonyms, but for those that do, thinking about their opposites requires students to evaluate the critical attributes of the words in question.

- **Paraphrase definitions.** Requiring students to use their own words increases connection-making and provides the teacher with useful informal assessment—"Do they really get it?"

- **Provide examples.** The more personalized the example, the better. An example for the new word *egregious* might be *Ms. Kinsella's 110-page reading assignment was egregious indeed!*

- **Provide nonexamples.** Similar to using antonyms, providing nonexamples requires students to evaluate a word's attributes. Invite students to explain why it is not an example.

- **Ask for sentences that "show you know."** Students construct novel sentences confirming their understanding of a new word, using more than one new word per sentence to show that connections can also be useful.

- **Teach word sorting.** Provide a list of vocabulary words from a reading selection and have students sort them into various categories (e.g., parts of speech, branches of government). Students can re-sort words into "guess my sort" using categories of their own choosing.

---

4. Stahl, S. A. *Vocabulary Development*. Cambridge, MA: Brookline Books, 1999.

© Pearson Education, Inc., publishing as Pearson Prentice Hall.

Restrict your selections to approximately six to eight words that are critical to comprehending the reading passage/segment you intend to cover in one lesson (e.g., one Science chapter section; a three-page passage from a six-page short story.)

- Choose **"big idea"** words that name or relate to the central concepts addressed in the passage (in subject areas outside of English Language Arts, these central lesson terms are typically highlighted by the publisher).

- Choose high-use, widely applicable **"academic tool kit"** words that student are likely to encounter in diverse materials across subject areas and grade levels (e.g., *aspect, compare, similar, subsequently*).

- Choose high-use **"disciplinary tool kit"** words for your subject area that you consider vital for students to master at this age and proficiency level (e.g., *metaphor, policy, economic, application, species*).

- Choose **"polysemous"** (multiple meaning) words that have a new academic meaning in a reading in addition to a more general, familiar meaning (e.g., "wave of immigrants" in U.S. History vs. a greeting or an ocean wave).

- Identify additional academic words, not included in the reading selection, that students will need to know in order to engage in **academic discourse** about the central characters, issues, and themes (especially for literary selections).

- Be careful not to overload students with low-frequency words that they are unlikely to encounter in many academic reading contexts, especially words that are not essential to comprehend the gist of the text.

© Pearson Education, Inc., publishing as Pearson Prentice Hall.

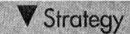

Possible Sentences (Moore and Moore[6]) is a relatively simple strategy for teaching word meanings and generating considerable class discussion.

1. The teacher chooses six to eight words from the text that may pose difficulty for students. These words are usually key concepts in the text.

2. Next, the teacher chooses four to six words that students are more likely to know something about.

3. The list of ten to twelve words is put on the chalkboard or overhead projector. The teacher provides brief definitions as needed.

4. Students are challenged to devise sentences that contain two or more words from the list.

5. All sentences that students come up with, both accurate and inaccurate, are listed and discussed.

6. Students now read the selection.

7. After reading, revisit the Possible Sentences and discuss whether they could be true based on the passage or how they could be modified to be true.

Stahl[7] reported that Possible Sentences significantly improved both students' overall recall of word meanings and their comprehension of text containing those words. Interestingly, this was true when compared with a control group and when compared with Semantic Mapping.

---

6. Moore, P. W., and S. A. Moore. "Possible Sentences." In E. K. Dishner, T. W. Bean, J. E. Readence, and P. W. Moore (eds.). *Reading in the Content Areas: Improving Classroom Instruction*, 2nd ed. Dubuque, IA: Kendall/Hunt, 1986, pp. 174–179.
7. Stahl, op. cit.

 © Pearson Education, Inc., publishing as Pearson Prentice Hall.

Word Analysis/Teaching Word Parts helps many underprepared readers who lack basic knowledge of word origins or etymology, such as Latin and Greek roots, as well as discrete understanding of how a prefix or suffix can alter the meaning of a word. Learning clusters of words that share a common origin can help students understand content-area texts and connect new words to those already known. For example, a secondary teacher (Allen[8]) reported reading about a character who suffered from amnesia. Teaching students that the prefix *a-* derives from Greek and means "not," while the base *-mne-* means "memory," reveals the meaning. After judicious teacher scaffolding, students were making connections to various words in which the prefix *a-* changed the meaning of a base word (e.g., *amoral, atypical*).

The charts below summarize some of the affixes worth considering, depending on your students' prior knowledge and English proficiency.

| Prefix | Meaning | Percentage of All Prefixed Words | Example |
|---|---|---|---|
| *un-* | not; reversal of | 26 | uncover |
| *re-* | again, back, really | 14 | review |
| *in-/im-* | in, into, not | 11 | insert |
| *dis-* | away, apart, negative | 7 | discover |
| *en-/em-* | in; within; on | 4 | entail |
| *mis-* | wrong | 3 | mistaken |
| *pre-* | before | 3 | prevent |
| *a-* | not; in, on, without | 1 | atypical |

| Suffix | Meaning | Percentage of All Suffixed Words | Example |
|---|---|---|---|
| *-s, -es* | more than one; verb marker | 31 | characters, reads, reaches |
| *-ed* | in the past; quality, state | 20 | walked |
| *-ing* | when you do something; quality, state | 14 | walking |
| *-ly* | how something is | 7 | safely |
| *-er, -or* | one who, what, that, which | 4 | drummer |
| *-tion, -sion* | state, quality; act | 4 | action, mission |
| *-able, -ible* | able to be | 2 | disposable, reversible |
| *-al, -ial* | related to, like | 1 | final, partial |

**8.** Allen, J. *Words, Words, Words: Teaching Vocabulary in Grades 4–12.* York, ME: Stenhouse, 1999.

© Pearson Education, Inc., publishing as Pearson Prentice Hall.

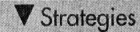

Following are three meaningful and alternative assessment formats that require relatively little preparation time:

1. Select only four to six important words and embed each in an accessible and contextualized sentence followed by a semicolon. Ask students to add another sentence after the semicolon that clearly demonstrates their understanding of the underlined word as it is used in this context. This assessment format will discourage students from rote memorization and mere recycling of a sample sentence covered during a lesson.

   **Example:** Mr. Lamont had the most <u>eclectic</u> wardrobe of any teacher on the high-school staff.

2. Present four to six sentences, each containing an underlined word from the study list, and ask students to decide whether each word makes sense in this context. If yes, the student must justify why the sentence makes sense. If no, the student must explain why it is illogical and change the part of the sentence that doesn't make sense.

   **Example:** Mr. Lamont had the most <u>eclectic</u> wardrobe of any teacher on the high-school staff; rain or shine, he wore the same predictable brown loafers, a pair of black or brown pants, a white shirt, and a beige sweater vest.

3. Write a relatively brief passage (one detailed paragraph) that includes six to ten words from the study list. Then, delete these words and leave blanks for students to complete. This modified cloze assessment will force students to scrutinize the context and draw upon a deeper understanding of the words' meanings. Advise students to first read the entire passage and to then complete the blanks by drawing from their study list. As an incentive for students to prepare study cards or more detailed notes, they can be permitted to use these personal references during the quiz.

Because these qualitative and authentic assessments require more rigorous analysis and application than most objective test formats, it seems fair to allow students to first practice with the format as a class exercise and even complete occasional tests in a cooperative group.

   © Pearson Education, Inc., publishing as Pearson Prentice Hall.

# List-Group-Label

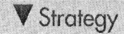

▼ Strategy

List-Group-Label (Taba[5]) is a form of structured brainstorming designed to help students identify what they know about a concept and the words related to the concept while provoking a degree of analysis and critical thinking. These are the directions to students:

| |
|---|
| 1. Think of all the words related to _____.<br>(a key "big idea" in the text) |
| 2. Group the words listed by some shared characteristics or commonalities. |
| 3. Decide on a label for each group. |
| 4. Try to add words to the categories on the organized lists. |

Working in small groups or pairs, each group shares with the class its method of categorization and the thinking behind its choices, while adding words from other class members. Teachers can extend this activity by having students convert their organized concepts into a Semantic Map that becomes a visual expression of their thinking.

List-Group-Label is an excellent prereading activity to build on prior knowledge, introduce critical concepts, and ensure attention during selection reading.

---

5. Taba, H. *Teacher's Handbook for Elementary Social Studies.* Reading, MA: Addison-Wesley, 1988.

© Pearson Education, Inc., publishing as Pearson Prentice Hall.

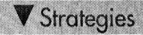
Research by Frayer et al.[9] supports the strategy of teaching by Concept Mapping:

1. identifying the critical attributes of the word.
2. giving the category to which the word belongs.
3. discussing examples of the concept.
4. discussing nonexamples.

Others have had success extending this approach by guiding students through representation of the concept in a visual map or graphic organizer. The Clarifying Routine, designed and researched by Ellis,[10] is a particularly effective example:

1. Select a critical concept/word to teach. Enter it on a graphic clarifying map like the sample for *satire.*
2. List the clarifiers or critical attributes that explicate the concept.
3. List the core idea—a summary statement or brief definition.
4. Brainstorm for knowledge connections—personal links from students' world views/prior knowledge (encourage idiosyncratic/ personal links).
5. Give an example of the concept; link to clarifiers: "Why is this an example of —————————?"
6. Give nonexamples. List nonexamples: "How do you know ————————— is not an example of —————————
7. Construct a sentence that "shows you know."

| Term: SATIRE | | |
| --- | --- | --- |
| **Core Idea: Any Work That Uses Wit to Attack Foolishness** | | |
| **Example** <br> • A story that exposes the acts of corrupt politicians by making fun of them <br><br> **Nonexample** <br> • A story that exposes the acts of corrupt politicians through factual reporting <br><br> **Example sentence** <br> • Charles Dickens used satire to expose the problems of common folks in England. | **Clarifiers** <br> • Can be oral or written. <br> • Ridicule or expose vice in a clever way. <br> • Can include irony, exaggeration, name-calling, understatement. <br> • Are usually based on a real person or event. | **Knowledge Connections** <br> • Political cartoons on the editorial pages of our paper <br> • Stories TV comics tell to make fun of the President— as on *Saturday Night Live* <br> • My mom's humor at dinner time! |

9. Frayer, D. A., W. C. Frederick, and H. J. Klausmeier. *A Schema for Testing the Level of Concept Mastery* (Technical Report No. 16). Madison, WI: University of Wisconsin Research and Development Center for Cognitive Learning, 1969.
10. Ellis, E. *The Clarifying Routine.* Lawrence, KS: Edge Enterprises, 1997.

© Pearson Education, Inc., publishing as Pearson Prentice Hall.

Students benefit from graphic presentations of the connections between the ideas they are learning. Each Unit Resources booklet includes Concept Maps—graphic organizers that illustrate the logical relationship among the skills taught in a Part or a Unit. In Grades 6 through 10, the Concept Maps focus on the Literary Analysis, Reading Skill, and Academic Vocabulary skills in each Part. In Grades 11 and 12 and in *World Masterpieces,* each Map connects the Literary Analysis skills in a Unit to the trends and themes of the period covered.

## Steps

1. Review the Concept Map and identify the skills you will cover.

2. Distribute copies of the Concept Map to students. Identify those skills and concepts you will teach and have students circle or otherwise note them. Elicit from students any prior knowledge they may have about the ideas you have introduced. In addition, you may wish to ask them about their own interests in connection with the ideas. In later classes, you can make connections to students' prior knowledge and interests as relevant.

3. Briefly note the connections between ideas on the Concept Map. For example, you might explain that the "Big Picture" or "Main Idea" in the Part is the short story. Using the Concept Map, explain that a plot is an important part of a short story.

4. Emphasize for students that the skills you have identified represent a goal for the class: Everyone will be working toward mastery of those skills.

5. In succeeding lessons, refer students to their Concept Maps at appropriate junctures. As you introduce a selection, review the relevant portion of the Concept Map with students so that they clearly grasp the goals you are setting.

6. As you conclude teaching the selection, review the Concept Map with students to see how the skills are connected with other concepts they have learned. Have students add the name of the selections they have completed to the appropriate blanks. Have students log the additional assignments they complete, such as Extension Activities, in the Learning Log on the chart.

7. As you conclude instruction for a Part or for a Unit, review with students the skills they have covered and the logical connections among the skills.

Grateful acknowledgment for the idea of the Concept Map is made to B. Keith Lenz and Donald D. Deshler, who develop the idea in their book *Teaching Content to All: Evidence-Based Inclusive Practices in Middle and Secondary Schools* (New York: Pearson Education, Inc., 2004).

© Pearson Education, Inc., publishing as Pearson Prentice Hall.

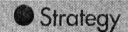

- Students listen while the teacher poses a question or task.
- Students are given quiet time to consider what they know about the topic and record a number of possible responses. This may be a simple list of words and phrases or a focused quick-write. It is also helpful to provide students with a series of response prompts to complete prior to being asked to share aloud. In this way, less proficient academic language users will have a linguistic scaffold to bolster their linguistic output along with their confidence in sharing aloud.

  For example, if students are being asked to make predictions about what will happen in the next chapter of *The Joy Luck Club*, they might be provided with these sentence prompts to complete:

  I predict that Waverly's mother will be (disappointed in / proud of) her daughter's behavior because . . .

  Based on Waverly's relationship with her mother, I assume that her mother will react very (positively / negatively) because . . .

- The teacher whips around the class in a relatively fast-paced and structured manner (e.g., down rows, around tables), allowing as many students as possible to share an idea in 15 seconds or less.
- After several contributions, there tends to be some repetition. Students point out similarities in responses using appropriate language strategies (e.g., *My idea is similar to / related to . . .*), rather than simply stating that their ideas have already been mentioned. This fosters active listening and validation of ideas.
- The teacher can record these ideas for subsequent review or have students do a quick-write summarizing some of the more interesting contributions they heard during the discussion.

© Pearson Education, Inc., publishing as Pearson Prentice Hall.

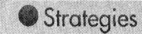

## Numbered Heads

- Students number off in teams, one through four.
- The teacher asks a series of questions, one at a time.
- Students discuss possible answers to each question for an established amount of time (about 30 seconds to 90 seconds, depending on the complexity of the task).
- The teacher calls a number (1–4), and all students with that number raise their hand, ready to respond.
- The teacher randomly calls on students with the specified number to answer on behalf of their team.
- Students are encouraged to acknowledge similarities and differences between their team's response and that of other teams (e.g., *We predicted a very different outcome. Our reaction was similar to that of Ana's group.*).
- The teacher continues posing questions and soliciting responses in this manner until the brainstorming or review session is finished.

## Think-Write-Pair-Share

- Students listen while the teacher poses a question or a task.
- Students are given quiet time to first answer the question individually in writing.
- Students are then cued to pair with a neighbor to discuss their responses, noting similarities and differences. Students encourage their partners to clarify and justify responses using appropriate language strategies:

  How did you decide that?

  In other words, you think that . . .

- It is often helpful to structure the roles (first speaker, first listener) and designate the time frames:

  First speakers, you have 90 seconds to share your answers with your partner.

- After rehearsing responses with a partner, students are invited to share with the class.
- The teacher asks a series of questions, one at a time.
- Students discuss possible answers to each question for an established amount of time (about 30 seconds to 90 seconds, depending on the complexity of the task).

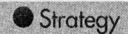
Strategy

Students who bring special learning needs to the writing process are more likely to internalize the assignment expectations if the task is first clearly outlined on the board or in a handout. They must, in turn, hear the assignment described and, subsequently, have the opportunity to paraphrase what they understand the actual assignment expectations to be—ideally, orally to a partner and in writing to the teacher. If all students are then encouraged to turn in two clarification questions about the assignment, less proficient writers will have a safe and structured venue for monitoring their comprehension and articulating instructional needs. In so doing, passive or apprehensive students are more likely to vocalize any misunderstandings about the task in a timely and responsible manner, rather than realizing the night before the paper is due that they are unsure how to proceed.

**Sample Description of a Writing Assignment**

---

**Writing Assignment Guidelines:**
***A Color That Has Special Significance***

Write a detailed expository paragraph providing specific reasons that your chosen color has special meaning in your life. Your justification paragraph must include these qualities of effective expository writing:

- An appropriate title (e.g., *Jade Green: A Link to My Heritage*)
- A topic sentence that lets the reader know that you will be discussing the relevance of a particular color to specific aspects of your life
- Transition words that introduce each of your new points about your chosen color (e.g., *first of all, in addition, furthermore, moreover*)
- Specific reasons for selecting this color, including details and relevant commentary that help the reader easily understand the color's special significance
- A visible effort to include new vocabulary from this unit
- An effort to use subordinating conjunctions to join related ideas
- A concluding statement that thoughtfully wraps up your paragraph
- Proofreading goals for the final draft:
  - complete sentences (no fragments or run-on sentences)
  - correct verb tenses
  - correct spelling

Your first draft is due on _____. Please bring two copies of your draft for a peer-response session

---

© Pearson Education, Inc., publishing as Pearson Prentice Hall.

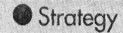

As demonstrated in your *Prentice Hall Literature* Teacher's Edition, one concrete way to structure linguistic equity and to scaffold the vocabulary demands of a challenging writing assignment is to provide students with an array of sentence starters, including practical vocabulary options relevant to the specific writing task and topic. Another equally important scaffold for students writing in a second language or second dialect is a word-form chart that highlights important forms of a base word germane to the assignment.

Following is a list of sentence starters and a relevant word-form chart for a writing assignment on a personally significant color.

---

**Sentence Starters to Discuss a Color You Value**

_____ is my favorite color because I associate it with _____. (my future career, my love of nature, my personality, my hobby)

This color reflects/represents/is associated with my interest in _____. (salsa dancing, R & B music, physical fitness, environmental protection)

This color symbolizes/is a symbol of _____. (my culture, my ethnicity)

I have included/selected/chosen the color _____ because _____.

The color _____ is meaningful/valuable/significant to me because _____.

I appreciate/value/like/am fond of the color _____ because/since _____.

---

**Sample Word-Form Chart**

| Noun | Adjective | Verb | Adverb |
|---|---|---|---|
| symbol | symbolic | symbolize | symbolically |
| meaning | meaningful | | meaningfully |
| value | valuable | value | valuably |
| relevance | relevant | | relevantly |
| importance | important | | importantly |
| relationship | related | relate | |
| association | associated | associate | |
| significance | significant | signify | significantly |
| preference | preferred; preferable | prefer | preferably |
| fondness | fond | | fondly |

© Pearson Education, Inc., publishing as Pearson Prentice Hall.

# Language Arts Instruction

## Professional Articles

## Introduction

The number of children in the country who can be classified as diverse learners because of the special circumstances they bring to public education is growing at a pace that currently outstrips educators' abilities to keep up. Unless significant educational changes are made in response to the dramatic changes occurring in classrooms throughout the country, including the development and utilization of instructional strategies that address the needs of diverse learners, the number of children who "fall through the cracks" in public education will continue to rise.[1]

The 2000 census confirmed what demographers had been documenting for the previous decade: America is more diverse than ever. Certainly, the diversity of our population is a significant asset to our nation in many ways; however, it also places considerable stress on our educational system to effectively accommodate the range of learning needs found in students today. A typical high-school classroom includes students who are diverse in terms of their experiential, linguistic, cultural, socioeconomic, and psychological backgrounds. The range of student needs, interests, motivation, and skill levels often presents heightened challenges to both curriculum and instruction. It should be clearly acknowledged that the individual needs of some students require additional specialized support in basic reading skills, English language development, study skills, and behavioral/emotional/social domains. However, the goal of a comprehensive Language Arts program remains the provision of "universal access" for all students to an intellectually rich and challenging language arts curriculum and instruction, in addition to whatever specialized intervention may be required.

Universal access exists when teachers provide curriculum and instruction in ways that allow all learners in the classroom to participate and to achieve the instructional and behavioral goals of general education, as well as of the core curriculum. Teachers will succeed in providing universal access if they teach in heterogeneous, inclusive classrooms and consistently

---

1. Kame'enui, Edward, and Douglas Carnine. *Effective Teaching Strategies That Accommodate Diverse Learners.* Upper Saddle River, NJ: Prentice Hall, 1998.

   © Pearson Education, Inc., publishing as Pearson Prentice Hall.

and systematically integrate instructional strategies that are responsive to the needs of typical learners, gifted learners, less proficient readers, English language learners, and students who are eligible for and receiving special education services.

Although each student population represented in the classroom may require specific interventions and supports, these learner populations also share many common characteristics, such as the need to build on prior knowledge, the need for systematic vocabulary development, and the need for systematic instruction in strategic reading approaches, to name a few key curricular and instructional areas. Through identification of these shared needs and the implementation of teaching and learning strategies responsive to these needs, the general education teacher, with the support of specialists and other staff, can make significant inroads in designing inclusive lessons that are responsive to the learning and behavioral needs of all learners.

This book provides numerous suggestions to assist teachers in designing English Language Arts lessons that strive for universal access. The suggestions focus specifically on the instructional needs of students who are less proficient readers, students who are English language learners, and students with identified special education needs. The next section describes the reading process and what it takes to be a proficient reader. The remaining sections explore the specific needs of the three focus student populations: English language learners, less proficient readers, and students with special education needs.

© Pearson Education, Inc., publishing as Pearson Prentice Hall.

A clear consensus has emerged in the field of reading education supporting the notion that reading is a complex process of constructing meaning from text. Successful readers must bring an array of interrelated skills, knowledge, and strategies together in order to understand written English. Skillful readers are able to decode the words accurately and fluently, connect their meanings to prior knowledge, and continually monitor their emerging understanding as they read. In other words, successful readers are active, thoughtful, and strategic learners able to make meaning from what they are reading.

## Factors That Affect Reading Success

Successful reading is largely determined by the elaborate interaction of four factors: learner characteristics, skill and instructional variables, demands of the text, and nature of the classroom environment. To better understand these elements, we will examine each in turn, as well as the way they interact to affect successful reading.

## Learner Characteristics

Each learner brings unique characteristics to the learning experience. For example, students who are less proficient readers may experience attention and memory issues that make reading especially challenging. English language learners may be highly capable students who, because of limited vocabulary or experiences in their new country, lack the schema for understanding the ideas encountered in text. Students with disabilities may experience cognitive, behavioral/social, and/or physical challenges that make the development of reading skill more challenging.

## Skill and Instructional Factors

Reading success is largely determined by the particular skills an individual reader brings to the reading act. For example, the ability to fluently and accurately decode the words in a given reading selection is a necessary but not sufficient condition for successful reading. In addition, the ability to activate and build prior knowledge along with the related ability to connect what one is reading to existing knowledge are essential for proficient comprehension. Moreover, comprehension is significantly determined by a student's level of English acquisition, vocabulary, and skillful use of various reading comprehension strategies such as summarization or self-questioning.

 © Pearson Education, Inc., publishing as Pearson Prentice Hall.

An essential personal aspect of successful reading is the extent to which a reader is actively engaged in the reading, has a clear purpose for reading, and is interested in the content being explored. Skillful readers have learned helpful mental habits such as perseverance, managing and directing attention, being aware of and monitoring their thoughts and feelings as they read. Skilled readers are active participants in the reading act—reading is not a spectator sport.

Instructional interventions provided in the classroom play a significant role in students' development of these skills. Explicit, systematic instruction in decoding and fluency, the incorporation of activities that build and enhance prior knowledge, the provision of explicit vocabulary instruction, and the direct teaching, modeling, and practicing of comprehension strategies will lead to students' skill development and their enhanced engagement and interest in the complexities of the reading act.

## Text-Based Factors

It is immediately apparent that the types of texts encountered by students vary widely and create different levels of challenge for different readers. Just as the make and model distinguish one automobile from another, text-based factors differentiate one text from another. While some of these factors may be largely cosmetic in nature, others, such as sentence length, novel vocabulary, density of the concepts, or clarity of the organizational pattern, can have a significant influence on reader comprehension. For example, the presence of well-designed reader aids, including pictures, charts, graphs, and focus questions, can provide additional support to naive readers.

Perhaps the most fundamental distinction in text-based factors affecting reading success is that of narrative (story) reading vs. expository (informational) reading. Expository texts are generally written to inform or persuade the reader using very different organizational patterns from those typically utilized in narratives. For example, information in content-area reading, such as in science and social studies, is often arranged according to structures such as chronological sequence, comparison and contrast, cause and effect, main idea and supporting details, and so forth. Many students are quite comfortable reading stories but find themselves ill equipped to deal with the demands of informational content-area texts.

## Classroom Environment

The classroom environment affects everything and everyone within it, including the nature of the reading/literacy program. Specifically, the classroom environment can be viewed as composed of both physical and social-psychological dimensions.

© Pearson Education, Inc., publishing as Pearson Prentice Hall.

Research suggests that students learn best in a friendly, respectful setting where

- they feel a sense of safety/order and are comfortable taking risks.
- they understand the purpose of and value the tasks at hand.
- they have high expectations/goals for learning.
- they feel accepted by their teacher and peers.

These general factors are of particular import when thinking about what accounts for successful reading. Students will often have significant gaps in their skill, knowledge, proficiency in English, and be self-conscious concerning their lagging literacy.

It is important to be respectful and truthful with students about what it will take to significantly improve their abilities in the Language Arts: It takes PRACTICE, and lots of it. Literacy cannot be "done to" students—it is a collaborative enterprise that is "done with" students. To be sure, teachers provide excellent direct instruction, guided practice, specific feedback, coaching, and more, yet students must understand their roles as active self-directed learners. The intentional design of a caring yet "on purpose" classroom climate creates the condition within which the hard work of improving literacy can take place.

## Summary

Understanding that successful reading comprises a complex interaction of factors—learner, skills and instruction, text, and environment—provides a template for thinking about how classrooms can provide universal access to a rich core curriculum for the diverse range of learners in today's high-school classrooms. Secondary students need a balanced Language Arts program based on their individual needs. All students require a firm foundation in fluent/automatic decoding, broad background knowledge of various subjects, ever-expanding vocabularies, all coupled with an array of comprehension strategies to fit the purpose for reading as well as the type of text being read.

In the following section, we examine strategies for developing lesson plans that support diverse learners in meeting rigorous grade-level standards in the Language Arts.

© Pearson Education, Inc., publishing as Pearson Prentice Hall.

The number of immigrant, migrant, and refugee students in the United States who have little knowledge of the English language is growing exponentially. In fact, students who are learning English as an additional language are the fastest-growing segment of the school-age population. While the number of English language learners (ELLs) nationwide has skyrocketed, their academic achievement trails behind that of their native English-speaking peers. National studies of English language learners have shown that they are likely to come from disadvantaged socioeconomic backgrounds, attend low-income schools, and have parents with limited English proficiency. These students are also judged by their teachers to have weaker academic abilities, receive lower grades, and score well below their classmates on standardized tests of mathematics and reading.[1] Moreover, in a large-scale California study, secondary schools reported that even long-term resident ELLs entered high school with only fourth to sixth grade academic competencies.[2]

## Differential Preparation for Second-Language Schooling

Secondary-school curricula are based on assumptions about basic reading and writing skills and elementary subject matter foundations. However, the growing population of secondary English language learners is tremendously diverse, particularly with regard to their educational backgrounds. These students enter U.S. schools with varying degrees of curricular preparation and a vast range of language proficiencies, in English and their native language. At times, it may seem that the one thing these diverse students have in common is the need to accelerate their English language and literacy acquisition in order to participate more fully in their secondary schooling.

Although some have parents with impressive levels of formal education and professional job experiences, many come from less privileged families, challenged by limited functional literacy even in their native language. Newcomers from war-torn regions and rural areas of developing countries are apt to arrive severely under-schooled, with fragmented native language literacy training and weak subject matter foundations.

---

1. Moss, M., and M. Puma. *Prospects: The Congressionally Mandated Study of Educational Growth and Opportunity.* Washington, DC: U.S. Department of Education, 1995.
2. Minicucci, C., and L. Olsen. "Programs for Secondary Limited English Proficiency Students: A California Study." *Focus,* Vol. 5. Washington, DC: National Clearinghouse for Bilingual Education, 1992.

© Pearson Education, Inc., publishing as Pearson Prentice Hall.

These youths predictably require compassion, considerable time, and patient modeling simply to adjust to basic school routines and expectations before they can ever begin to concentrate on phonemic awareness lessons, let alone literary analysis.

On the other hand, more fortunate immigrant youths have benefited from rigorous and sustained elementary schooling in their native country and make the transition to American classrooms more effortlessly. Literate in their home language, these second-language learners have already internalized critical scripts for schooling and often function above equivalent grade levels in math or science. However, these traditionally educated newcomers still face a daunting transition to daily instruction in a language they have only begun to study, along with curriculum content, teaching practices, and skills that may not have been emphasized in their native schooling.

Our secondary schools also serve increasing numbers of students who have been raised and educated entirely in the United States but who speak a language other than English at home. These continuing English language learners were either born in the United States or arrived here as very small children. Many of these long-term U.S. residents are not literate in their home language and remain struggling English readers well into the upper grades and beyond. They may demonstrate a comfortable handle on the social domain of both languages but flounder with grade-level reading and writing tasks.

In summary, with regard to prior schooling, secondary English language learners tend to fall into one of three general and frequently overlapping categories:

1. Recent adolescent immigrants who have received continuous native language schooling prior to immigration to the United States and are prepared with relatively strong academic and study skills to apply to new subject matter

2. Language minority students continuing into secondary schools from U.S. elementary schools with insufficient English fluency and literacy to compete in challenging academic areas

3. Immigrant, refugee, and migrant students with sporadic or no prior schooling who consequently enter lacking basic literacy and elementary curricular foundations.

### Second-Language Literacy Development

Statistics on the academic achievement of English language learners demonstrate a dire need for informed attention devoted to literacy, the cornerstone of all academic abilities.

© Pearson Education, Inc., publishing as Pearson Prentice Hall.

Nonetheless, given the extreme variability in these students' educational histories, they must be offered different pathways to eventual academic success. One approach to literacy instruction will not fit all English language learners. However, the instructional practices outlined in this chapter and throughout this manual should greatly assist them in participating more fully in a heterogeneous secondary Language Arts classroom.

Those with significant gaps in their elementary educational backgrounds will require a thoughtful and sustained literacy intervention program, complemented by a substantive and protracted English language development program. Their acute and compelling academic needs cannot be accommodated solely within the confines of the general education Language Arts classroom, an after-school tutorial, or a reading intervention program.

Similarly, literate and academically prepared newcomers will still need a viable English language development program to enable them to transfer the knowledge and skills they acquired in their native language schooling to the curricula they are studying in the United States. Literate adolescents who are virtual beginners in English will also benefit from a separate reading support class, to help them readily acquire the basic phonology, morphology, and syntax of English and to more efficiently transfer the reading skills they have already mastered in their native language. Students who can already read relatively fluently in their first language will make an easier transition to English decoding than bilingual classmates who are nonreaders. These literate second-language learners will therefore need to move more rapidly than struggling ELL readers, from initial skill-building lessons that focus on decoding, word recognition, and pronunciation to explicit instruction in comprehension strategies such as prediction, questioning, and summarizing that will help them deal more productively with the reading demands of content-area classrooms.

## Reading in a Second Language

Research findings suggest that reading processes in a second language are not significantly different from those in a first language.[3] For example, both rely on the reader's background knowledge regarding the topic and text structure to construct meaning, and both make use of cueing systems (graphic,

---

**3.** Grabe, W. "Current Developments in Second Language Reading." *TESOL Quarterly* (1991), 25, 375–406.

syntactic, phonological, semantic) to allow the reader to predict and confirm meaning.

While literacy processes in first and second languages may be quite similar, two crucial areas of difference must be addressed. First, initial reading and writing in English will be slower and more painstaking for second-language learners because of their lack of overall fluency. The second-language learner is often in the process of acquiring basic oral language while simultaneously developing literacy skills in English. Limited proficiency in a second language can cause a proficient reader in the native language to revert to poor reading strategies, such as reading word by word. Also, some students may not even have the native language literacy skills to transfer concepts about print and strategies to the second language.

Secondly, ELL students are likely to have less prior knowledge and relevant vocabulary to process new information while reading academic English assignments. Furthermore, readers' background knowledge is often culture-bound and may not match the content needed for a given reading text. ELL students with a limited range of personal and educational experiences on a reading topic will therefore have little to draw upon to construct meaning from a selection even if they are able to accurately decode.

## Academic Language Development

Many adolescent ELL students come to school with sufficient social language for everyday classroom interactions yet are severely lacking in the academic English foundations to tackle a poem or follow the instructions on a standardized test. This is because academic vocabulary is primarily developed through school-based reading and repeated exposure during content-based classroom activities.

The average native English-speaking student enters elementary school with an internalized understanding of the syntax and phonology of English, plus a working vocabulary of several thousand words. This vocabulary base is enhanced each year through new school experiences and reinforced in home and community settings. In striking contrast, the language minority student enters U.S. schooling with a tenuous grasp of the phonology and syntax of the English language, a scant working English vocabulary, and rare opportunities for practice and expansion of this knowledge outside the classroom. As a consequence, they must develop content-specific language and literacy skills along with conceptual foundations, all the while competing with native English-speaking classmates who may

© Pearson Education, Inc., publishing as Pearson Prentice Hall.

also be challenged by grade-level Language Arts curricula, but who at least operate from a relatively firm foundation in basic academic English and years of exposure to high-frequency social English vocabulary.

## Implications for English Language Arts Instruction

A number of implications for instruction can be drawn from these descriptions of the academic language and literacy challenges of ELL students. Novice English readers will require extensive and dynamic instructional "front-loading" in order to effectively grapple with challenging literacy tasks. Teachers all too often concentrate their energies on the damage-control phase, when it becomes clear that students either failed to comprehend or felt too overwhelmed to even try to tackle a reading task. Explaining critical concepts and language after the fact does little to engender reader confidence or competence for the next task. The students may walk away with a better grasp of the plot development in *The Joy Luck Club* but have no sense of how to proceed with the next chapter. Instead, conscientious literacy mentors essentially "teach the text backwards" by devoting far more instructional time to the preparation and guidance phases of lessons. Since a second-language reader may be approaching an assignment with impoverished background knowledge and weak English vocabulary, it makes sense to concentrate on classroom activities that build strong conceptual and linguistic foundations, guide them into the text organization, model appropriate comprehension strategies, and provide a clear purpose for reading. This responsible preparation will in turn help to create the kind of nurturing affective and cognitive arena that communicates high expectations for their literacy development and encourages them to persist and take risks.

## Instructional Considerations When Preparing Lessons to Support English Language Learners

All of the instructional practices detailed in Part 3 of this booklet will support ELL students in making strides in their second-language literacy development and in becoming vibrant members of the classroom community of learners. Following are some additional reminders of ways in which you can support ELL students at various stages of your lesson planning to deal more productively with the reading and writing demands of English Language Arts curricula.

© Pearson Education, Inc., publishing as Pearson Prentice Hall.

## Phase 1: Preteach

- Pull out a manageable number of key concepts.

- Identify vocabulary most critical to talking and learning about the central concepts. Don't attempt to cover all of the vocabulary words you anticipate they will not know. Do more than provide synonyms and definitions. Introduce the essential words in more meaningful contexts, through simple sentences drawing on familiar issues, people, scenarios, and vocabulary. Guide students in articulating the meanings of essential terms through these familiar contexts and hold them responsible for writing the definitions in their own words.

- Present key words when they occur within the context of the reading selection or activity. Make the words as concrete as possible by linking each to an object, photo, drawing, or movement.

- Post the new essential vocabulary in a prominent place in the classroom to create a word bank of organized lesson terminology.

- Examine your lesson to see what types of language functions students will need to participate in various activities. For example, if they are being asked to make predictions about upcoming paragraph content in an essay based on transition words (e.g., *therefore, in addition, consequently*), students will need to be taught some basic sentence patterns and verbs to express opinions (e.g., "I predict that . . ."; "Based on this transition word, I conclude that . . ."). If being asked to agree or disagree with the arguments in a persuasive article, students will need to learn some sentence patterns and verbs to convey agreement or disagreement (e.g., "I don't agree with the author's argument that adolescents don't have a work ethic because . . .").

- Engage students in prereading activities that spark their curiosity and involve them in all four language modes.

- Assess students' prior knowledge related to key concepts through participation structures and collaborative group discussions with realia (e.g., photographs, objects) serving as a visual trigger.

- Utilize realia and visuals needed to make the concepts less abstract.

- Use multimedia presentations such as CD-ROM and videos to

© Pearson Education, Inc., publishing as Pearson Prentice Hall.

familiarize students with the plot, characters, and themes of a narrative text prior to reading, but don't use it as a replacement for reading.

- Provide a written and oral synopsis of the key content prior to actually asking students to read a selection if the sentence structures and vocabulary are particularly demanding.

- Use graphic organizers and semantic maps to help students grasp the central content in an accessible manner prior to reading.

- Lead a quick text prereading, or "text tour," focusing student attention on illustrations; chapter title and subtopics; boldface words; summary sections; and connection of chapter to theme, previous chapters, activities, and concepts.

- When possible, build in opportunities for "narrow reading," allowing students to read more than one selection on the same topic, to build concept and vocabulary recognition that will support their reading more fluently and confidently.

## Phase 2: Teach

- Clearly establish a reading purpose for students prior to assigning a manageable amount of text.

- Describe and model strategies for navigating different kinds of text. Provide a convincing rationale for each new strategy and regularly review both the purpose and process.

- Familiarize students with a manageable tool kit of reading comprehension and study strategies and continue practicing these selective strategies. In this way, students end the school year with a viable approach unattainable through sporadic practice with a confusing array of new reading behaviors.

- Introduce a new strategy using a text that isn't too difficult in order to build credibility for the strategy and ensure student success. Otherwise, if a selection is too difficult and the strategy fails to deliver for students, they will have little faith in experimenting with the new strategy on future texts.

- Whenever possible, get students physically involved with the page, using highlighters, self-sticking notes, and a small piece of cardboard or heavy construction paper to focus and guide their reading from one paragraph or column to the next.

© Pearson Education, Inc., publishing as Pearson Prentice Hall.

- Alternate between teacher-facilitated and student-dominated reading activities.
- Do "think-aloud" reading to model your cognitive and metacognitive strategies and thought processes.
- Assign brief amounts of text at a time and alternate between oral, paired, and silent reading.
- Guide students through the process of reading and comprehending a passage by reading aloud to them and assisting them in identifying the text organization and establishing a clear reading purpose.
- Allow students to read a passage while listening to an audiotape recorded by a classmate, cross-age tutor, or parent volunteer.
- Have students engage in "repeated readings" of the same brief passage to build word recognition, fluency, and reading rate.
- Provide some form of study guide in order to focus their reading on the critical content and prevent them from getting bogged down with nonessential details and unfamiliar vocabulary. A partially completed outline or graphic organizer is more task based and manageable than a list of questions to answer, which often results in simple scanning for content without really reading and comprehending material.
- Demonstrate your note-taking process and provide models of effective study notes for students to emulate.

## Phase 3: Assess

- Prepare both text-based and experientially based questions, which lead students from simply getting the gist of a selection to establishing a personal connection to the lesson content.
- Build in task-based and authentic assessment during every lesson to ensure that ELL students are actually developing greater proficiency with new content and strategies. Quick writes, drawings, oral and written summaries, and collaborative tasks are generally more productive indicators of lesson comprehension than a closing question/answer session.
- Provide safe opportunities for students to alert you to any learning challenges they are experiencing. Have them submit

© Pearson Education, Inc., publishing as Pearson Prentice Hall.

anonymous written questions (formulated either independently or with a partner) about confusing lesson content and process, and then follow up on these points of confusion at the end of class or in the subsequent class session.

- Ask students to end the class session by writing 3–5 outcome statements about their experience in the day's lesson, expressing both new understandings and needs for clarification.

- Make sure that assessment mirrors the lesson objectives. For example, if you are teaching students how to preread expository text, it isn't relevant to assess using comprehension questions. A more authentic assessment of their ability to apply this strategy would be to provide them with a photocopy of an expository selection and ask them to highlight and label the parts one would read during the actual prereading process. It would be relevant, however, to ask them to identify two reasons for engaging in a text prereading before tackling the entire selection.

- Build in opportunities for students to demonstrate their understandings of texts that draw upon different language and literacy skills: formal and informal writing assignments, posters, small-group tasks, oral presentations, and so on.

- Don't assign ELLs tasks that require little or no reading or lesson comprehension. For example, don't allow them to simply draw a picture while other students are writing a paragraph. Instead, make sure that you have adequately scaffolded the task and equipped them with a writing frame and model to guide them through the process. While one might argue that this is multimodal and tapping into multiple intelligences, it is actually conveying expectations for their development of academic competence in English.

- Make sure that students understand your assessment criteria in advance. Whenever possible, provide models of student work for them to emulate, along with a nonmodel that fails to meet the specified assessment criteria. Do not provide exemplars that are clearly outside their developmental range. While this may be an enriching reading task, it will not serve as a viable model. Save student work that can later serve as a model for ELLs with different levels of academic preparation.

- Develop accessible and relevant rubrics for various tasks and products that are customized to the task rather than generic assessment tools. Introduce a rubric in tandem with exemplars of successful and less productive work to help them internalize the assessment criteria. Guide students in identifying the ways in which sample work does or does not meet established grading criteria.

## Phase 4: Extend

- Consider ways in which students can transfer knowledge and skills gleaned from one assignment/lesson to a subsequent lesson.
- Build in opportunities for students to read a more detailed or challenging selection on the same topic in order to allow them to apply familiar concepts and vocabulary and stretch their literacy muscles.
- Recycle pre- and postreading tasks regularly, so students can become more familiar with the task process and improve their performance. If they are assailed with curricular novelty, ELLs never have the opportunity to refine their skills and demonstrate improved competence. For example, if you ask them to identify a personality trait of an essential character in a story and then support this observation with relevant details in an expository paragraph, it would make sense to have them shortly afterwards write an identical paragraph about another character.
- Discuss with students ways in which they can apply new vocabulary and language strategies outside the classroom.
- Praise students' efforts to experiment with new language in class, both in writing and in speaking.
- Demonstrate the applicability of new reading and writing strategies to real-world literacy tasks. Bring in potentially more engaging reading selections that will pique their interest and provide a more compelling rationale for applying a new strategic repertoire. Design periodic writing tasks for an authentic audience other than the teacher: another class, fellow classmates, and so on.

© Pearson Education, Inc., publishing as Pearson Prentice Hall.

## Characteristics of Less Proficient Learners

Every classroom has a number of less proficient students, individuals who begin the year one, two, or more years below grade level yet who do not qualify for special education services and may not be English language learners. It is important to keep in mind that most accommodations made for English learners and special needs students will be helpful for all kinds of diverse learners, including less proficient learners. However, it is worthwhile to briefly examine some of the learner characteristics of less proficient students in comparison with their average achieving peers. An appreciation of these distinctions will provide a useful foundation for understanding the importance of using the various "universal access" strategies described throughout this section and incorporated into the Prentice Hall Literature program.

## Attention and Memory

Research suggests that underachieving students have difficulty in organizing and categorizing new information during instruction. Typically, less skillful students do not effectively order, classify, and arrange information in meaningful ways during learning, frequently leaving them confused and missing the "big picture." Long-term memory is often adversely affected due to the lack of meaningful connections established and difficulty with noticing how new information relates to prior knowledge. In addition, underprepared students frequently do not know how to focus their attention on the important aspects of a classroom presentation, demonstration, or reading selection. In either case, the intentional use of explicit strategies coupled with interactive review and extension activities can make a significant difference in providing poorly prepared students full access to the Language Arts curriculum.

© Pearson Education, Inc., publishing as Pearson Prentice Hall.

# Lesson Planning and Instructional Accommodations for Attention and Memory

## Phase 1: Preteach

- Gain attention requesting a simple physical response (e.g., "Everyone, eyes on me please," "Touch number one," and so forth). Students need to show you they are ready.
- Keep the lesson pace moving along briskly—a "perky not pokey" pace is helpful.
- Clarify or introduce critical "big ideas" or conceptual anchors that the reading or lesson or activity is built around (e.g., an example, a metaphor, a demonstration).
- Use brief choral responses when the answer is short and identical (e.g. "Everyone, the answer to number one is _____.").
- Use brief partner responses when the answer is open-ended and longer (e.g., "Ones, tell twos the most important new information revealed in the last paragraph.").
- After students have had a chance to rehearse or practice with a partner, randomly call upon them to build prior knowledge or raise questions the text may answer.
- Use graphic organizers, charts, and concept maps to assist students with focusing on critical concepts as well as categorizing and organizing information to be studied/learned.

## Phase 2: Teach

- Engage students in a "read/reflect/discuss/note" cycle of filling out the graphic organizers/concept maps collaboratively as you progress through the reading or lesson.
- Do a brief oral review using partners (e.g., think-write-pair-share) to ensure that all students are firm on the big ideas/critical concepts.
- Cue students to take special note of crucial information and explore why this information is so critical.
- Engage students in the active use or processing of the new information (e.g., paraphrase, give an example, write a response).
- Emphasize connections between new and known information.
- Connect new learning to student's personal experience (e.g., coach students to create analogies or metaphors using prior knowledge).

© Pearson Education, Inc., publishing as Pearson Prentice Hall.

## Phase 3: Assess

- Ask students to explain their graphic organizer/concept map to a partner. Monitor selected students and determine their level of understanding—reteach/provide additional examples as necessary.
- Provide students the opportunity to reorganize, prioritize, and otherwise reflect on the key aspects of the lesson.
- Systematically monitor retention of key information or "big ideas" over time using "quick writes" (brief written summaries to a prompt), random questioning, observing student interactions, written assignments, and so on. Reteach, provide additional examples, invite students to elaborate, and so on, as necessary.

## Phase 4: Extend

- Have students design investigations or projects using the information in new ways.
- Design homework assignments that require students to go beyond the text to apply lessons learned to their lives or to other circumstances.
- Challenge students to organize information in novel ways, come up with different categories, and otherwise elaborate the information being studied.
- Draw explicit connections and prompt students to induce connections between information studied earlier in the term and new ideas encountered in the current reading selection.

## Learning Strategies and Use

Perhaps the most ubiquitous characteristic of less proficient students is their lack of effective and efficient strategies for accomplishing various academic tasks, from writing a persuasive essay to taking notes during a lecture to responding to a piece of literature. Less skillful students tend to have a very limited repertoire of learning strategies and have little awareness of how to monitor the use of learning strategies during reading, writing, and other academic activities. In contrast, successful learners are active, "strategic," and flexible in their employment of appropriate learning strategies tailored to the demands of a particular academic task or assignment.

Kame'enui and Carnine[4] suggest three critical design principles teachers need to keep in mind when addressing the issue of learning strategies with underprepared or diverse learners.

---

4. Kame'enui, Edward and Douglas Carnine, op. cit.

© Pearson Education, Inc., publishing as Pearson Prentice Hall.

1. Important learning strategies must be made overt, explicit, and conspicuous.

2. Strong verbal and visual support, or "scaffolding," should be provided to ensure that diverse learners understand when, where, and how to use the strategies.

3. Judicious review of new learning strategies is required to allow less prepared students enough practice to incorporate the new strategy into their learning routines.

It is important to note that differences between less proficient students and average achievers in their use of learning strategies is not based on organic or biological differences. In other words, it is their lack of experience and preparation that is the critical difference. Fortunately, less proficient learners are quite capable of acquiring effective learning strategies and significantly improving their academic performance when provided with direct instruction in the "what-why-how-when" of strategy use in a highly focused educational setting.

## Lesson Planning and Instructional Accommodations for Learning Strategies

### Phase 1: Preteach

- Clarify the rationale for learning the new strategy in terms, examples, and results the students value (e.g., "Where in school or life would it be useful to know how to write a persuasive essay?").
- Brainstorm for examples of successful strategy usage with interactive tactics such as "give one, get one" to involve all students (e.g., each student lists as many ideas as possible in 3–4 minutes and then has 3–5 minutes to compare with a peer and "give one" idea to them as well as "get one" from them to extend their brainstormed list).
- Provide personal examples of how you have used this strategy to your academic advantage.
- Directly teach any "pre-skills," or prerequisite skills, students need to perform the strategy.

### Phase 2: Teach

Explicitly model the use of the strategy, including a significant focus on thinking aloud during the execution of each step in the strategy.

© Pearson Education, Inc., publishing as Pearson Prentice Hall.

- Provide students with a brief summary of the strategy steps or an acronym to facilitate retention of the strategy.

  **Example:**

  **POWER: P**repare, **O**rganize, **W**rite, **E**dit, **R**evise

  (Archer & Gleason 2000)

- Guide students in practicing the strategy using less demanding content that allows students to focus on the new strategy. Gradually transition to more difficult content.

- Break the strategy down into explicit steps, ensuring that students are able to perform each step and combine steps to use the whole strategy.

- Structure partner-mediated practice in which students take turns practicing the strategy and providing feedback to one another (e.g., taking turns reading a paragraph or page and paraphrasing the gist in 12 words or less).

## Phase 3: Assess

- Monitor partners during strategy practice to observe competence, areas for review, and so forth.

- Randomly call on students to informally demonstrate their strategy knowledge.

- Include explicit use of strategies taught as part of the quiz, paper, report, project, and other formal assessments.

## Phase 4: Extend

- Discuss with students where else in or out of school they could use the strategy.

- Provide extra credit or some other incentive to encourage the use of the strategy in other content area classes.

- After they have gained some degree of mastery, encourage students to modify and otherwise personalize the strategy to better fit their learning style or needs.

### Vocabulary and Reading Fluency

Vocabulary differences between struggling and average students are apparent from the primary years in school and tend to get worse over time. It is not surprising that less prepared learners engage in far less reading in and out of school, resulting in substantially impoverished vocabularies.

© Pearson Education, Inc., publishing as Pearson Prentice Hall.

In addition, their ability to read fluently and accurately is often diminished, further compounding the issue and rendering reading a frustrating and defeating experience.

There is no shortcut, or "quick fix," for vocabulary building, but teachers can make a tremendous difference by sustained attention to the following practices:

- Directly teaching key conceptual vocabulary using strategies that take students beyond simple memorization
- Teaching students how to learn words and concepts from context
- Encouraging wide reading in and out of school; students who have serious fluency problems (e.g., reading below 100 words per minute in grade-level text) will require sustained practice daily in repeated reading of instructional level/age-appropriate texts

## Lesson Planning and Instructional Accommodations for Vocabulary and Fluency

### Phase 1: Preteach

- Select conceptually rich, critical vocabulary for more detailed instruction before reading.
- Choose age- and level-appropriate passages for students to use repeated reading strategies (e.g., on prerecorded tapes, partner reading, choral reading with small groups).

### Phase 2: Teach

- Directly teach the meanings of critical, conceptually rich vocabulary required for full understanding of the passage or lesson.
- Pick vocabulary strategies that take students beyond simple repetition of the definition to prompt active construction of new connections between the concept and their prior knowledge. Such strategies include
  —creating semantic maps showing how words are related
  —using the words in sentences that "show you know" the meaning
- Define the critical attributes of the concept in short bulleted phrases and create examples and nonexamples of the concept, prompting students to explain why the exemplar does or does not have the attributes of the concept under consideration (a graphic organizer showing the attributes and examples/nonexamples can be very useful).

 © Pearson Education, Inc., publishing as Pearson Prentice Hall.

- Engage students in word sorts: Provide 10–20 vocabulary words for students to place into preset categories (e.g., parts of speech, words descriptive of the character or not, and so on).

- Pair students at similar instructional levels for repeated reading practice; have the more proficient student read a paragraph or a page and then have the less proficient student reread the same section.

- Practice repeated reading of instructional-level passages of 150–200 words in length with prerecorded tapes, set goals, and individually graph and monitor fluency daily, finishing with a written retelling of the passage.

- Teach students important generative word roots (e.g., Latin and Greek) and common affixes. Practice sorting and combining to examine how they work (e.g., -spec-: spectrum, spectacle, inspection, speculation).

- Model and practice the use of context in predicting word meanings during reading, thinking aloud to demonstrate to students how textual cues direct your thinking.

## Phase 3: Assess

- Randomly call on students to provide examples of the vocabulary word under examination.

- Monitor students during partner discussion of selected critical vocabulary words.

- Evaluate students during small-group discussion, written products, and so on.

- Directly monitor the fluency of selected students via one-minute timings. Note rate, accuracy, and expression.

## Phase 4: Extend

- Encourage students to informally use recently taught vocabulary words in "show you know" sentences during classroom conversations, written products, and so on.

- Intentionally revisit newly acquired vocabulary during discussion, while thinking aloud during demonstrations, and so on.

- Encourage students to practice fluency building via repeated reading at home, appropriate CD-ROM technology, and cross-age tutoring of younger students, in which the target student must prepare a story to read fluently with his or her tutee.

## Motivation and Academic Identity

Motivation is complex and difficult to define, but most experts agree that it is significantly related to how much success or failure one has experienced relative to the activity in question. Less proficient secondary students typically do not see themselves as capable of sustained reading, inquiry, or writing in a challenging academic setting. The old cliché "Nothing succeeds like success" is relevant to this discussion. To build motivation and encourage the development of a productive "academic identity," it is important to engage less proficient students in challenging lessons while simultaneously incorporating adequate support or instructional scaffolding to increase the likelihood students will experience success. In addition, helping students to explore their thinking as they read and write through structured dialogues and thinking aloud can be very helpful. Noted reading researcher David Pearson calls this process a "metacognitive conversation," allowing less proficient students to gain an understanding of how successful readers and writers think as they work. In a manner of speaking, teachers can provide less proficient students with an academic or cognitive role model. For example, modeling a simple self-monitoring strategy during writing such as "remember your audience" can assist students in keeping multiple perspectives in mind as they compose.

## Lesson Planning and Instructional Accommodations for Motivation and Academic Identity

Motivation and academic identity do not lend themselves to the Preteach, Teach, Assess, and Extend lesson format. In a sense, motivation is more "caught than taught" and will be the result of successfully engaging students in the curriculum. However, there are a number of general strategies that are useful to consider including:

- **Self-selected reading** Allow less proficient students regular opportunities to read material they are interested in, at their instructional level.

- **Goal setting** Engage students in setting personal goals for various academic tasks, such as pages/chapters read per week, strategy usage, words read per minute during fluency practice, and so forth.

© Pearson Education, Inc., publishing as Pearson Prentice Hall.

- **Metacognitive dialogues** Ask students to informally share their perceptions, approaches, and fears regarding various school-related challenges. Students and teachers then share their thoughts and feelings about how they used various strategies to become more successful.

- **Book clubs, book reviews, newsletter reviews, e-mail postings** These provide an audience for students' opinions about books they have read.

- **Partnerships** Have students build partnerships with peers and with younger students, community members, and business personnel.

- **Negotiated choices** As appropriate, involve students in negotiating alternative assignments, options, and novel ideas to reach common goals.

- **Model an "academic identity"** Invite teachers/students/ other adults into the classroom to share how they developed as literate citizens.

## Summary

Less proficient high-school students are underprepared for the academic challenges of a rigorous grade-level Language Arts program in a variety of ways. Many of their difficulties can be linked to difficulties with attention and memory, learning strategies, vocabulary and reading fluency, and motivation/academic identity. Secondary Language Arts teachers can have an extremely beneficial effect on the learning of less proficient students by the sustained focus on appropriate strategies for preteaching, teaching, assessment, and extension beyond the lesson.

Students with special education needs are a highly diverse student group. Although their learning needs vary greatly, a majority of children identified as special education students will experience mild to severe difficulties in becoming proficient and independent readers and writers. Through instruction that incorporates adaptations and modifications and is delivered in collaborative ways, students with disabilities can gain literacy skills and be active participants in general education Language Arts curricula and instruction.

### Characteristics of Special Education Learners

### Eligibility for Special Education

Federal law IDEA '97 (Individuals with Disabilities Education Act, P.L. 105–17) specifies the disabling conditions under which students are found eligible to receive special education services. These disabling conditions may be clustered into the two broad categories of high incidence and low incidence disabilities (see chart on the following pages for descriptions of disabling conditions). Each student with a disability may experience specific cognitive, communicative, behavioral/social/emotional, physical, and learning issues. Students may exhibit all, or some combination, of the characteristics listed for their particular disability and, in the case of some students, have more than one disability (e.g., a student identified as having a learning disability may also have a communicative disorder). Because of the heterogeneity of the special education student population, even within categories of disability, an Individualized Education Program (IEP) is created for each student found eligible to receive special education services.

© Pearson Education, Inc., publishing as Pearson Prentice Hall.

# Disabling Conditions

| High Incidence Disabilities | Descriptors | Reading Instruction Consideration |
|---|---|---|
| • *Speech or Language Impairment* | • Speech disorders include difficulties in articulation, voice, and fluency.<br><br>• Language impairments may include difficulties in phonology, morphology, syntax, semantics, and pragmatics. | • When possible, provide opportunities for intensive instruction in decoding and word-recognition skills (e.g., computer drill and practice programs; flash cards of frequently encountered words).<br><br>• Provide time for students to read the text multiple times to gain fluency (e.g., repeated readings; paired reading).<br><br>• Explicitly teach vocabulary and provide strategies for dealing with unknown words (e.g., teaching syllabification skills; teaching meaning of prefixes and suffixes).<br><br>• Explicitly teach more complex language patterns (e.g., compound sentences) and literary elements (e.g., idioms; metaphors). |
| • *Learning Disabilities* | • Students exhibit average to above-average intelligence combined with uneven academic performance patterns (i.e., perform at an average to above-average level in some academic subjects, while experiencing significant difficulties in others).<br><br>• Students experience processing difficulties (e.g., have difficulty taking in oral and print information and in expressing ideas orally and in writing).<br><br>• Students may experience attention and social/behavioral challenges. | • Preteach "big ideas" and vocabulary.<br><br>• Provide multiple opportunities for students to read text to gain fluency.<br><br>• Explicitly teach vocabulary using activities that are multisensory and require active participation (e.g., acting out meanings of words; drawing images to represent word meanings; tape-recording words and word meanings; using computer software programs).<br><br>• Explicitly teach comprehension strategies by modeling the steps, guiding the students through the steps, and monitoring for implementation (e.g., webbing and outlining; predicting; summarizing).<br><br>• Provide multiple avenues for demonstrating comprehension of text (e.g., writing, drawing, speaking, acting out scenes). |
| • *Emotional Disturbance* | • Students experience difficulty learning that is not due to cognitive, sensory, or health factors.<br><br>• Students may have difficulty forging and maintaining interpersonal relationships. | • Make students accountable during large-group, small-group, and paired reading (e.g., have them take notes and make and check predictions; ask questions of all group members, not just a spokesperson; have students complete individual quizzes to check for understanding).<br><br>*continued* |

© Pearson Education, Inc., publishing as Pearson Prentice Hall.

| | | |
|---|---|---|
| | • Students may display inappropriate behaviors or feelings under normal circumstances.<br><br>• Students may experience feelings of unhappiness or depression.<br><br>• Students may have physical symptoms or fears associated with personal or school problems. | • Explicitly teach skills for working in groups (e.g., how to ask questions; how to state an opinion; how to disagree with another person's ideas).<br><br>• Provide structure and establish routines for reading activities and transitions (e.g., specify expectations during large-group reading; establish routines for how students are to complete comprehension activities).<br><br>• Become familiar with the student's behavior plan and systematically implement it in the classroom (e.g., use the reinforcers and consequences identified in the plan to build consistency for the student). |
| • *Mental Retardation* | • Students will demonstrate subaverage (in students with mild/moderate mental retardation) to significantly subaverage (in students with severe mental retardation) intellectual functioning.<br><br>• Students will demonstrate overall low performance in adaptive behavior domains (e.g., taking care of personal health needs). | • Preteach and reteach vocabulary and concepts as needed.<br><br>• Make concepts concrete by linking concepts to the students' daily lives.<br><br>• Explicitly model what is expected, and when able, provide examples of completed projects.<br><br>• Provide multiple avenues for students to engage with text (e.g., books on tape, paired reading, passages in hypertext format).<br><br>• Provide multiple exposures to the same text and its key vocabulary.<br><br>• Provide multiple ways for students to demonstrate understanding of text. |
| • *Low Incidence Disabilities* | **Note:** Students with low incidence disabilities may have average to above-average intelligence or may experience cognitive impairments ranging from mild to severe. | **Note:** Students with low incidence disabilities may have average to above-average intelligence or may experience cognitive impairments ranging from mild to severe. |
| • *Deaf/Hard of Hearing* | • Students who are deaf or who have some degree of hearing loss | • Present ideas visually.<br><br>• Capture key ideas from discussions in written form on the overhead or chalkboard.<br><br>• Use FMI systems when available.<br><br>• When orally reading text, reduce background noise as much as possible; when conducting small-group or paired reading activities, consider having the groups move to other rooms or spaces.<br><br>• Work with the interpreter or special education staff to identify adaptations and modifications. |

*continued*

© Pearson Education, Inc., publishing as Pearson Prentice Hall.

| | | |
|---|---|---|
| • *Blind/Low Vision* | • Students who are blind or who have some vision | • Present ideas auditorially and through tactile modes to support student access. |
| | | • Work with the special education teacher to secure large-print text, Braille text, books on tape, and AAC reading devices. |
| | | • Work with the special education staff to identify specific adaptations and modifications. |
| • *Deaf/Blindness* | • Students who have concomitant hearing and visual impairments | • Work with the special education staff to identify specific adaptations and modifications. |
| | | • Gain understanding and a level of comfort in using the AAC devices the student is using in the classroom. |
| • *Other Health Impaired* | • Students with health conditions that limit strength, vitality, or alertness (e.g., heart condition, sickle cell anemia, epilepsy, AIDS) | • Work with the special education staff to identify adaptations and modifications. |
| | | • Gain understanding of the child's condition and day-to-day and emergency medical needs. |
| | | • Develop plans for dealing with students' absences. |
| • *Orthopedic Disabilities* | • Students with physical disabilities (e.g., club-foot, bone tuberculosis, cerebral palsy) | • Work with the special education staff to identify specific adaptations and modifications. |
| | | • Work with the special education staff to secure adapted materials and AAC devices, as appropriate (e.g., book holder; computer voice-recognition system that allows student to dictate written assignments). |
| | | • Adapt routines and activities to take into consideration the student's physical needs (e.g., room arrangement that allows for mobility in a wheelchair; procedures for distributing and collecting materials; procedures for forming work groups.) |
| • *Autism* | • Students experience difficulty in verbal and nonverbal communication<br><br>• Students experience difficulties in social interactions<br><br>• Is commonly referred to as a "spectrum disorder" because of the heterogeneity of the group | • Work with the special education staff to identify specific adaptations and modifications. |
| | | • Structure group and paired activities to take into consideration the child's needs; teach social skills and supports for working in small group and paired situations. |
| | | • Connect concepts and vocabulary to the interests of the student. |
| | | • Work with the special education staff to implement behavioral/social plans to provide consistency. |
| | | • Establish and maintain routines to ensure predictability within the classroom. |

*continued*

© Pearson Education, Inc., publishing as Pearson Prentice Hall.

| | | |
|---|---|---|
| • *Traumatic Brain Injury* | • Students who experience an acquired injury to the brain <br><br> • Injury results in total or partial functional disability or psychological impairment (e.g., cognition, language, memory, attention, reasoning) | • Work with the special education staff to identify specific adaptations and modifications. <br><br> • Adapt routines and activities to take into consideration the student's physical needs (e.g., room arrangement that allows for mobility in a wheelchair). <br><br> • Take into consideration student's language, memory, and attention skill needs when constructing class assignments and activities. <br><br> • Preteach and reteach concepts and vocabulary as appropriate. |

## Individualized Education Plan

The IEP serves to guide general and special education teachers, related service providers, and parents in designing and delivering educational programs that maximize students' school participation and learning. The IEP includes goals, objectives, and benchmarks that outline what an individual student is expected to learn and achieve during the course of the academic year, as well as the types of services and special adaptations and modifications that are to be put into place to support the educational achievement of the student. For example, in the area of Language Arts instruction, a student's IEP may include the following goal and objectives:

*Goal:* Jamal will improve in reading comprehension skills as measured by the district-adopted standardized test.

*Objective:* Given narrative passages written at the seventh-grade level, Jamal will correctly write the name(s) of the main character(s) and outline, in writing, the main events of the passages in correct sequence for three out of four passages by December.

*Objective:* Given expository passages written at the seventh-grade level, Jamal will correctly write the main idea of the passages and at least three supporting details for three out of four passages by February.

The IEP goes on to identify specific services the student will need in order to achieve these goals and objectives. A range of services is available to students with disabilities through their IEP. Services fall along a continuum and include the option of

© Pearson Education, Inc., publishing as Pearson Prentice Hall.

students receiving instruction in general education classrooms with special education supports and participating in specialized instruction delivered by special education teachers in special education classrooms for one or more periods a day. The type of service delivery to be provided is determined individually for each student through the IEP meeting. The general education teacher, in partnership with the special education staff and the student's parents and, when appropriate, the student, determine the type of service delivery that is most appropriate for a student based on his or her learning needs.

Many students with disabilities are educated in general education classrooms alongside their general education peers. Service-delivery models that support student participation in general education classrooms go by various names, including mainstreaming, integration, and inclusion. All have the underlying same intent—to provide for the needs of students with disabilities in the least restrictive environment, alongside their general education peers.

In the case of Jamal, the service delivery option selected and specified in his IEP may look something like this:

> Student will participate in the general education Language Arts class and in one period of special education reading resource support each day. The special education teacher will team with the general education Language Arts teacher at least two days per week to provide instruction in the general education Language Arts class.

IEPs also specify the types of curricular, instructional, and behavioral adaptations and modifications that are to be put into place to support the student's achievement. For Jamal, the following adaptations and modifications may be specified in the IEP:

> The student will receive instruction in learning strategies to identify characters, story sequence, and main ideas and supporting details. The student will be provided a story map for identifying the main character(s) and for sequencing story events. The student will be provided a main idea/supporting details map when working with expository passages.

The IEP is a guide that details the types of goals, educational program, and adaptations and modifications a special education student is to receive. The IEP is developed by a team and is reviewed at least annually. General education teachers, special education professionals, administrators, parents, and students all have a voice in the development of the individual IEP.

## Lesson Planning and Instructional Accommodations

When developing Language Arts lesson plans for inclusive classrooms of general and special education learners, teachers will want to consider the addition of teaching and learning strategies that will support universal access to the content. Teachers will need to be familiar with the unique learning needs and requirements of the students and their goals, objectives, and benchmarks and, through collaboration with other IEP team members, incorporate those needs and strategies into the classroom.

This process does not need to be as intimidating as it sounds because there are some common, relatively unintrusive teaching and learning strategies that can be implemented in the classroom to address students' specific needs, as well as support the learning of the other students present in the classroom. For example, students with disabilities can greatly benefit from activities that preteach and reteach concepts, that explicitly link lesson content with prior experience and knowledge, that directly teach the meaning of critical vocabulary words, and that explicitly model how tasks are to be completed. This is true for other learners as well, including less proficient readers and students who are English language learners. Lesson plans that include explicit instruction in behavioral and social expectations also help to ensure student participation and learning. Pacing is also an issue. Some students with disabilities will require a somewhat slower pace or an ongoing review of key concepts if they are to grasp key understandings and skills. Also, activities need to be considered in light of the students' disabilities. For example, will special materials be needed (such as materials with enlarged print for students with low vision or adapted manipulatives that can be used by a student with a physical disability)? If participating in student-mediated instruction (e.g., small-group learning), what type of preparation will students receive for participating in these activities? Will the activities provide necessary supports to ensure student participation (e.g., will directions be explicit and in writing as well as presented verbally)?

There are a number of other simple adaptations and modifications general education teachers can implement in the classroom to directly address the literacy learning needs of students with disabilities. In fact, in many cases, these adaptations and modifications will assist all learners in the classroom, including typically developing readers, English learners, and less proficient readers. A beginning list of suggestions for meaningfully including students with disabilities in the general education Language Arts curriculum

© Pearson Education, Inc., publishing as Pearson Prentice Hall.

is presented in the chart at the end of this section. Although presented in terms of disabling conditions, the suggestions apply across conditions.

It is also helpful to think of instructional considerations that specifically apply to the four phases of instruction: Preteach, Teach, Assess, and Extend. A beginning list of suggestions is provided below.

## Phase 1: Preteach

- Identify the most critical and high-utility vocabulary words for comprehension of the passage. Provide explicit instruction in the meaning of these words that incorporates instruction in the understanding of prefixes, suffixes, word roots, synonyms, and antonyms.
- Provide an overview of key ideas and concepts presented in the text using study guides, outlines, or maps.
- Explicitly connect text content with the students' lives.
- Preteach key concepts.

## Phase 2: Teach

- Present all ideas orally and visually and, when possible, incorporate tactile and kinesthetic experiences as well.
- Stop often to discuss key ideas and check for understanding.
- Limit the presentation of information or discussion of key topics to short periods of time (no more than ten minutes) to enhance attention.
- Require students to demonstrate that they are listening and following along (e.g., taking notes, running a finger along the text).
- Incorporate active reading strategies (e.g., choral reading, paired reading) to assist students in maintaining attention.
- Provide necessary adaptive materials as appropriate (e.g., enlarged print).
- Incorporate the same comprehension and learning strategies over extended periods to allow for mastery. This will provide students with multiple opportunities to practice a strategy and to become comfortable in its application. This will also prevent "strategy clutter," which can occur when a student has too many strategies to draw from and is not facile enough with any to allow for ease of use.

© Pearson Education, Inc., publishing as Pearson Prentice Hall.

- Provide specific and step-by-step instructions. Model what the students are to do, step-by-step.

## Phase 3: Assess

- Go beyond questioning techniques to assess students' understanding by having them write questions about what they have learned, identify those sections they find are unclear or confusing, or complete short writes of the key points.
- When having students work in groups or pairs, set up procedures that maintain individual student accountability (e.g., students each having to write, draw, or state a response).
- When appropriate, have students self-manage and chart their performance. Academic performance, homework and assignment completion, and behavior could be charted.

## Phase 4: Extend

- Provide examples of completed projects.
- Allow students to work in pairs or small groups.
- Provide outlines of what is to be done, with suggested dates and timelines for project completion.

## Collaboration as a Key to Student Achievement

One of the most critical things a general education teacher can do is to collaborate with the special education teachers and staff. Special education staff have extensive expertise in working with students with disabilities and are there to support each student with an IEP. These professionals are available as support systems for general education teachers and parents. The chart that follows presents a brief list of potential special educators that you may want to contact when working with students with disabilities in your general education classroom.

General education teachers can do a great deal to ensure that students with disabilities are meaningfully included in the life of the classroom. The attributes listed on the next page are important to all classrooms, but they play a key role in the creation of a classroom culture and climate that supports the participation and achievement of students with disabilities.

© Pearson Education, Inc., publishing as Pearson Prentice Hall.

- Exploring differences and the importance of the acceptance of differences
- Setting clear expectations for all students that take into consideration students' learning styles and needs
- Providing students with reasonable choices
- Setting up instructional activities that foster the development of relationships between students and between students and teachers
- Demonstrating mutual respect, fairness, and trust

For example, in the case of Jamal, you could work with the special education teacher to identify those learning strategies you are already teaching in the classroom that will assist Jamal. You may want to invite the special education teacher into the classroom to provide instruction in other critical learning strategies that would assist all of your students in becoming better readers and writers, including Jamal. Because Jamal is receiving resource-room support one period per day, you may want to discuss with the special education teacher the type of instruction he is receiving during the support period and together work to develop a plan that links the curriculum of the two learning environments. You will most likely be involved in assessing whether Jamal is achieving his goals and objectives and in providing instruction to support their achievement.

## Summary

Students with disabilities are a highly heterogeneous group of learners. Their cognitive and behavioral, social, and physical needs can present unique challenges in the classroom, but through careful and strategic planning and collaboration among professionals and parents, these students can be contributing and vital members of the classroom community, as well as readers and writers. It is the professionals' responsibility, in consultation with the parents, to ensure universal access to the curriculum for these students. Lesson planning and the inclusion of adaptations and modifications within lessons are beginning points for achieving the goal of universal access for students with disabilities.

# Special Education Teachers and Service Providers

| Support Provider | Roles | How They Can Support the General Education Teacher |
|---|---|---|
| Special Education Teacher<br><br>• resource teacher<br>• itinerant teacher<br>• special-day class teacher<br>• inclusion specialist | • Is intimately familiar with students' IEP goals, objectives/benchmarks, and the students' academic, communicative, and behavioral/emotional needs<br><br>• Has expertise in how to adapt and modify curriculum and instruction to meaningfully include students with disabilities in general education classrooms and curriculum<br><br>• Has expertise for providing remedial support and intensive intervention services for students with disabilities | • Can answer questions about students' learning needs<br><br>• Can explain the students' IEP and what can be done in the general education class to support student achievement of IEP goals and objectives/benchmarks<br><br>• Can help you develop ways to adapt and modify instruction that will help students learn<br><br>• Can work with you in the classroom to support the students' participation and achievement |
| Para-professional | • May be assigned to "shadow" a student in the general education classroom<br><br>• Can assist in adapting and modifying curriculum and instruction for the particular student(s)<br><br>• May serve to monitor students' academic and behavioral/emotional needs and intervention plans<br><br>• May assist students in meeting physical, mobility, and health needs | • Can assist you in addressing the student's needs (e.g., can provide a one-on-one explanation that you may not be able to furnish because of the other students in the classroom)<br><br>• Can be responsible for adapting and modifying instructional activities and assignments, with guidance from you and the special education teachers<br><br>• Can oversee the implementation of specialized intervention plans<br><br>• Can be responsible for the student's physical, mobility, and health needs |
| Audiologist | • Expertise in measuring students' hearing levels and evaluating hearing loss | • Can give you suggestions for how to work with students who have partial or total hearing loss<br><br>• Can give you suggestions for how to deal with a student who refuses to wear his or her hearing aids in class<br><br>*continued* |

© Pearson Education, Inc., publishing as Pearson Prentice Hall.

| | | |
|---|---|---|
| Physical and Occupational Therapist | • Physical therapist generally focuses on gross motor development (e.g., walking, running)<br><br>• Occupational therapist generally focuses on fine motor development (e.g., using writing tools) | • Can give you suggestions for how to modify requirements to take into consideration students' motor and physical needs |
| School or Educational Psychologist | • Expertise in educational testing administration and interpretation<br><br>• May also have training in counseling and working with students in crisis situations | • Can help you understand testing results and may be able to come into the classroom to observe and give you suggestions for working with a particular student<br><br>• Can help you work with a student who is in crisis (e.g., divorce, death) |
| Augmentative and Alternative Communicative Specialist | • Expertise in assessing students' AAC needs<br><br>• Expertise in developing programs that assist students in using alternative means for communicating verbally and in writing (e.g., communication boards; using speech synthesizer software) | • Can explain to you how a student's AAC device works<br><br>• Can give you suggestions for how to make adaptations and modifications that support the student's use of the AAC device in the classroom (e.g., physical arrangement of the learning environment; assignment adjustments) |
| Educational Therapist | • Expertise in assessment and remediation for students experiencing learning problems<br><br>• May serve as a case manager and build communicative links between school, home, and related service providers | • Can give you suggestions for how to adapt instruction to meet the student's needs<br><br>• Can give you suggestions for communicating with parents and for working with the special education staff |

© Pearson Education, Inc., publishing as Pearson Prentice Hall.

# ANSWERS

## LITERARY ANALYSIS AND READING SKILLS
### Adjusting Reading Rate

**Practice,** p. 2

1. F; **Sample answer:** I would scan or skim a table of contents in a textbook to find a particular chapter.
2. F; **Sample answer:** I would definitely skim headings to see what topics were covered in a chapter.
3. F; **Sample answer:** Captions of photos and graphs are always worth scanning.
4. T
5. T
6. F; **Sample answer:** Headings give main ideas and key points in a textbook, so I would look at headings when looking for a main idea.
7. T

**Assess,** p. 3

**A** Students should indicate appropriate skimming and scanning strategies: they might check the table of contents for the location of Chapter Three; they might skim the headings within the chapter looking for "taxation without representation"; they might look for a map that would show the colonies; they might look in a glossary or look at photos to see if they can find a "lobsterback," the British redcoat soldier; they might skim paragraphs looking for key words. Some combination of these strategies would be needed to pass the open book quiz.

**B** 1. D; 2. A; 3. B

### Allegory

**Practice,** p. 4

**A Sample answers:**
1. love; friendship; 2. old age;
3. wealth; good fortune; 4. happiness; good luck

**B** 1. B; 2. C; 3. B

**Assess,** p. 5

**A Sample answers:**
1. winter; 2. warmth; a sunny day; good weather;
3. hunger; 4. autumn

**B** 1. A; 2. D; 3. D

### Analogy

**Practice,** p. 6

1. The old woman and the old house are analogous. Both are the same age, both are still around though fragile with great age. The old woman remembers the past, and the house contains memories of the past.
2. The scene and a tennis match are analogous. The actors are analogous to players, and each time one says a line, it is like a tennis player sending the ball back across the net.
3. The street map and a snapshot are analogous. Both show a place at a given time—the snapshot with visual images, and the street map with references to once-important places that may no longer exist.
4. The car and the horse are analogous. Both are forms of transportation, both are old, and both can still move but do so slowly and reluctantly.

**Assess,** p. 7

1. The bits of advice and diamonds are analogous. Each is a single unit, valuable, "brilliant," and "rare," or hard to come by. The analogy emphasizes the great value of the advice.
2. A chess game and a battle are analogous. Both involve advancing through territory by means of strategy; both use a hierarchy of soldiers (living soldiers in one case, chess pieces in the other). The analogy emphasizes the patterns of battle.
3. Being a weightless astronaut in a space capsule and being a cork in a bowl of water are analogous. Both are very buoyant and tend to float around. The difference is that the astronaut has some control over movement, whereas the cork does not. The analogy emphasizes the buoyancy of a being in space.

**B** Students should develop an analogy of their own choosing into a short paragraph of at least three sentences. These sentences should discuss similarities between the two items. Students should write another sentence commenting on the point the analogy makes.

### Analyzing Text Features

**Practice,** p. 8
1. C; 2. B; 3. D; 4. A

**Assess,** p. 9
1. C; 2. B; 3. A; 4. C

© Pearson Education, Inc., publishing as Pearson Prentice Hall.

5. Robert Frost's poems are written in a regular meter—sometimes in rhyming iambic pentameter, and sometimes in blank verse.

## Analyzing the Usefulness and Credibility of Web Sources

### Practice, p. 10
1. B
2. A

### Assess, p. 11
1. C; 2. B; 3. C; 4. D

## Annals

### Practice, p. 12
**A** 2
**B** 1. —; 2. C-E; 3. C-E

### Assess, p. 13
**A** 1. F; 2. T; 3. T; 4. T; 5. F; 6. T; 7. F
**B** a, d, c, f, e, b
**C** 1. —; 2. C-E

## Anticipating Events

### Practice, p. 14
Sample answers:
1. (nowhere on earth/ Had he met a man whose hands were harder; His mind was flooded with fear); I think Beowulf will win the fight.
2. In the story of St. George and the Dragon, St. George kills the dragon. If *Beowulf* is similar to this story, Beowulf will kill Grendel.

### Assess, p. 15
Sample answers:
1. (It did not lead him to meditate upon his frailty as a creature of temperature, and about man's frailty in general); I think the man will get into trouble because it is so cold.
2. In "Contents of the Dead Man's Pocket," the character is stranded outside his apartment on the window ledge. He figures out a way to get back inside, though. If "To Build a Fire" is similar to this story, the man will figure out a way to save himself from the cold.
3. (for he would have to build a fire and dry out his footgear. . . .); I think he will build a fire.
4. (the fire was blotted out!); The man will start all over again and try to build another fire.
5. I think the man is in trouble. I feel suspense and worry about whether he will survive.

## Aphorisms

### Practice, p. 16
**A** 1. T; 2. F; 3. T; 4. T; 5. T
**B.** 1. —; 2. A; 3. A; 4. —; 5. A

### Assess, p. 17
**A** 1. A; 2. A; 3. —; 4. A; 5. A; 6. —; 7. —; 8. A; 9. —; 10. A
**B** 1. It is silly to spend all of your time wishing for things because that will not help you get them.
2. People who cannot admit they are wrong do not stop to check whether they are wrong. They do not ask for help. For these reasons, they are more often wrong than other people.
3. It is better not to interfere too much with what people are doing. If you leave them alone, they will do the right thing.

## Applying Background Information

### Practice, p. 18
Sample answers:
1. one, so far
2. at age 8, after reading many comic books
3. the fact that he became interested in time travel at 8 while reading comic books; the fact that he has explored the subject of time travel in many ways; the fact that his favorite period is Ancient Egypt
4. Barnett seems to have a sense of humor (the comment about the cats) and seems really passionate about his subject (his concentration on time travel); the fact that he writes about time travel suggests that he likes history and is imaginative and curious.

### Assess, p. 19
Sample answers:
1. She has always loved train travel, and her other writings have involved train travel.
2. about 15 years
3. She seems lively and friendly ("Call me Paige"), easygoing (her full answers to the questions), passionate about traveling (since she has written so much about it).
4. "Do you know what your next book is going to be about?" "What was the strangest/funniest/scariest/most wonderful thing that happened to you while you were riding trains?"

## Applying the Author's Biography

### Practice, p. 20
1. C

© Pearson Education, Inc., publishing as Pearson Prentice Hall.

**Assess,** p. 35

**A** 1. C; 2. B; 3. A; 4. B

**B** In their answers, students should clearly restate the author's main point: Following one's own ideas leads to happiness, whether or not those ideas are good ones. Students should then give relevant experiences of their own. Relevant experiences include these cases: following good advice and being happy; following bad advice and wishing one had applied one's own ideas instead; applying one's own ideas and being happy even though the outcome was not the best. Students should clearly relate their experiences to the writer's point. They should express their agreement or disagreement with the point on the basis of their examples.

### Characterization

**Practice,** p. 36

**A** 1. Direct; 2. Indirect; 3. Direct; 4. Indirect

**B** Sample answers:
   1. "Attention, everyone, I have arrived," said Olivia energetically; She handed her varsity cheerleading jacket to Alice, the freshman who followed her everywhere; designer shirt and expensive sneakers; She spun around so that others could admire her. Olivia is full of herself and likes to be the center of attention.

**Assess,** p. 37

**A** 1. Direct; 2. Direct; 3. Indirect; 4. Indirect; 5. Direct

**B** Sample answers:
   1. She knew a way around that problem, though. She would tell him she was worried about the test, too, and ask him to help her study; clearly labeled folders; quickly found the one in which she had filed her old math tests; Rachel is smart, organized, and neat. She is not just smart in math. She is smart about how she deals with her friends.
   2. When the coach said George had not made the varsity team, George did not say anything; George said no—he had too much homework. Later, though, his friends saw him walking down the side of the road, kicking stones; George keeps his feelings to himself. He is not a loner or a spiteful person, since he is nice to Phil. He is keeping his disappointment about not making the team bottled up inside, though.

### Characterization in Drama

**Practice,** p. 38

**A** 1. B; 2. B

**B** Sample answers:
   1. Henry is opinionated.

   2. Irene is stubborn and difficult.
   3. John wants the approval of others.

**Assess,** p. 39

**A** 1. F; 2. T; 3. T; 4. F; 5. F

**B** Sample answers:
   1. Warren is romantic.
   2. Brian is materialistic and ambitious.
   3. Tim is depressed.
   4. Barb is not concerned about others.
   5. Will is proud to be a father.

### Characters: Dynamic and Static

**Practice,** p. 40

   1. static; 2. static; 3. dynamic; 4. dynamic

**Assess,** p. 41

**A** 1. dynamic; 2. static; 3. static

**B** Sample answers:
   1. Dr. Bad finds a stray kitten. He is filled with pity. He adopts the kitten and spends millions of dollars to build a shelter for homeless animals.
   2. Eliana sees posters advertising auditions for her favorite play, *The Crucible*. She decides to try out for the production. Eliana is so engrossed in the character that she forgets to be nervous during her audition.

### Characters' Motives

**Practice,** p. 42

**A** 1. hope; 2. anger; 3. fear

**B** Sample answers:
   1. B; The tears in Vicki's eyes suggest that she feels bad for the dog.
   2. C; The fact that they keep trying despite their failures shows they are determined to come up with a solution.

**Assess,** p. 43

   1. C; 2. B; 3. A; 4. A

### Chinese Poetic Forms

**Practice,** p. 44

   1. T; 2. F; 3. F; 4. T; 5. F; 6. F; 7. F; 8. T

**Assess,** p. 45

   1. A; 2. B; 3. B; 4. B; 5. B; 6. A; 7. B

© Pearson Education, Inc., publishing as Pearson Prentice Hall.

## Chronological Order

### Practice, p. 46

**Sample answers:**

1. <u>All five children had squeezed into the back seat of their father's car.</u> (Also accept <u>Then, Anne's father had driven the whole family to a beach two hours away.</u>) This is described as a trip that Anne remembers taking during her childhood. This part of the story is written in the past perfect tense.

2. <u>As she drove south</u>; <u>Anne passed miles of empty beaches</u>; <u>Anne turned the car</u>; <u>parked it</u>; <u>walked inside.</u> These phrases tell of a time when Anne is old enough to drive on her own. They are not written in the past perfect tense, so they must come from a time later than events told in that tense.

### Assess, p. 47

**A** 1. C

2. **Sample answers:** <u>John could now laugh about this terrible moment</u>; <u>These days, John carefully recorded his appointments on a calendar.</u> The words "now" and "these days" signal to the reader that the action occurs in the present.

3. **Sample answers:** The transition phrase "John could now laugh" tells the reader that the action is moving from past to present.

**B** <u>cast her mind back</u>; <u>had felt</u>; <u>in time</u>; <u>had learned</u>; <u>Today</u>

1. She had brought her twin daughters home from the hospital.
2. She had felt tired and overwhelmed.
3. She had learned how to manage caring for the girls.
4. Sarah watched her children playing in the yard.
5. The children did not notice her watching.
6. Sarah could not imagine her life without them.

## Comparing and Contrasting Characters

### Practice, p. 48

**Sample answers:**

1. O'Malley: dresses well and looks like an executive

   Junior: wears casual clothing and dresses like "one of the guys"

2. O'Malley: has held many jobs; chats with employees

   Junior: only worked in the high-paying jobs; has a good education

3. O'Malley: hard-working; cares about appearance; knowledgeable; friendly

   Junior: educated; privileged

### Assess, p. 49

**Sample answers:**

**A** 1. background; Victoria and Kirsten are similar because they come from the same family; they both lived on a farm.

2. motives; Victoria and Kirsten have different goals. Victoria wants to be popular, while Kirsten wants to perform well academically.

3. fate: Victoria and Kirsten both end up happy, but Kirsten is happy because she gets what she wanted. Victoria is happy because she changes what she wants.

**B** 1. A. friendly; B. lonely
2. A. calm; B. restless

## Comparing and Contrasting Critical Reviews

### Practice, p. 50

1. The book is a novel, 628 pages long; it is a love story set in the Civil War.

2. Besides agreeing about factual matters such as the length and plot of the novel, the reviewers both agree that the book is long and that it opens well.

3. Reviewer #1 found the characters "paper-thin" and the story a "cliché" and "yawnful." Reviewer #2 found the characters "winning" and the story "gripping."

### Assess, p. 51

1. The rock concert took place at the Asher Auditorium and featured the rock band Wet Paint Drying. On the whole, the group did well.

2. Both reviewers seem to like the concert (though Reviewer #1 was much more positive). Both really liked the guitar solo in the first number.

3. Reviewer #1 seemed to love everything. This reviewer enjoyed the first number, with its "weird and wonderful" vocals. Reviewer #2 had a mixed opinion of the first number, calling the vocals "muddy" and lacking in energy. This reviewer was more reserved in praising the group.

4. Since both reviews were basically positive, it is likely that most students would find the concert appealing.

## Conflict

### Practice, p. 52

1. External; 2. Internal; 3. External; 4. Internal; 5. External; 6. External; 7. Internal

© Pearson Education, Inc., publishing as Pearson Prentice Hall.

5. Students should give specific reasons for their answers based on concrete details from the passage.

## Evaluating Characters' Decisions

### Practice, p. 74

Sample answers:

1. Rakesh's decisions make his father miserable. He can't eat what he wants.

2. Rakesh is a doctor, so he probably made the right decision. Still, he could let his father have a treat sometimes, just to make him happy.

3. Yes, he benefits because he has a son he can be proud of and who gives him medical advice. No, because his son is making his life miserable.

4. He made a good decision. Even if Rakesh is making him miserable now, the father did the best thing for his son.

### Assess, p. 75

1. C
2. B
3. Della's decision to sell her hair affects Jim as well. He also loves her hair. He will be disappointed when he finds out that she sold her hair because he bought combs for her to wear.
4. Some students may think that Jim and Della benefit from their decisions because they realize that their sacrifices for each other are a symbol of their love.
5. Some students may think that Jim and Della made good decisions because they cared more about their spouse than about themselves. Other students may say that they made bad decisions because they both ended up with nothing.

## Existentialism

### Practice, p. 76

Sample answer:

Mrs. Telford is on her own, seems isolated, and, at that moment, must deal with a choice with completely unknown consequences. Her decisions to give the young men a ride and to invite them to lunch at her home are completely independent, not based on any political or religious system or other code of conduct.

### Assess, p. 77

**A** Sample answers:

1. Henry is entirely on his own. He has been traveling apparently for the sake of travel itself, with no prior plan.

2. He makes his choices based on his immediate physical needs and emotional impulses. He is entirely free and makes no judgments based on any pre-existing set of principles.

**B** Sample answer:

If Henry had been obeying a standard code of behavior, he might feel that he needed to have some larger purpose, rather than simply traveling freely and randomly. He might not have been so willing to change his mind, as he does in the passage. At first, he thinks that he will just stop for the night and then move on the next day. Then, when he finds the hotel, he decides instead to spend more time there.

## Fables

### Practice, p. 78

1. the grasshopper and the ant; The grasshopper represents people who do not plan for the future and just spend their time enjoying themselves. The ant represents people who think ahead and don't sacrifice the future for today's pleasure.

2. The fable makes fun of the laziness and lack of foresight of the grasshopper.

3. **Sample answer:** Don't sacrifice the future for the present.

### Assess, p. 79

**A** 1. the sun and the wind; The sun represents age and experience; the wind, youth and physical strength.

2. The fable makes fun of the overconfidence of someone who thinks he knows everything but does not.

3. **Sample answer:** Knowledge is more powerful than physical strength.

**B** Students might describe a situation in which a physically strong bully is tricked by someone who is smarter. Or they might describe a situation in which someone gets into trouble because of inexperience and has to be rescued by someone with wider knowledge of the world.

## Folk Tales

### Practice, p. 80

1. A; 2. B; 3. D

### Assess, p. 81

1. D; 2. C; 3. B

## Follow Directions

### Practice, p. 82

1. Desk Lamp Diagram and Parts

© Pearson Education, Inc., publishing as Pearson Prentice Hall.

2. Desk Lamp Diagram and Parts
3. clockwise

## Assess, p. 83

1. Cordless Telephone Diagram and Parts
2. Cordless Telephone Installation Instructions
3. It will be easier to perform these steps if you also look at the diagram.

### Hyperbole and Understatement

## Practice, p. 84

1. F; 2. U; 3. H; 4. U; 5. H; 6. F

## Assess, p. 85

**A** 1. H; 2. F; 3. U; 4. F; 5. U; 6. H

**B** Sample answers:

1. Joanne is as unfriendly as a hive of angry bees.
2. As icicles formed on the shower door, Stefanie said, "It's a little chilly in here."
3. Because my father's car got stuck in the snow last night, no one should drive.
4. It's just pneumonia; I'll be fine.
5. Randy is funnier than a roomful of clowns.
6. I'm sure to get an A today because I'm wearing this shirt.

### Hypothesizing

## Practice, p. 86

1. Something is going to happen that night. The events of the night may be famous, so readers already know what is going to happen.
2. She is observant and has a good memory, especially if something has upset her.
3. She has a long-term fear or dislike of this man, based on the fact that he put her off the bus twelve years before, for some reason that she has not yet revealed

## Assess, p. 87

Sample answers:

1. We should not take Pangloss's ideas seriously. He is a ridiculous character and might be a fraud.
2. Pangloss seems to be simplemindedly optimistic, rather than realistic. Or he is a hypocrite who is flattering his master.
3. Pangloss is indeed simplemindedly optimistic. He actually seems to believe these ridiculous ideas.
4. Pangloss's belief that noses were made to wear spectacles and that spectacles exist because we have noses to wear them shows that he has almost no grasp on reality.

### Identifying With a Character

## Practice, p. 88

Sample answers:

1. **Basic situation:** One person keeps trying to do better than another. They are rivals. **My own experience:** I had two friends who were always trying to do better than each other. **How I would react:** I would be annoyed by the constant competition.
2. **Basic situation:** A person moves away and leaves a friend behind. **My own experience:** I moved when I was in second grade. I still keep in touch with my best friend from the time. **How I would react:** I would feel sad and lonely.

## Assess, p. 89

**A** Sample answers:

1. A new person arrives in a group and is nervous.
2. A person is relieved when a problem she is responsible for turns out all right.
3. Two partners have a fight about a decision one of them makes.

**B** Sample answers:

1. **My own experience:** When new students arrive at our school, they generally seem a little uncomfortable at first. Then, they adjust. **How I would react:** I would be nervous too.
2. **My own experience:** I wandered away in the mall when I was a kid. When they found me, my parents were angry and relieved. **How I would react:** I would feel relieved.
3. **My own experience:** I have a friend who is always doing stupid things. It makes me frustrated. **How I would react:** I would be angry.

### Imagery

## Practice, p. 90

**A** 1. A; 2. A

**B** Sample answer:

I see the unmoving rocks on the seashore, with the waves coming in and pulling back. I also see how the moving water spins the seaweed.

## Assess, p. 91

**A** 1. C; 2. C; 3. B

**B** Sample answers:

1. I see a young soldier lying in the grass asleep. His mouth is wide open, and there's no hat on his head.
2. I can hear violin music. It sounds as if the violins are crying because autumn has come again.

© Pearson Education, Inc., publishing as Pearson Prentice Hall.

3. I hear people selling vegetables calling out in the street for customers. I see a boat with a yellow sail getting closer to an island.

### Indian Fable

## Practice, p. 92
**A** 1. T; 2. F; 3. F; 4. F
**B** 1. B; 2. B; 3. A; 4. B

## Assess, p. 93
**A** 1. F; 2. F; 3. T; 4. F; 5. F
**B** 1. Not good, because the situation is not likely to produce a lesson about behavior.
2. Good, because the situation can serve as the basis for a lesson about the dangers of believing flattery.
3. Good, because the situation provides the basis for a lesson about how to act.

### Interpreting Imagery

## Practice, p. 94
**A** 1. C; 2. B; 3. A
**B** Sample answers:
1. loneliness, paranoia, fear
2. beginning of spring, joy, hope
3. sickness, old house, decay
4. love, happiness, contentment
5. terror, fright, being startled, panic

## Assess, p. 95
**A** 1. E; 2. D; 3. C; 4. A; 5. B
**B** Sample answers:
1. shyness, delicacy; 2. stirring action, pride;
3. nervous, eerie; 4. sadness, an ending;
5. peaceful, relaxed, happiness

### Irony

## Practice, p. 96
1. Dramatic; 2. Verbal; 3. No irony; 4. Dramatic;
5. Situational; 6. Dramatic

## Assess, p. 97
**A** 1. Dramatic; 2. No irony; 3. Situational;
4. Verbal
**B** 1. **What Amanda thinks:** She won the music scholarship. **What the audience knows:** She did not get the music scholarship.
2. **What Marcus thinks:** He has to buy a computer. **What the reader knows:** Marcus will be getting a computer as a gift.

### Japanese Poetic Forms

## Practice, p. 98
1. T; 2. T; 3. F; 4. F; 5. F; 6. T; 7. T; 8. T; 9. F; 10. T

## Assess, p. 99
**A** 1. B; 2. A; 3. D; 4. C
**B** Sample answers:
1. The poem has three lines with the right number of syllables: five, seven, and five. The poem has a *kigo*, the word *autumn*. The poem contains a contrast, which is emphasized in the last line.
2. The poem has five lines, as a tanka should. Like many tanka, the poem is about love and nature. However, the translation does not have the correct number of syllables in each line. For instance, the first line should have five syllables, but the translated line has six. The next line should have seven syllables, but the translated line has six.

### Journal

## Practice, p. 100
**A** Sample answers:
1. The writer describes the mood at campaign headquarters on the day before an election.
2. feeling the pressure; snapping at one another
3. Yes, because the entry relates events in a way that is more factual than personal.
**B** 1. T; 2. F; 3. T; 4. T

## Assess, p. 101
**A** 1. √; 2. —; 3. √; 4. √; 5. —; 6. √
**B** Sample answers:
1. Columbus is charmed by the beauty of nature.
2. *exquisite; delicious*
3. It was hard for soldiers to get muskets during the war.
4. Goss complains that is it difficult because the muskets are very heavy.

### Locating Information Using Maps and Atlases

## Practice, p. 102
**A** Sample answers:
1. They farm the land.
2. "Population"
3. a star in a circle

## Assess, p. 103
1. The Nile River provides fertile ground for farming in otherwise desert-like areas.

2. "Population"

3. a star in a circle

## Lyric Poetry

## Practice, p. 104

1. **Sample answer:** The main impression is the coziness of being inside when it is cold out.

2. **Sample answer:** The writer conveys the sadness of not being able to talk to someone she loves. She has the insight that she can show her love in a hug.

## Assess, p. 105

**A** 1. F; 2. T; 3. T

**B** 1. **Sample answer:** The main feeling is hope or courage. The speaker realizes life can be hard. Her insight is that we need to keep hope alive.

2. **Sample answer:** The speaker expresses longing. He wishes he were back in the past or back home.

3. **Sample answer:** The speaker expresses desire or longing. He wants his love to stand by him. His insight is that the world is an empty place without love.

## Magical Realism

## Practice, p. 106

**A** 1. B

2. the hidden strength of his heart popped the buttons on his shirt

**B** **Fantasy:** the giant's body; fish are blind; divers die of nostalgia

**Reality:** using an anchor as a weight

## Assess, p. 107

**A** 1. B; 2. C

**B** 1. he could have drawn fish out of the sea simply by calling their names; springs would have burst forth from among the rocks

2. **Sample answers:** magnificent man, widest doors, highest ceilings, strongest floor, happy wife.

## Making Generalizations

## Practice, p. 108

Sample answer:

3; Each person gets the wrong idea about the elephant because he touches only part of it. If they put their ideas together, they would get the right answer. For this reason, the poet says that they should have gone in together. The story shows that people need to put their ideas together and use logic to see the truth.

## Assess, p. 109

**A** **Sample answer:**
3; All the other statements are facts rather than generalizations. This statement makes a broad point about Rumi's work.

**B** **Sample answer:**
3; In his poems, Rumi is expressing his values. If you found a number of passages in which he says that spirituality is more valuable than book learning, you could assume that he believed this to be true.

**C** **Sample answer:**
2; The details of the poem seem to point to the idea that you have an intelligence already inside you and that you can rely on it. Rumi says that the idea expressed in number 1 is true, but it is not the generalization that he is trying to support. As for number 3, Rumi never says not to study.

## Metaphor

## Practice, p. 110

1. D; 2. D; 3. I; 4. E; 5. I; 6. E

## Assess, p. 111

**A** 1. F; 2. F; 3. F; 4. T

**B** 1. IE; 2. DE

**C** 1. (claws); (snarling and hissing); (raced down the hallway); (flaming mane).

2. C

## Modern Realistic Drama

## Practice, p. 112

Sample answers:

1. Not suitable; The subject is not from ordinary life.

2. Suitable; The subject involves everyday life and also an internal conflict.

3. Suitable; The subject involves a social issue and a possible internal conflict for Kayla.

## Assess, p. 113

**A** 1. C; 2. A; 3. B; 4. B

**B** 1. Suitable, since the situation suggests realistic conflict between characters in contemporary life.

2. Suitable, since the main character is pitted against the forces of the larger society.

3. Not suitable, since the situation involves larger-than-life, exotic, and legendary elements.

© Pearson Education, Inc., publishing as Pearson Prentice Hall.

## Modernism

**Practice,** p. 114

**A** 1. B; 2. A; 3. B

**B** 1. F; 2. F; 3. T; 4. F

**Assess,** p. 115

**A** 1. F; 2. T; 3. F; 4. T

**B** 1. A; 2. A; 3. B; 4. B; 5. A; 6. B

## Monologue

**Practice,** p. 116

   1. C; 2. B; 3. B

**Assess,** p. 117

**A** 1. Not suitable because the situation involves a telephone conversation.

   2. Suitable because the brother's practicing could form the basis for a monologue.

   3. Not suitable because the two participants are involved in a conversation.

**B** 1. B; 2. C

## Myth

**Practice,** p. 118

   1. B; 2. A; 3. D; 4. B

**Assess,** p. 119

   1. B; 2. B; 3. B; 4. C; 5. B

## Narrative Accounts

**Practice,** p. 120

**A.** 1. C; 2. D

**B** Sample answer:

The writer includes feelings and thoughts about the game. These include the following details: I thought the home team would fall apart before we even got started; We had never been defeated, so I thought it could never happen; I learned a lesson in humility.

**Assess,** p. 121

**A** 1. D; 2. C

**B** 1. The reader knows this is a first-person narrative account because the author writes in the first person and relates a story.

   2. The purpose of this account is to give an insider's perspective about an important discovery. <u>It was not until we enlarged the pictures and studied them that we realized what we had found.</u>

3. A historian or other scholar might want to read this account to better understand the thoughts, actions, and decisions that contributed to an important discovery.

4. The author says that their discovery was almost an accident; their original intention had been something entirely different. This is a detail someone who had not participated in the event would not have known or would have had to conduct research to learn.

## Narrative Poetry

**Practice,** p. 122

**A** 1. A; 2. C

**B** Sample answers:

1. (the waves); What Daedalus thinks: <u>cursed his talents</u>; What Daedalus does: <u>saw the wings on the waves</u>; <u>Buried the body in a tomb</u>

2. The myth explains how the land came to be named—for Icarus.

**Assess,** p. 123

**A** 1. C; 2. D; 3. A

**B** Sample answers:

1. (Samos, Juno's sacred island. / Delos and Paros toward the left, Lebinthus / Visible to the right, and another island, / Calymne, rich in honey.); (the vast heaven, / Nearer the sun); (the blue sea); (the dark water / Men call the Icarian now)

2. Thoughts: "And the boy / Thought *This is wonderful!*" Actions: "And left his father, / Soared higher, higher, drawn to the vast heaven"; "*Father!* he cried, and *Father!*"

3. The myth tells how the Icarian Sea came to be named.

## Novella

**Practice,** p. 124

1. a tiny little farm, Campi, the country

2. without seeking assistance from anyone, he patiently resigned himself to a life of poverty

3. Federigo managed his affairs more prudently, and lived with her in happiness to the end of his days.

4. D

**Assess,** p. 125

**A** 1. C; 2. A

**B** 1. hard-working, successful, proud, caring

2. Story A; Julia wants to sell her store, but she doesn't want to do something that will be bad for the town.

3. C

© Pearson Education, Inc., publishing as Pearson Prentice Hall.

## Paradox

### Practice, p. 126
**A** 1. P; 2. NP; 3. P

**B** Sample answers:

Idea 1: The student thinks that drawing the fish well means that he has to study it closely.

Idea 2: The student draws the fish well only when it is gone.

Truth or Lesson: When you really know something well, then it is inside you and you do not need reminders.

### Assess, p. 127
**A** 1. NP; 2. P; 3. P

**B** 1. C; 2. B; 3. A

**C** Sample answers:

Idea 1: The students are proud of their ideas and want to show off.

Idea 2: The wise man thinks that their showing off is foolish.

Truth or Lesson: Theories about the best way to live do not mean much if you are a fool. What matters is how you act.

## Parallelism

### Practice, p. 128
1. Parallelism; 2. No parallelism; 3. Parallelism; 4. Parallelism

### Assess, p. 129
Sample answers:

Examples of parallelism: we can not dedicate—we can not consecrate—we can not hallow; what we say here . . . what they did here; that from these honored dead we take increased devotion to that cause for which they gave the last full measure of devotion—that we here highly resolve that these dead shall not have died in vain—that this nation, under God, shall have a new birth of freedom—and that government of the people, by the people, for the people, shall not perish from the earth; of the people, by the people, for the people

Sample answer: Parallelism increases the effectiveness of the Gettysburg Address by helping Lincoln to emphasize the most important ideas. He uses parallelism to list points that seem to build up to a strong emotional climax. Lincoln's use of parallelism also helps create a rhythm to the speech that probably made people listen to it with more interest.

## Paraphrasing

### Practice, p. 130
**A** Sample answers:

1. desire; wish; 2. notice; observe; 3. brothers; 4. languages; 5. People have the same thoughts and feelings all over the world.

**B** Sample answer:

As I sit here alone with my thoughts and dreams, I imagine that there are other people just like me in foreign lands with the same thoughts and dreams, and I feel that they are my brothers.

### Assess, p. 131
**A** Sample answers:

1. echoing; 2. bird; 3. go down; 4. a grassy park or recreational area; 5. It lifts the spirits to play outside amid the beauties of nature.

**B** Sample answer:

The bright sun and singing birds make a joyous setting for playing outside until it gets dark and we get tired.

## Parody

### Practice, p. 132
Sample answers:

1. A; Louie was so mean that his own dog growled at him. He got his nickname because he liked to blow bubbles in his bathtub.

2. A; One look at her and my heart stopped. My socks bunched up, and my shoelaces untied themselves; She opened her mouth and reached in with her graceful, dainty hand to pull out a fat wad of chewing gum.

### Assess, p. 133
**A** 1. A; 2. B

**B** Sample answers:

1. Type of story being parodied: private-eye or gangster stories; Element parodied: a. plot; "We got you a contract to go on the new quiz show," said Louie. "Waddya say?"

2. Type of story being parodied: fantasy or science-fiction stories; Element parodied: b. theme; "Still, if you're about to be squashed like a bug, who cares if you break the rules?"

## Picturing the Action

### Practice, p. 134
1. knocking; champed

2. The picture is one of a ground thick with green ferns; the words indicate that the house is in the middle of a forest.

3. A bird flies out of a turret.

© Pearson Education, Inc., publishing as Pearson Prentice Hall.

4. A unnamed man, the Traveler, stops at a door covered with moonlight; he is at a house in the middle of the forest. He knocks and calls out, "Is there anybody there?" as his horse munches ferns on the forest floor. The only response is a bird flying out of a high window. The Traveler knocks again and repeats his words, "Is there anybody there?"

## Assess, p. 135

Sample answers:

**A** 1. He creates a picture of powerful wind battling rising waves of flood water.
2. He is saying that all other humans are dead. The phrase creates a picture of stillness, of all life stopped, and of humans blending into the earth.
3. The phrase is one of stillness and solidity, in contrast to the violent action of wind and water in the first sentence. There is a sense that you can see very far.
4. The speaker bows down and weeps. He creates a picture of himself with tears pouring down his face.

**B** The storm and flood rage for six days, battling each other in a terribly violent attack on the earth and mankind. On the seventh day, the storm stops and everything becomes terribly still. The speaker sees that the sea is flat and all human life has stopped. He bows down and weeps over the devastation he sees.

### Point of View

## Practice, p. 136

1. T-P; 2. F-P; 3. F-P; 4. T-P; 5. T-P

## Assess, p. 137

**A** 1. A; 2. B; 3. A; 4. B
**B** 1. First-person point of view
2. Students should state that readers do not know whether the narrator's view of Daniel is correct. In the first-person point of view readers only get information from the narrator; the information may not be correct.
3. Third-person point of view

### Political Poetry

## Practice, p. 138

1. a raisin in the sun, a sore, rotten meat, a syrupy sweet, a heavy load
2. A
3. Hughes is saying that society kept African Americans from fulfilling their dreams. He says that the effect was anger and frustration.

## Assess, p. 139

**A** Sample answers:
1. poetry written to express personal feelings about political events or situations
2. a war people do not support

**B** Sample answers:
1. B
2. He compares them to bees. He wants them to realize that, like worker bees in a hive, their labor benefits only the Queen (or, in their case, the King).
3. He thinks it is oppressive, greedy, and lazy. Words and phrases: tyrants, ungrateful drones, stingless drones.

### Reading Between the Lines

## Practice, p. 140

1. Portia means that a husband should share his secrets with his wife and that Brutus should trust her with his secret and share it with her.
2. David thinks the watch is too expensive and that John cannot afford to buy it as a present for his best friend.

## Assess, p. 141

1. Brutus says that he is dealing with an internal conflict.
2. Beth means that she thinks that Cathy is exaggerating the nature and extent of the injury to her thumb.
3. Bob means that Paul needs to think about how to approach the situation before rushing into it.

### Reading Drama

## Practice, p. 142

**A** 1. B; 2. A
**B** 1. SD; 2. SD; 3. —; 4. SD; 5. SD

## Assess, p. 143

Sample answers:
1. The scene takes place in a cave.
2. A strange blue light fills the stage.
3. The pirates are sleeping on the right.
4. The Queen of the Pirates is sleeping on the bed.
5. Squidge waves his arms around while he yells.
6. Squidge is still asleep and dreaming, and he is acting out his dream.
7. Inkle puts his hand over Squidge's mouth to shut him up.
8. The Queen is very angry that Squidge woke her up.

© Pearson Education, Inc., publishing as Pearson Prentice Hall.

## Reading in Sentences

**A** 1. C; 2. B; 3. A
**B** 1. four; 2. two; 3. I should pause slightly for the comma.

**Assess, p. 145**
**A** 1. C; 2. A; 3. B
**B** 1. six
   2. two
   3. 3 and 6
   4. I learn that people used to tell the speaker that if she dug a hole deep enough, she would reach China.

## Reading Stanzas as Units of Meaning

**Practice, p. 146**
   1. The letter writer says she was 14 years old when she married her husband. As a young bride, she scowled and avoided her husband.
   2. The letter writer says that at the age of 15 she stopped being disagreeable and began to respond to her husband. She no longer avoided him. By then she wanted to be buried with her husband after their deaths.
   3. The River Merchant's Wife seems to have fallen in love with her husband after being married to him for a year. Also, she also may be more mature at 15 than at 14. She is changing from a moody girl into a loving woman.

**Assess, p. 147**
**A** 1. The speaker says he is in the middle of his life—probably middle-aged. He feels that he is lost in a dark wood.
   2. The speaker describes the dark wood where he is lost. It is a wilderness, difficult to walk through, dreary, and terrifying.
   3. The speaker says that this wood is almost as bitter as death itself. However, since his experience came to something good, he feels he can retell it to the reader. The purpose of the next stanzas is likely to be to tell of the speaker's difficult journey through the forest.
**B** The overall point of the stanzas is to set up the situation for the important story that the speaker will tell, a story that turned out well. The implication is that the speaker will tell how he went from being lost at the beginning to being saved or finding his way.

## Recognizing Author's Bias

**Practice, p. 148**
**A** Sample answers:
   1. P; calm presence helped restore order
   2. N; tyrannical, unfortunate, unjust
   3. N; a scab that won't heal

**B** Sample answers:
   1. Peers: less refined; Tracie: most remarkable, superior, most flattering, fine, perfectly complement. The words used to describe Tracie's peers have negative associations. The words used to describe Tracie and her wardrobe have positive associations.
   2. Tracie prefers designer clothing and accessories.
   3. The author appears to approve of an upper-class lifestyle and expensive goods and to have a bias against other tastes and lifestyles.

**Assess, p. 149**
**A** Sample answers:
   1. It can help you understand why the author stresses certain facts or makes certain statements.
   2. Clues to an author's bias include phrases or assertions with negative or positive associations.
**B** 1. The author thinks that people who fuss too much about avoiding junk food and eating healthy foods are rude and ridiculous.
   2. Everyone but Val munched happily away; As usual; make a point of being fussy; prim lecturing; spoiling others' good time

## Recognizing Dramatic Tension

**Practice, p. 150**
**A** 1. C; 2. A
**B** Students should circle item 2. In their explanations, they should point out that this plot scenario would probably produce the most conflict and therefore the most dramatic tension.

**Assess, p. 151**
**A** 1. C; 2. B; 3. C; 4. A
**B** Students should circle item 2. In their explanations, they should point out that this plot scenario would probably produce the most conflict and therefore the most dramatic tension.

## Relating to Your Own Experiences

**Practice, p. 152**
Sample answers:
   1. experiences with puzzles or mysteries; frightening experiences

© Pearson Education, Inc., publishing as Pearson Prentice Hall.

2. experiences with challenges or wanting to be accepted by older adolescents

3. experiences with quarrels or conflict; experiences with ironic surprises

## Assess, p. 153

Sample answers:

1. experiences with grandparents or older people; reluctance to impose on others

2. conflicts with parents; evaluation of one's own ability or talents; challenges under pressure

3. cooperation and competition in friendships

### Reread for Clarification

## Practice, p. 154

**A** 1. A few years ago, Pam risked her own life and rescued Martha from a sinking boat.

2. Pam sent Martha the postcard to thank her for buying her the airline ticket.

**B** 1. Senator Michael Harris

2. Mark was the son of the influential, powerful, and famous Senator Michael Harris.

## Assess, p. 155

**A** 1. Mary associates the scent of jasmine with the joy of her father coming home.

2. Mary didn't notice her father immediately because she was busy playing in the backyard.

**B** 1. Linda pulls over to the side of the road because she witnessed a terrible car accident and wanted to help.

2. Linda has thirty years of experience as an emergency room nurse.

### Responding

## Practice, p. 156

Sample answers:

1. Both terms sound funny but interesting. *Gab* is very slangy and creates the sound of mindless chatter. *Barbaric yawp* is great— sounds squawky and uncivilized.

2. It is spooky in a good way.

3. Some students may be struck by the image of the spotted hawk scolding the poet. They may like the odd-sounding words Whitman uses and his very personal, direct way of talking to the reader, always addressing the reader as "you."

## Assess, p. 157

**A** Sample answers:

1. The image of the two ambulances stuck in the mud is weirdly funny, especially with the drivers yelling at each other, "tossing" the

blame back and forth like a beanbag. But there is also a feeling of helplessness, even tragedy, since the ambulances cannot move and the groaning people inside need help desperately.

2. It made me sad to see the dying soldier but I didn't want the lieutenant to ruin the man's peace by telling him that he was dying. Or maybe the man already knew?

3. The beginning of the passage feels noisy and confused, a little funny, and very frustrating, when you think of all the men who need help and the fact that the drivers are only concerned with blaming each other. The sight of all those bandaged men coming and going made me feel pity and concern, as did the image of the dying soldier. In that final image, I felt a kind of acceptance of the inevitable.

**B** Sample answer:

Dear Mr. Crane, This passage describing the lieutenant's view of the hospital tents, the stuck ambulances, quarreling drivers, pathetic wounded men, and the dying soldier was funny yet sad. It presented many different views of war in a very short space.

### Romanticism

## Practice, p. 158

1. B; 2. A; 3. C

## Assess, p. 159

**A** 1. T; 2. F; 3. T; 4. T

**B** 1. C; 2. A; 3. C

### Satire

## Practice, p. 160

1. pet owners

2. it mortified [embarrassed] him to be tied up

## Assess, p. 161

**A** 1. C; 2. B; 3. B

**B** 1. wars over beliefs

2. What better reason to fight than to decide how to break an egg!

### Setting

## Practice, p. 162

**A** 1. B; 2. C; 3. B

**B** 1. D; 2. C; 3. B; 4. A

## Assess, p. 163

**A** 1. A; 2. C

**B** 1. A; 2. C; 3. B

**C** 1. B; 2. A; 3. C

© Pearson Education, Inc., publishing as Pearson Prentice Hall.

## Setting a Purpose for Reading

**Practice,** p. 164
1. D; 2. C

**Assess,** p. 165

**A** 1. B; 2. C

**B** Sample answers:
to find out the history of the castle; to find out what visitors can see at the castle; to find out who lived in the castle

### Sonnet

**Practice,** p. 166
1. Group 1: free, see, me, furiously;
   Group 2: molest, west, protest, breast;
   Rhyme scheme: *abba abba*
2. The speaker describes the past.
3. The speaker still loves and longs for Laura.

**Assess,** p. 167

**A** 1. (despair), (fair), (air); Spring, prospering, thing; The rhyme scheme used is *abab abab*.
2. Spring has arrived, and it has brought love with it everywhere. [Love is in all the water, earth and air, /And love possesses every living thing.]

**B** 1. (sojourn), (burn); land, sand; The sestet rhyme scheme used is *cdcdcd*.
2. Even though spring has arrived, the speaker is sad because his love is gone. Therefore, he is unable to enjoy the beauty and love that spring brings with it. [But to me only heavy sighs return /For her who carried in her little hand /My heart's key to her heavenly sojourn.]; [The beasts still prowl on the ungreening sand.]
3. The sestet reveals the speaker's sorrow despite the joy of spring described in the octave.

### Speaker

**Practice,** p. 168
1. Writer; **Sample answers:** tough; proud of her mother
2. Fictional Character; **Sample answers:** lonely; troubled; shy

**Assess,** p. 169

**A** 1. T; 2. F; 3. T; 4. T

**B** Sample answer: The speaker is the writer himself. You can tell that he has a sense of humor about himself. He is not angry that people hated him. He realizes that they hated him because he was important.

**C** Sample answer: The speaker is a stream or a river. I can tell because the speaker says that he makes the "sunbeam dance" and that he "joins" the river.

### Speech

**Practice,** p. 170

**A** 1. T; 2. F; 3. T; 4. F; 5. T

**B** 1. B; 2. B; 3. A

**Assess,** p. 171

**A** 1. C; 2. D; 3. A; 4. B

**B** 1. A; 2. B; 3. C

### Summarizing

**Practice,** p. 172
1. C; 2. A; 3. C

**Assess,** p. 173

**A** 1. B; 2. D

**B** 1. B
2. Students' summaries should include the main ideas and key information: The Willow Grove botanical garden has rare purple roses that are very valuable, as well as many other varieties of roses. The botanical garden often gives bouquets of roses to the hospital, and it donates one purple rose bush to the auction every year.

### Surrealism

**Practice,** p. 174
1. The moon mends chipped plates, darns wedding sheets, and sorts old photographs. These activities are not logical, since the moon does not come down to Earth to do such work.
2. The winds blew into the woman's bureau drawers, bargained between her shutters, and swept "dream-crumbs" from the woman's sleeping mouth into town. This portrayal is dreamlike because these images are both vivid and illogical.
3. The passage is surrealistic because it uses concrete detail to combine ideas that would not logically go together; it is also vivid and dreamlike.

**Assess,** p. 175

**A** 1. A little girl is blowing bubbles that contain things: violets, mice, another girl blowing bubbles. Sometimes the bubbles break and their contents land on other objects, such as traffic lights. The girl keeps on blowing bubbles.

© Pearson Education, Inc., publishing as Pearson Prentice Hall.

7. looked at briefly and without focused attention
8. looked at carefully
9. looked at angrily

## Connotations: Words for Crowds

### Practice, p. 196

**A** 1. negative; 2. negative; 3. positive; 4. negative

**B** 1. pack; 2. swarm; 3. flock

### Assess, p. 197

**A** Sample answers:
1. masses; 2. flock; 3. Hordes; 4. mob;
5. Swarms; 6. Throngs; 7. Herds; 8. packs

**B** Sample answer:
Throngs of happy shoppers filled the mall, looking for holiday presents. Hordes of greedy shoppers raided the mall, looking for holiday presents. My first sentence suggests that the shoppers are happy and that their activity is peaceful. My second sentence suggests that they are pushy and greedy and that their activity is violent or at least unpleasant.

## Echoic Words

### Practice, p. 198

**A** Sample answers:
1. the sound of an owl
2. the sound of a car coming to a sudden stop
3. the sound of a small animal running through leaves
4. the sound of a twig breaking
5. the sound of a chicken or a rooster
6. the sound of a collision

**B** 1. barn; 2. drain; 3. pots

### Assess, p. 199

**A** 1. crunch; 2. click; 3. buzz; 4. pop; 5. blat;
6. murmur; 7. crinkle; 8. thump

**B** 1. whack; 2. creaking; 3. gulp; 4. roared

## Forms of *reciprocity*; Related Words: *awe*

### Practice, p. 200

**A** 1. reciprocal; 2. reciprocate

**B** 1. awfully; 2. awful

### Assess, p. 201

**A** 1. F; 2. E; 3. A; 4. D; 5. C; 6. B

**B** Sample answers:
1. No. You have not acted mutually if you do not repay your brother.
2. Yes. You are exchanging mutual services.

3. Yes. The Grand Canyon fills you with wonder and fear, so it is an awful sight.
4. No. If you laugh a little and then forget what the movie is about, it did not fill you with wonder and fear.

## Greek Prefix *hypo-*; Latin Prefix *re-*

### Practice, p. 202

**A** 1. hypotension; 2. hypodermic; 3. hypothermia;
4. hypoglycemia

**B** 1. retrieve; 2. resurface; 3. reload; 4. reemploy;
5. repel; 6. repeat

### Assess, p. 203

**A** 1. hypogastrium; 2. hypoallergenic;
3. hypokinesis; 4. hypoactive

**B** 1. reflect; 2. repeal; 3. resonate; 4. retrieve

**C** Sample answers:
1. **reflect:** to bend back; to send light back
2. **repeal:** to call back; to undo
3. **retrieve:** to find again; to bring back
4. **resonate:** to sound again; to echo

## Greek Word Parts *-logy* and *-path-*

### Practice, p. 204

**A** 1. ornithology; 2. anthropology; 3. geology;
4. biology

**B** 1. pathology; 2. apathy; 3. sympathy;
4. pathogen; 5. osteopath

### Assess, p. 205

**A** 1. A; 2. B; 3. B; 4. A; 5. A

**B** Sample answers:
1. doctor: A pathologist examined the blood sample.
2. uncaring: Sidney seemed apathetic about the good news.
3. virus: Tests identified the pathogen that was causing Hal's illness.
4. understanding: My sister is extremely empathic and can tell when I am feeling bad.
5. study of disease: Mark is going to specialize in the pathology of diabetes.

## Latin Prefixes *ab-* and *sub-*

### Practice, p. 206

**A** 1. A; 2. A; 3. A; 4. B; 5. A; 6. B

**B** 1. submerged; 2. abducted; 3. subterranean;
4. subsonic; 5. abnormal; 6. abstract

### Assess, p. 207

**A** 1. E; 2. A; 3. B; 4. C; 5. D

© Pearson Education, Inc., publishing as Pearson Prentice Hall.

**B** 1. subnormal; 2. subterranean; 3. subtitle;
4. subtract; 5. abnormal; 6. absent;
7. absorb; 8. abjure

## Latin Prefixes *ante-/anti-* and *en-*

### Practice, p. 208

**A** 1. antipasto; Antipasto is an appetizer that comes before the main meal.
2. antechamber; An antechamber is an outer room that leads to another room.
3. antebellum; *Antebellum* means "before war."

**B** 1. put into code
2. put into someone's trust or care; give to someone to watch over
3. make into a tangle

### Assess, p. 209

**A** Sample answers:
1. No; The prefix *anti-* means "before," so you are not remembering after the event.
2. Yes; The prefix *ante-* means "before," so the Golden Age of Greece must come before the Roman Empire.
3. No; The prefix *ante-* means "before," so antipasto probably comes before a meal, not after it, as a dessert does.
4. Yes; The prefix *ante-* means "before," so a book about antebellum life probably talks about life before the Civil War.

**B** Sample answers:
1. Yes; The prefix *en-* can mean "put into," so if you encourage someone you are putting courage in him or her.
2. No; The prefix *en-* can mean "put into," so if you enrage someone you are putting rage into him or her.
3. Yes; The prefix *en-* can mean "put into," so if you entomb a body, you put it in a tomb.
4. No; The prefix *en-* can mean "cause to be," so if you enable someone to drive home, you make him or her able to drive.

## Latin Prefixes *con-/com-*, *ex-*, and *im-/in-*

### Practice, p. 210

**A** 1. C; 2. A.; 3. B
**B** 1. exclude; 2. exclaim; 3. extract
**C** 1. Yes; 2. Yes; 3. No

### Assess, p. 211

Sample answers:
**A** 1. jeans; *Informal* means "*not* formal."
2. a talk between friends: The prefix *con-* means "with," not "alone."
3. reveal it; The prefix *ex-* means "out."

**B** 1. convention; 2. excel; 3. incomplete;
4. impatient; 5. immortal, 6. exhale

## Latin Prefixes *mal-* and *dis-*

### Practice, p. 212

**A** 1. garbage; *Malodorous* means "having a bad odor."
2. a twisted tree; *Malformed* means "formed badly."
3. spiteful; *Malicious* means "having an evil temper."
4. junk food; *Malnutrition* means "poor nutrition."

**B** 1. disentangle; 2. discontinue; 3. disbelieve;
4. dislocate; 5. dishonest

### Assess, p. 213

**A** 1. malignant; 2. malaria; 3. maltreat;
4. malpractice; 5. malfunction; 6. malice
**B** 1. dissolve; 2. disclose; 3. disappear;
4. disagree; 5. disloyal; 6. displease

## Latin Roots *-firm-*, *-tort-*, *-voc-/-vok-*

### Practice, p. 214

**A** Sample answers:
1. Root: -firm-; Meaning: strengthen; strong; Sample definition: a strong yes
2. Root: -tort-; Meaning: twist; Sample definition: twisted
3. Root: -voc-; Meaning: speak; voice; call; Sample definition: person who uses her voice; singer

**B** 1. F; 2. T; 3. F; 4. T

### Assess, p. 215

**A** 1. C; 2. B; 3. A
**B** 1. A; 2. D; 3. B; 4. C
**C** 1. vocal; 2. tortuous; 3. confirmed; 4. invoked

## Latin Roots *-naviga-*, *-temp-*, and *-ject-*

### Practice, p. 216

**A** 1. inject; 2. tempo; 3. navigated
**B** 1. B; 2. A; 3. D; 4. C

### Assess, p. 217

**A** 1. A; 2. C; 3. B
**B** 1. F; 2. T; 3. T; 4. T
**C** 1. A; 2. B; 3. C; 4. C

© Pearson Education, Inc., publishing as Pearson Prentice Hall.

## Latin Roots -pel-, -vert-, and -trem-; Anglo-Saxon Root -stead-

### Practice, p. 218
**A** 1. B; 2. A; 3. D; 4. C
**B** 1. instead; 2. divert; 3. tremble; 4. propel

### Assess, p. 219
**A** 1. D; 2. B; 3. C; 4. A
**B** 1. No; 2. Yes; 3. Yes; 4. No
**C** 1. compelled; 2. tremors; 3. diversions; 4. vertigo; 5. homestead

## Latin Roots -port-, -stup-, and -patr-/-pater-

### Practice, p. 220
**A** 1. Root: -stup-; Meaning: stunned; amazed
　　2. Root: -port-; Meaning: carry; move
　　3. Root: -pater-; Meaning: father
**B** 1. C; 2. A; 3. B; 4. A

### Assess, p. 221
**A** 1. *transport*; 2. *portable*; 3. *patriot*; 4. *stupor*
**B** 1. A; 2. A; 3. C; 4. B

## Latin Roots -sacr-, -lustr-, and -cred-

### Practice, p. 222
**A** 1. Root: -sacr-; Meaning: holy
　　2. Root: -lustr-; Meaning: light; shine
　　3. Root: -cred-; Meaning: believe
**B** 1. A; 2. C; 3. A; 4. B

### Assess, p. 223
**A** 1. B; 2. A; 3. C
**B** 1. A; 2. C; 3. D; 4. B
**C** 1. *luster*; 2. *credible*; 3. *sacrosanct*; 4. *incredulous*

## Latin Suffixes -ence, -ity, -ment, and -tion

### Practice, p. 224
**A** 1. reality; 2. insistence; 3. achievement; 4. illumination
**B** 1. C; 2. D; 3. B; 4. A

### Assess, p. 225
**A** 1. B; 2. D; 3. A; 4. C
**B** Sample answers:
　　1. From *prefer.* An instance of wanting one thing more than another.
　　2. From *narrate.* An act of telling a story.

3. From *actual.* An instance of being real.
4. From *employ.* The state of having a job.

**C** Sample answer:
The fiddler owed his great <u>eminence</u> to his amazing <u>capability</u> with the bow. When he let loose on an old-time tune, he filled his audience with <u>elation</u>. His playing was an <u>adornment</u> to any song.

## Legal Terminology: Latin Roots -domin-, -jur-, and Others

### Practice, p. 226
**A** 1. Root: -sec-; Meaning: follow; pursue
　　2. Root: -domin-; Meaning: rule
　　3. Root: -dict-; Meaning: state; say
　　4. Root: -jur-; Meaning: law
**B** 1. C; 2. B; 3. D; 4. A

### Assess, p. 227
**A** 1. Root: -dict-; Meaning: state; say
　　2. Root: -domin-; Meaning: rule
　　3. Root: -sec-; Meaning: follow; pursue
　　4. Root: -jur-; Meaning: law
**B** 1. D; 2. A; 3. C; 4. B
**C** 1. indicted; 2. prosecutor; 3. dominions; 4. juror

## Prefixes eu-, pro-, and mono-

### Practice, p. 228
**A** 1. B; 2. A; 3. C
**B** 1. promote; 2. produce; 3. propel
**C** 1. bored; A monotone is a speaking tone that never changes.
　　2. No. It has one pair of wings.

### Assess, p. 229
**A** 1. eulogize; 2. proceed; 3. projectile; 4. monocle
**B** 1. T; *Pro-* means "forward." A promotion is a move forward or upward for an employee.
　　2. F; *Eu-* means "good." Eupepsia means "healthy" or "good digestion."
　　3. T; *Mono-* means "one." A monolith is one stone that is large.
**C** 1. B; 2. D; 3. A; 4. C

## Related Words: glaze and glimmering; prime

### Practice, p. 230
1. A; 2. A; 3. C; 4. C; 5. B; 6. C

### Assess, p. 231
**A** 1. T; 2. T; 3. F
**B** 1. F; 2. F; 3. T
**C** 1. primary; 2. primacy; 3. glimmering; 4. prime; 5. glazier; 6. glint

© Pearson Education, Inc., publishing as Pearson Prentice Hall.

## Words Related to *vulgar* and *languish*

### Practice, p. 232

**A** 1. vulgar; 2. divulge; 3. vulgarize; 4. vulgarity

**B** 1. languish; 2. languid; 3. languishing;
4. languor

### Assess, p. 233

**A** 1. A; 2. B; 3. B

**B** 1. B; 2. D; 3. A; 4. C

**C** 1. languid; 2. languishing; 3. languor;
4. languish

# GRAMMAR SKILLS

## Absolute Phrases

### Practice, p. 234

**A** 1. We stayed inside watching DVDs, (the night being rainy and cold.)

2. (The chocolate cake baked,) Mrs. Patruni turned to the decorations.

3. The refugees can return from the mountains, (the war finally ending.)

4. The judges went home, (the prizes having been awarded.)

5. (The coach singing their praises,) the athletes felt proud.

**B** Sample answers:

1. The paint having dried, we could hang the pictures.

2. The holes being dug, we planted the bushes.

3. We had to spend hours at the library, the project still not done.

### Assess, p. 235

**A** 1. (The alarm set,) I turned off the light and went to sleep.

2. Sandra Cisneros began her second book, (the first one having been published,)

3. (The ice finally frozen solid,) we grabbed our skates and headed for the pond.

4. The plane took off, (the pilot having been given the all-clear.)

5. (The anthem being sung,) the game began.

6. Ali was quick to go to the store, (DVD recorders being sold for half price.)

7. (The air conditioner broken,) the hotel provided fans for the guests.

8. (The autumn air smelling crisp and fresh,) Ben and Maggie went for a walk.

**B** Sample answers:

1. The crime having been solved, the detectives were satisfied.

2. We decided to row to shore, the winds getting stronger.

3. We headed for the lake, the gas tank filled.

4. The cast having rehearsed, opening night was a success.

## Action and Linking Verbs

### Practice, p. 236

**A** 1. grows; 2. prefer; 3. eats; 4. believe

**B** 1. are; 2. taste; 3. seem; 4. feel

**C** 1. A, looked (up); 2. L, looked; 3. A, smell;
4. L, smell

### Assess, p. 237

**A** 1. appreciate; 2. need; 3. grow; 4. look (for);
5. understand

**B** 1. are; arrow from *popular* to *fundraisers*

2. seem; arrow from *happy* to *viewers*

3. will be; arrow from *help* to *donation*

4. feel; arrow from *good* to *people*

**C** 1. A, collected; 2. L, grew; 3. A, worried;
4. L, remained; 5. A, offered; 6. L, became

## Adjectival Modifiers

### Practice, p. 238

**A** 1. cl.; It was the (letters) that the soldiers appreciated most.

2. part.; After working hard all day, (we) were happy to relax.

3. inf.; The (time) to end the debate is now.

4. cl.; Fans cheered for the (team) that won the championship.

5. part.; (Rain) falling from the sky beat upon the rooftops.

6. prep.; The (decorations) in the window made a lovely display.

7. inf.; The new mayor was a (politician) to admire.

8. part.; The (shop) around the corner sells newspapers and candy.

**B** Sample answers:

1. The kids swimming in the lake were getting cold.

2. The camera that the customer ordered was out of stock.

3. We practiced soccer in the park across the street.

### Assess, p. 239

**A** 1. It is the bad (weather) that kept us at home.

2. Saying their last goodbyes, the (friends) parted.

3. The old people sat on (benches) along the boardwalk.

4. Trail (mix) to give you energy should always be in your backpack.

© Pearson Education, Inc., publishing as Pearson Prentice Hall.

5. The (road) that we take runs next to the river.

6. Picnickers were amazed at the (fireworks) exploding in the sky.

7. It was a (day) to remember.

8. You will find a (treasure) buried under that rock.

9. Badly burned, (Max) determined never to forget his sunscreen again.

10. She had a time-saving (plan) to order gifts online.

**B** Sample answers:

1. It is a new CD that Kyle is listening to for the first time.

2. Ann received a letter from her best friend.

3. Working out every day, the team became strong.

4. It was my father's decision to repaint the walls.

### Adjective Clauses

## Practice, p. 240

**A** 1. that you mentioned (book)

2. who should be ashamed (they)

3. which is beautiful (capital)

4. that she prefers (style)

5. whom you questioned (man)

**B** 1. who; 2. where; 3. when; 4. who; 5. where

## Assess, p. 241

**A** 1. C; 2. A; 3. D

**B** 1. that he wanted (map)

2. whom you wanted to see (woman)

3. whose car is outside (man)

4. which was on sale (jacket)

5. who is coming over (woman)

**C** 1. who; 2. that; 3. where; 4. when; 5. that

### Adverb Clauses

## Practice, p. 242

**A** 1. Pete opened his back door because he heard a cat crying.

2. Before Pete could blink, the cat was in the kitchen.

3. The cat purred gratefully when Pete offered it some leftovers.

4. Pete was able to find the cat's owner when he put an ad in the newspaper.

**B** Sample answers:

1. Before we left on vacation, we took the dogs to the kennel.

2. If you can make the trip, you will enjoy the scenery.

3. After she finished her homework, Cathy played basketball.

4. I hurried home because I was hungry.

## Assess, p. 243

**A** 1. Dana awakened before the winter sun rose.

2. She skated where her coach had told her.

3. She practiced daily because she wanted to be champion.

4. Before he left, Tom closed and locked the window.

5. When the clock struck six, Carrie started home for dinner.

6. My sister had long hair when she was in college.

7. Unless I call you, I will take the bus from the station.

8. She was late because the train was delayed.

9. A storm developed after we reached the turnpike.

10. While we're in Virginia, we should visit Williamsburg.

**B** Sample answers:

1. Because Bob was late to the show, he missed part of the first act.

2. After they picked two bushels of blueberries, they fell asleep.

3. We can begin the conference since all the participants have arrived.

4. She developed laryngitis whenever she caught a cold.

5. Although we played brilliantly, we lost the game.

### Adverb Phrases (Sentence Beginnings)

## Practice, p. 244

1. over our house, (flew)

2. For many years, (practiced)

3. about the bad weather, (Concerned)

4. because of favorable tail winds, (soon)

5. in the chess tournament, (competed); with her performance, (happy)

## Assess, p. 245

**A** 1. For two long hours

2. by the large crowd

3. During the student council meeting

4. due to a mechanical problem

5. across the open field

**B** 1. By midmorning, Dennis had finished polishing the silverware.

2. After a long, strenuous hike, a hearty meal suits me well.

3. From the darkened doorway, a small figure slowly emerged.

4. Up the tree trunk scampered two playful chipmunks.

5. Before the wedding, the bride had a long talk with her mother.

## Agreement and the Indefinite Pronouns *each* and *no one*

### Practice, p. 246
**A** 1. uses; 2. practices; 3. writes; 4. has;
   5. was created
**B** 1. his or her; 2. him or her; 3. his;
   4. his or her; 5. her

### Assess, p. 247
**A** 1. seems; 2. his or her; 3. eats;
   4. his or her; 5. it
**B** 1. No one in our class was ever late unless he
   or she had a good reason.
   2. Correct
   3. Correct
   4. Each of the job applicants left his or her
   résumé with the office manager.
   5. Luckily, each of us has brought enough
   money for the movie and a snack.

## Agreement in Inverted Sentences

### Practice, p. 248
**A** 1. lies; 2. are; 3. runs; 4. is; 5. are
**B** 1. sit; 2. were; 3. come; 4. are; 5. is

### Assess, p. 249
**A** 1. were; 2. were; 3. are; 4. are; 5. are; 6. were;
   7. have; 8. were
**B** 1. are; 2. are; 3. were; 4. is; 5. were;
   6. was; 7. were

## Appositives and Appositive Phrases

### Practice, p. 250
**A** 1. Servette, <u>who worked at the corner candy
   store</u>, always gave samples. arrow to *Servette*
   2. Mr. Chang, <u>the math teacher</u>, was my
   homeroom teacher for the year. arrow to *Mr.
   Chang*
   3. James K. Polk, <u>our eleventh president,</u> was
   born in North Carolina. arrow to *James K. Polk*
   4. Ms. Steffa, <u>the school principal</u>, canceled
   sports activities due to the storm. arrow to
   *Ms. Steffa*
   5. Winnie the Pooh, <u>a fictitious character</u>, was a
   friend of Christopher Robin. arrow to *Winnie
   the Pooh*
   6. Mollie and Max, <u>golden retrievers</u>, were the
   winners of the dog show. arrow to *Mollie and
   Max*
   7. The Racing Rocket, <u>a new thriller roller
   coaster</u>, is now open at the park. arrow to
   *The Racing Rocket*
**B** 1. Monica Gonzales's painting, an oil and batik,
   greatly impressed Vincent Goff.

2. The aurora borealis, sometimes called the
   northern lights, appears at night in northern
   latitudes.

### Assess, p. 251
**A** 1. (Norman Rockwell), <u>a twentieth-century
   American painter</u>, illustrated many covers of
   *The Saturday Evening Post.*
   2. A large black (cloud), <u>a sign of a
   thunderstorm,</u> appeared in the sky.
   3. (William Shakespeare), <u>a playwright and poet,</u>
   wrote during the fourteenth and fifteenth
   centuries.
   4. (Appomattox Court House), <u>a National
   Historical Park</u>, is where Robert E. Lee
   surrendered to Ulysses S. Grant.
   5. (Pete), <u>my brother's friend</u>, makes the best
   popcorn over a campfire.
**B** Sample answers:
   1. The dusty piece of paper, a treasure map,
   was hidden inside a chest.
   2. Checkers, a popular game, is easy to play
   once you know the rules.
   3. Larry, my best friend, was given the lead in
   the school play.
   4. David Beckham, an inspiration to all soccer
   players, should write a book about his
   experiences.
   5. *Beloved*, an award-winning novel, was written
   by Toni Morrison.

## Colons

### Practice, p. 252
**A** 1. Danger: This water is polluted.
   2. Four states border Mexico: California,
   Arizona, New Mexico, and Texas.
   3. The box contained the following items: rocks,
   marbles, shoes, and rope.
   4. The process is somewhat involved: It requires
   three separate stages.
   5. This is what I have to do on Sunday: clean
   my room, baby-sit for my brother, and finish
   my homework.
   6. He excelled in one sport: soccer.
   7. Dear President Bush:
**B** Sample answers:
   1. I am taking the following subjects this year:
   math, science, social studies, English, and
   Spanish.
   2. You need these supplies for a picnic: hot
   dogs, carrot sticks, potato chips, and soft
   drinks.
   3. We have seen the following birds this
   summer: blue jays, robins, sparrows, and
   bald eagles.

© Pearson Education, Inc., publishing as Pearson Prentice Hall.

**A** 1. Four team sports are popular in U.S. schools: basketball, baseball, football, and soccer.

2. The day after Thanksgiving is a holiday in these states: Florida, Maine, Minnesota, Nebraska, and Washington.

3. Caution: Read this manual completely before using your chain saw.

4. Marianne chose three different poets to study: Dickinson, Frost, and Poe.

5. The president banged the gavel: "Let the meeting come to order."

6. Greetings, fellow club members:

7. The salad contains three ingredients: lettuce, tomatoes, and mushrooms.

8. My father grows a variety of vegetables: carrots, squash, and cucumbers.

9. Warning: This cabinet contains dangerous electrical equipment.

10. We have the following trees on our property: maple, elm, and oak.

**B** Sample answers:

1. Dear Governor Jones:

2. Ellen waved goodbye: "I'll miss you both very much while you're at camp"

3. Danger: Poisonous snakes inside

4. The little girl asked Santa for the following presents: a baby doll, a dump truck, and some wooden blocks.

5. The job can be very involved: You must first know everyone's name and birthday.

### Commas After Introductory Words

**Practice,** p. 254

**A** 1. By the way,; 2. Yes,; 3. Tomorrow;

4. In the meantime,; 5. No,; 6. Incidentally,

**B** 1. Hey, don't you want to come to the movie with us?

2. Unfortunately, I have too much to do today.

3. However, I'll be happy to meet you for dinner later on.

**C** Sample answers:

1. Of course, rain may delay the game.

2. Oh, there is the other earring.

3. Nevertheless, you will have to take the exam.

**Assess,** p. 255

**A** 1. Of course,; 2. However,; 3. First;

4. Hey,; 5. Oh,; 6. Indeed,

**B** 1. At last, the flight has arrived.

2. Fortunately, the snow is great for skiing.

3. Nevertheless, you need to be on the lookout for ice patches.

4. Well, let's get going.

**C** Sample answers:

1. Yes, there is a dance tonight.

2. Well then, let's start over.

3. By the way, you should bring a jacket because it gets cold.

4. Good, the rain stopped.

### Commas With Quotations

**Practice,** p. 256

1. Jared called his friend's scheme "ridiculous" and refused to take part in it.

2. *Correct*

3. Major Morris warned, "If you keep it, don't blame me for what happens."

4. Louise Erdrich refers to her mother's movements as "catlike."

5. *Correct*

6. *Correct*

7. The Blackfeet referred to horses as "Elk Dogs."

8. The appearance of the moon a few days before or after it is full is described as "gibbous."

**Assess,** p. 257

**A** 1. Venus angrily inquired, "Am I then to be eclipsed by a mortal girl?"

2. *Correct*

3. *Correct*

4. Mr. Darcy shocks Elizabeth by confessing, "You must allow me to tell you how ardently I admire and love you."

5. *Correct*

6. Roberto found the white-water challenge "a wonderful wilderness experience."

7. The doctor noted that the test results were "promising" and vowed to do all that he could.

8. The counselor advised, "Grades are certainly an important factor in college admissions."

**B** Students' paragraphs should include at least two direct quotations and one partial quotation. Students should use commas before direct quotations and should not use commas before partial quotations.

### Commonly Confused Words: *fewer, less; sit, set; in, into*

**Practice,** p. 258

**A** 1. setting; 2. into; 3. fewer

**B** Sample answers:

1. There are fewer rain clouds in the sky than there were an hour ago.

2. We will have less rain for sure.

© Pearson Education, Inc., publishing as Pearson Prentice Hall.

3. It is peaceful in the forest.

4. Sal went into the forest to look for his lost dog.

5. Angela set the baby in his stroller.

## Assess, p. 259

**A** 1. fewer; 2. less; 3. sits; 4. setting; 5. in; 6. into

**B** 1. set; 2. fewer; 3. into

**C** Sample answers:

1. There are fewer chocolate cookies on the plate.

2. There is less sugar in the raisin cookies.

3. The packages are in the car.

4. Get into the car so we can leave.

5. The waiter set the table for a party of five.

## Comparative and Superlative Adjectives and Adverbs

### Practice, p. 260

1. worst; 2. taller; 3. friendliest; 4. better; 5. more patiently

### Assess, p. 261

**A** 1. more difficult; 2. more expensive; 3. better; 4. freshest; 5. more enthusiastically; 6. more cheerfully; 7. more optimistically; 8. funnier; 9. farthest; 10. colder

**B** 1. Which was harder for you to learn, skiing or skating?

2. *Correct*

3. Of the three pitchers on the team, Julio is the most accurate.

4. I tried on all five pairs of shoes and then bought the pair I liked most.

5. *Correct*

## Compound Adjectives

### Practice, p. 262

1. eye-opening, (experience)

2. ten-year-old, (boy); highly active, (puppy)

3. crosshatched, (pattern)

4. mixed-breed, (dogs)

5. face-to-face, (confrontation)

### Assess, p. 263

**A** 1. well respected, (designer); out-of-date, (kitchen)

2. Hard-boiled, (eggs)

3. finely tuned, (instrument)

4. country-and-western, (singer); crossover, (hits)

5. lifelong, (commitment); low-income, (families)

6. mold-infested, (house)

7. five-speed, (transmission)

8. brainstorming, (session)

**B** 1. a world-famous athlete

2. an all-purpose cleaner

3. a six-lane highway

4. the five-year-old computer

5. the dirt-covered floor

6. a smoothly running machine

7. a fast-moving storm

8. a one-week vacation

## Compound Predicates

### Practice, p. 264

1. Subject: Boaz. Compound Predicates: ate; drank. Conjunction: and.

2. Subject: He. Compound Predicates: came over; sat down; Conjunction: and.

3. Subject: He. Compound Predicates: will renew your life; sustain your old age. Conjunction: and.

4. Subject: Naomi. Compound Predicates: took the child; held it to her. Conjunction: and.

5. Subject: She. Compound Predicates: prostrated herself with her face to the ground; spoke to him. Conjunction: and.

6. Subject: I. Compound Predicates: locked myself in; sat writing every evening till late in the night. Conjunction: and.

7. Subject: He. Compound Predicates: took over; decided what I should be; planned my costume. Conjunctions: and; and.

8. Subject: I. Compound Predicates: will stop by then; have a look at you all dressed up. Conjunction: and.

### Assess, p. 265

**A** 1. Compound Predicate: journeyed to Moab; took his wife and two sons. Subject: a man. Conjunction: and.

2. Compound Predicate: returned from Moab; brought her daughter-in-law Ruth. Subject: Naomi. Conjunction: and.

3. Compound Predicate: talked to Ruth gently; showed her what to do. Subject: Boaz. Conjunction: and.

4. Compound Predicate: stayed close to the maidservants of Boaz; gleaned until the end of the harvests. Subject: Ruth. Conjunction: and.

5. Compound Predicate: went to the threshing floor; did what her mother-in-law said. Subject: Ruth. Conjunction: and.

6. Compound Predicate: will show in Mrs. Linde; take care of the children. Subject: The maid. Conjunction: or.

7. Compound Predicate: breaks out into laughter; does not clap her hands. Subject: Nora. Conjunction: but.

© Pearson Education, Inc., publishing as Pearson Prentice Hall.

**B Sample answers:**

(Students should correctly use a compound predicate, either drawing on the Book of Ruth and *A Doll House* for details or making up their own.)

1. Ruth keeps faith with Naomi and succeeds as a result.
2. Naomi welcomes her daughter-in-law and brings her back to Bethlehem.
3. The doctor visits Nora but does not solve her problem.

## Compound-Complex Sentences

### Practice, p. 266

**A** 1. Ind: David raked the leaves / and Kenny helped him.
   Sub: before he mowed the lawn,
2. Ind: Marla trimmed the hedge and painted the mailbox.
   Sub: After the lawn was mowed and the gardens were weeded,
3. Ind: The dog was close to the road, / he ran to me.
   Sub: and when I called him,
4. Ind: we clipped on our microphones and went out onto the stage.
   Sub: When the time came,
5. Ind: John suggested the show, and Rebecca and Megan were all for it
   Sub: when they heard his idea.

**B Sample answers:**

1. The book was long and dull, but I read it when I was sick.
2. The dancers who traveled from Russia were excellent, and the audience applauded loudly.
3. Since the party was tonight, Susan baked the bread, and Ron prepared the salad.

### Assess, p. 267

**A** 1. Ind: We waited until the rain stopped, and then we went into the stadium
   Sub: where the baseball game would begin.
2. Ind: they missed the beginning of the movie / but they still understood the plot.
   Sub: Because they were late / that was being shown,
3. Ind: Mary hoped that she could buy a new television set, but she did not purchase one
   Sub: because the sets were too expensive.
4. Ind: we missed our morning flight, but we took an afternoon flight.
   Sub: Because traffic was bad,
5. Ind: We unloaded the car, and the guide led us through the woods
   Sub: until we found a good campsite.

**B Sample answers:**

1. Last January was cold, but February was even colder despite the two-day warm spell.
2. Because you are my brother, I understand your problems fully, and I sympathize with you.
3. When darkness descended, the wolves howled at the moon, and the campers cowered in their tents.

**C** 1. When Julie went to Chicago, she took the train, but when she goes to New York, she will fly.
2. As the storm increased in force, Ivan crawled under the bed, and Hillary covered her head with a pillow.

## Concrete and Abstract Nouns

### Practice, p. 268

**A** 1. concrete; 2. abstract; 3. concrete; 4. abstract; 5. concrete; 6. abstract

**B** 1. Concrete: sketches; Abstract: thoughts
2. Concrete: Mr. Brett, car, driveway; Abstract: None
3. Concrete: America, Abstract: tradition; liberty, justice

### Assess, p. 269

**A** 1. concrete; 2. abstract; 3. concrete; 4. concrete; 5. abstract; 6. abstract

**B** 1. Concrete: class, discussion, play; Abstract: None
2. Concrete: rainbow, children; Abstract: pleasure
3. Concrete: brother, vacation; Abstract: idea
4. Concrete: generations, heroes; Abstract: ideals

## Direct Address

### Practice, p. 270

**A** 1. Dr. Metz, your next patient is ready.
2. Lovely sunshine, you make me so happy today!
3. In another five minutes, Ashley, you may start the movie.
4. What did I tell you, John, about leaving the lights on?
5. I'll never trust you again, you liar!
6. Fellow students, today we celebrate our graduation.
7. Okay, campers, don't forget your sunscreen.

**B Sample answers:**

1. Uncle Earl, will you give me a ride to school?
2. Today, my friends, we will finish this project.
3. Please bring us the check, waiter.

© Pearson Education, Inc., publishing as Pearson Prentice Hall.

**A** 1. <u>Mrs. Sanchez</u>, the book you ordered is in.

2. Your wish is my command, <u>Mother</u>.

3. In that case, <u>Mr. Jackson</u>, I will give you my answer on Friday.

4. <u>O mighty ocean</u>, what adventures do you hold?

5. Please take your seats, <u>ladies and gentlemen</u>.

6. When you finish the hallway, <u>painters</u>, you may start on the bedroom.

7. Whoa there, <u>Nellie</u>!

8. <u>Mr. and Mrs. Kumar</u>, your table is ready for you.

9. Again today, <u>little bird</u>, your sweet song awakens me.

10. You are an exciting city, <u>Nashville</u>!

**B** Sample answers:

1. Today, my fellow Americans, we celebrate a great victory.

2. Please enter through this gate, ticket holders.

3. Beautiful elm tree, I love to sit in your shade.

4. After today, Lita, you will lead the team.

5. Wait on this side of the rope, those of you without reservations.

## Elliptical Clauses

**Practice,** p. 272

1. I never felt happier <u>than</u> [I felt] <u>on that train ride to Seattle</u>.

2. President Kennedy told <u>Americans</u> [that] <u>they should find ways to serve their country</u>.

3. E-mail travels almost instantaneously, <u>so much faster than so-called snail mail</u> [travels].

4. I believe [that] <u>Jen read Momaday's story more eagerly than</u> [she read] <u>any other selection</u>.

5. My sister said [that] <u>we were never closer than</u> [we were] <u>when she was preparing to leave for college</u>.

6. Max told Ellen the secret [that] <u>he had promised to keep</u>.

**Assess,** p. 273

**A** 1. Wise people understand [that] <u>they cannot do everything they might want</u> [to do].

2. It is vital to discover the one thing [that] <u>you want to do more than</u> [you want to do] <u>anything else</u>.

3. There is no holiday [that] <u>I love better than</u> [I love] <u>Thanksgiving</u>.

4. Thanksgiving involves less work <u>than some other holidays</u> [involve], and yet I feel [that] <u>it is more satisfying than most</u> [are].

5. Of course, I also eat more on Thanksgiving <u>than</u> [I eat] <u>on any other holiday, too</u>.

**B** Students' passages may contain elliptical expressions such as "The sport [that] I like best." Their passages may also include elliptical expressions comparing items, such as "I like to read more than [I like] any other activity." Check that these elliptical clauses are formulated correctly.

## Gerunds and Gerund Phrases

**Practice,** p. 274

**A** 1. OP; Is this the line for <u>buying tickets</u>?

2. S; <u>Designing computer graphics</u> is an excellent profession.

3. PN; My hobby is <u>singing</u>.

4. DO; The scientists continued <u>looking for a cure</u>.

5. OP; The negotiators worked at <u>achieving a good settlement</u>.

6. PN; This subject of the article was <u>protecting the environment</u>.

7. DO; The audience stopped <u>paying attention to the speaker</u>.

8. S; <u>Writing to persuade</u> requires practice.

**B** Sample answers:

1. Watching television makes me tired.

2. Mark and Rebecca are paid well for shoveling snow.

3. The Martins enjoy traveling around the country.

**Assess,** p. 275

**A** 1. PN, PN; Our fall activities are <u>raking leaves</u> and <u>planting bulbs</u>.

2. S, S; <u>Singing</u> and <u>dancing</u> raise a person's spirits.

3. OP; Before <u>starting out on a trip</u>, we highlight the route on a map.

4. DO; Alicia enjoyed <u>getting a good night's sleep</u>.

5. PN; An admirable activity is <u>volunteering at an animal shelter</u>.

6. OP; The article presented tips for <u>protecting against identity theft</u>.

7. OP; The chess players continued for four hours without <u>stopping</u>.

8. S; <u>Winning a scholarship</u> was Tyler's goal.

9. DO; Would you mind <u>keeping quiet</u>?

10. S; <u>Learning a foreign language</u> takes time and practice.

© Pearson Education, Inc., publishing as Pearson Prentice Hall.

**B** Sample answers:

1. Running for town council was Mr. Moran's goal.

2. Carlos got the information he needed by Web surfing.

3. During the summer, my favorite activity is watching tennis matches.

4. Ashley teaches water skiing.

## Indefinite and Demonstrative Pronouns

### Practice, p. 276

**A** 1. <u>Most</u> is; 2. <u>All</u> were; 3. <u>Each</u> has; 4. <u>Several</u> are

**B** 1. <u>those</u> belong; 2. <u>this</u> tells; 3. <u>that</u> is

### Assess, p. 277

**A** 1. *IP*; The committee hopes that <u>everybody</u> will want to help with the coat drive.

2. *IP*; Will <u>someone</u> please take charge of putting up the posters?

3. *IP*; <u>Several</u> bags of coats have already been donated.

4. *DP*; Carrie, will you take <u>these</u> to the Recreation Center?

5. *DP*; <u>This</u> is the last load for today.

6. *IP*; <u>All</u> of the volunteers will meet at the Center on Saturday.

7. *DP*; Please arrive at 9:00 A.M. <u>That</u> is the time the doors open.

8. *IP*; Check the coats to be sure <u>all</u> are in good shape.

9. *IP*; Do not keep <u>any</u> with bad stains or rips.

10. *DP*; <u>Those</u> should be returned to their owners or discarded.

**B** 1. *C*; <u>that</u> is

2. <u>some</u> of it ~~make~~ **makes**

3. <u>Those</u> ~~is~~ **are**

4. <u>Each</u> ~~are~~ **is**

5. *C*; <u>everything</u> **is**

## Infinitives and Infinitive Phrases

### Practice, p. 278

**A** 1. Rudolf wants (to play hockey this winter.)

2. Beverly learned how (to cook soufflé) at the culinary institute.

3. <u>To err</u> is human, <u>to forgive</u> divine.

4. Practicing is important if you want (to improve your swimming techniques)

5. (To create a work of art,) you first need (to get an idea.)

**B** 1. Jerry likes <u>to play golf every day</u>. (phrase serving as the object of the verb *likes*)

2. We went <u>to listen to the opera</u>. (phrase modifying the verb *went*)

3. I like <u>to read stories to my brother</u>. (phrase serving as the object of the verb *like*)

4. Max left <u>to join the Peace Corps.</u> (phrase serving as an adverb modifying the verb *left*)

### Assess, p. 279

**A** 1. Her goal, <u>to write a novel</u>, was never realized.

2. The purpose of the class was <u>to teach conservation skills</u>.

3. <u>To achieve the highest grade</u>, the students created a multimedia presentation.

4. Alex and Anna wanted <u>to ride their bikes to the beach</u>.

5. Felix began <u>to paint the house last summer</u>.

**B** 1. All the leaders wanted <u>to sign the peace agreement</u>. noun

2. The tailor made the dress <u>to fit the actress</u>. adverb

3. The sound vibrations caused the table <u>to shake</u>. adjective

4. Ethan was excited <u>to fish in the lake</u>. adverb

5. The student artists began <u>to paint watercolors</u>. noun

**C** Sample answers:

1. It took several hours of preparation before they were ready to eat the turkey.

2. They began to anticipate the date of the trip the second they agreed on a destination.

3. Against my better judgment, I decided to lend my friend a sum of money.

## Interjections

### Practice, p. 280

**A** Sample answers:

1. Ouch; 2. Wow; 3. Yuck, Ugh; 4. Yikes; 5. Uh; 6. Whew

**B** Sample answers:

1. Aw,; 2. Wow!; 3. Ouch!; 4. Whew,; 5. Darn,; 6. Ugh!

### Assess, p. 281

**A** Sample answers:

1. Wow,; 2. Yuck!; 3. Yikes!; 4. Hey,; 5. Oops!

**B** Sample answers:

1. Yuck, this broccoli tastes horrible.

2. Hey, I'm over here.

3. Wow, that car sure is fast!

4. Hmm, I wonder what he means by that.

5. Oops, I dropped the butter.

## Interrupting Phrases and Clauses

### Practice, p. 282

1. I just finished reading *Romeo and Juliet*—what a great work of literature!

© Pearson Education, Inc., publishing as Pearson Prentice Hall.

2. The flight to Atlanta was extremely long—about eight and a half hours—for such a young child.

3. The gymnast—what amazing balance and strength—impressed everyone in the crowd.

4. Your examination—someone should have already told you this—has been rescheduled.

5. "May I please speak to—oh, no, I've been put on hold," Phil said.

6. The wide receiver made an amazing circus catch—I couldn't believe how high he leapt!

7. The day of my trip to China—a lifelong dream of mine—finally arrived.

## Assess, p. 283

**A** 1. B; 2. A; 3. A; 4. B; 5. A

**B** 1. Wild rabbits—look! there's one now—often come to this field to graze.

2. The items in the wheelbarrow—some rocks, a mallet, and two pieces of rope—had spilled onto the ground.

3. I think Derrick will reach his goal—getting an academic scholarship for college.

4. Then my sister showed me—watch out for that car!—the way to the bus station.

5. What I'm trying to say—please try to focus—is that you need to study more.

## Noun Clauses

## Practice, p. 284

1. what I expected; predicate nominative
2. Whatever price they ask; subject
3. what they suggest; direct object
4. whoever called; indirect object
5. what Lester needs; predicate nominative
6. What most surprised Rita; subject

## Assess, p. 285

**A** 1. A; 2. B

**B** 1. S; How this business manages to survive
2. DO; how they can go
3. OP; whatever time you say
4. IO; whoever asks
5. PN; what my father prefers

**C** Sample answers:
1. how they plan to do it
2. what we had seen
3. whoever is here
4. what you need
5. which movie to see

## Parallel Structure

## Practice, p. 286

**A** 1. to the department store, to the library, and to the town hall
2. Twisting and turning
3. to wash his truck, to change the oil, and to fix the radio
4. Karl, Brandy, and I
5. that one of his cousins liked rock and that the other preferred jazz

**B** 1. Penelope would rather visit a new restaurant than go to an old favorite.
2. Nick knows how to plan, how to take notes, and how to use different sources.
3. Brad likes jogging, playing tennis, and going on hikes.
4. The mayoral candidate is intelligent, compassionate, and trustworthy.

## Assess, p. 287

**A** 1. washed the dishes, did the laundry, and waxed the floors
2. wrapping presents and tying ribbons
3. typed her report, printed it out, and bound it
4. Shouting and splashing
5. neither a credible plot nor effective characterization
6. to accept a difficult challenge and to succeed on their quest
7. a march, an overture, and a full-length symphony
8. purchase the ingredients, bake the cookies, and prepare the pies
9. moved around the room, explored the house, and then jumped on the table

**B** 1. Barb likes visiting new places and exploring foreign countries.
2. Ms. Harlan loves to bake, to sew, and to watch television.
3. Herb bought the car because it was stylish and because it was well priced.
4. The candidate endorsed the sale of state bonds, the establishment of a new state park, and a cut in property taxes.

## Participial Phrases

## Practice, p. 288

**A** 1. spent on this project (money)
2. Saving money from each paycheck (Cheryl)
3. wearing a turquoise bonnet (woman)
4. parked illegally (car)
5. held in their honor (concert)

© Pearson Education, Inc., publishing as Pearson Prentice Hall.

**B** Sample answers:

1. The small boy sitting at the end of the pier has caught nothing all day.
2. The sun setting behind the mountains is a beautiful sight.
3. Many books written by that author have been bestsellers.

## Assess, p. 289

**A** 1. B; 2. D

**B** 1. <u>Fractured in the accident</u> (arm)
2. <u>Crossing the finish line</u> (Jerry)
3. <u>announcing my prize</u> (letter)

**C** Sample answers:

1. Appearing somewhat nervous, the speaker approached the microphone.
2. The players sitting on the bench cheered for their teammates.
3. The children playing in the park built sand castles in the sandbox.
4. Noticing that the laundry was dry, my mom immediately removed the clothes from the dryer.

### Participles as Adjectives

## Practice, p. 290

**A** 1. fencing (class); exciting (duels); experienced (students)
2. identifying (marks)
3. soaked (grass); gleaming (wall)
4. fatigued (travelers); inviting (beds); made (beds)
5. wandering (cat); locked (door)

**B** 1. making; made
2. breaking; broken
3. forgetting; forgotten
4. losing; lost

## Assess, p. 291

**A** 1. broken; chattering
2. missing; forgotten
3. quavering; terrified; poised
4. doomed; hypnotizing
5. driven; haunted; stunning; intriguing; teeming; shattered

**B** Students' passages should contain at least three participles appropriately used as adjectives and following the correct form. The participles should be underlined, and the nouns they modify should be circled.

### Past Perfect Verb Tense

## Practice, p. 292

Wording of students' explanations may vary.

1. had reached; The hikers reached the lake sometime before 12:00 noon.
2. had run; The players ran the laps, and then the coach let them rest.
3. had traveled; Ken's traveling took place before he turned thirty.
4. had been destroyed; The firefighters arrived, but not until after most of the building had been destroyed.
5. had expected; Tina's expectation ended sometime before she finished college.

## Assess, p. 293

**A** 1. (none); 2. had looked; 3. had called;
4. had reminded; 5. (none); 6. had learned;
7. had thanked; 8. had seen

**B** 1. had hoped; 2. had become; 3. had blocked;
4. had written; 5. had anticipated; 6. had gained;
7. had called; 8. had remembered;
9. had arrived; 10. had forgotten

### Predicate Adjectives

## Practice, p. 294

**A** 1. (intelligent); 2. (powerful); 3. (dirty);
4. (susceptible); 5. (hoarse); 6. (sour)

**B** Sample answers:

1. burned; 2. older; 3. salty;
4. exhausted; 5. cold and damp

## Assess, p. 295

**A** 1. <u>policy</u>, (important)
2. <u>Jennie</u>, (famous)
3. <u>roads</u>, (dangerous)
4. <u>Susie</u>, (tall)
5. <u>senator</u>, (tired)
6. <u>sky</u>, (threatening)
7. <u>English and science</u>, (difficult)
8. <u>crowd</u>, (restless)
9. <u>Adam</u>, (loyal)
10. <u>albums</u>, (popular)

**B** Sample answers:

1. dark; 2. proud; 3. warm and sunny;
4. expensive; 5. disgusting; 6. kind

### Prepositional Phrases

## Practice, p. 296

**A** 1. <u>over the fence</u>; (fence)
2. <u>into the room</u>; (room)
3. <u>about the newspaper</u>; (newspaper)
4. <u>behind the couch</u>; (couch)
5. <u>within the cave</u>; (cave)

© Pearson Education, Inc., publishing as Pearson Prentice Hall.

**B** 1. <u>around the entire nature preserve</u>; ADV
   2. <u>under Robert Falcon Scott</u>; ADJ
   3. <u>with the green silk cover</u>; ADJ
   4. <u>on the proposed highway route</u>; ADJ
   5. <u>before Columbus's birth</u>; ADV
   6. <u>of modern music</u>; ADJ

## Assess, p. 297

**A** 1. <u>for Calgary</u>; <u>behind schedule</u>
   2. <u>among the actors</u>; <u>during rehearsal</u>
   3. <u>As a child</u>; <u>underneath some old clothes</u>; <u>inside a musty closet</u>
   4. <u>Under the pen name A. M. Barnard</u>; <u>of mystery and horror</u>
   5. <u>from the end</u>; <u>of school</u>; <u>until dusk</u>; <u>against a playground wall</u>

**B** 1. <u>behind pen names</u>; ADV
   2. <u>with huge front wheels</u>; ADJ
   3. <u>in Westminster Abbey</u>; ADV
   4. <u>in early June</u>; ADV
   5. <u>on Earth</u>; ADJ

**C** Sample answers:
   1. Jack poured the milk into the cup.
   2. She agreed to meet us at the restaurant.
   3. The actress waited patiently behind the curtain for her cue.

### Present Perfect Verb Tense

## Practice, p. 298

**A** 1. N
   2. I <u>have decided</u> to write my paper about Zora Neale Hurston.
   3. <u>Have</u> you ever <u>been</u> to Hawaii?
   4. N
   5. The power of the individual will <u>has remained</u> a major theme in American literature.
   6. N
   7. How long <u>have</u> you ever <u>gone</u> without watching television?
   8. Several U.S. universities <u>have existed</u> for centuries.
   9. N
   10. My sister's e-mails <u>have given</u> me a close-up view of college life.

**B** 1. have studied; 2. have been; 3. has assigned; 4. have read

## Assess, p. 299

**A** 1. N
   2. I <u>have been</u> wrong many times, but this mistake <u>has been</u> spectacular.
   3. N
   4. N

5. Readers <u>have enjoyed</u> Alcott's novels for more than 150 years.
6. At least three film versions of *Little Women* <u>have appeared</u>.
7. <u>Have</u> you <u>seen</u> the latest one?
8. N

**B** 1. has produced; 2. has continued;
   3. have been; 4. have watched

**C** Sample answers:
   1. I have thought about this problem for a while.
   2. I have read chapters three and four.
   3. Caroline has forgotten to pay me for her concert ticket.
   4. We have won the competition for the first time in five years.
   5. Manuel and Nadia have met before.

### Pronouns and Antecedents

## Practice, p. 300

**A** 1. (Vermont); 2. (mountains); 3. (visitors);
   4. (Vermonters); 5. (woman)

**B** 1. (It); <u>state</u>; 2. (their); <u>British</u>; 3. (his); <u>Ethan Allen</u>; 4. (they); <u>Vermonters</u>; 5. (it); <u>Vermont</u>;
   6. (it); <u>monument</u>; 7. (They); <u>Calvin Coolidge and Chester A. Arthur</u>

## Assess, p. 301

**A** 1. <u>his</u>; 2. <u>them</u>; 3. <u>They</u>; 4. <u>their</u>; 5. <u>His</u>

**B** 1. (Mr. Garcia); 2. (seeds); 3. (birds); 4. (Mrs. Suzuki); 5. (Mr. Garcia)

**C** 1. it; 2. his; 3. it; 4. he; 5. their

### Punctuating Dialogue

## Practice, p. 302

**A** 1. Harry complained, "This flight is always late."
   2. "I'll be there in ten minutes," Josh replied.
   3. "Is the Internet connection working?" Paula asked.
   4. "We're almost out of gas," Eddie warned, "so we had better get some."
   5. "How old are you, Grandpa?" Jenna inquired.

**B** Examine students' passages of dialogue to make sure that punctuation and paragraphing are correct.

## Assess, p. 303

**A** 1. David replied, "I think I'd prefer to visit the mountains rather than the beach."
   2. "What happened to my new slippers?" Dad inquired.
   3. "The shed needs a coat of paint," Sally observed, "but the job shouldn't take too long."

© Pearson Education, Inc., publishing as Pearson Prentice Hall.

4. "What an extraordinary work of art!" Timothy exclaimed.

5. "Swimmers going to the meet must board the bus by 10:00 o'clock," Coach Johnson announced.

**B** Examine students' passages of dialogue to make sure that punctuation and paragraphing are correct.

## Restrictive and Nonrestrictive Adjective Clauses

### Practice, p. 304

**A** 1. that we will all remember; (day)
2. that he wrote about; (statue)
3. who was recently appointed by the university; (Professor Johnson)
4. which were on sale; (jackets)
5. whose mother is the district attorney; (Len)

**B** 1. restrictive; 2. nonrestrictive; 3. restrictive; 4. nonrestrictive

### Assess, p. 305

**A** 1. that she had described to me; (color)
2. who works at the bank; (woman)
3. whose strings are hit by hammers to produce sound; (piano)
4. on which the argument centered; (issue)
5. which I bought two years ago; (bicycle)

**B** Sample answers:
1. The people who live on that street all drive fancy cars.
2. George, to whom I owe money, went to the hockey game with his friends.
3. Here is the tuna sandwich that you asked for.
4. The man whom Peter told you about has just entered the room.
5. Mrs. Roth, whose house is filled with valuable antiques, sings in the adult choir.

## Transitions and Transitional Phrases

### Practice, p. 306

1. although; Relationship: contrast
2. Because; Relationship: cause and effect
3. When; Relationship: order in time (chronological)
4. therefore; Relationship: cause and effect

### Assess, p. 307

**A** Sample answers:
1. After Socrates explained his actions to the citizens of Athens, he went to the place where the sentence was to be carried out.
2. Socrates was a wise and good man, but the judges condemned him to death anyway.

3. Because the words of Socrates are eloquent, Plato's "Apology" is still read today.
4. After Socrates thought about the statement that he was the wisest of men, he decided to test the statement by looking for a man wiser than himself.

**B** Sample answer:
When rock 'n' roll exploded onto the scene in the 1950s, some people claimed it was immoral. Consequently, they argued that it should be banned. A similar debate about the morality of music took place more than 2,000 years ago in ancient Greece. This debate, however, focused on Greek musical scales, called modes. Each Greek mode had seven notes. Also, the names of modes were associated with groups and regions. Since Lydia was viewed as a corrupt place, songs in the Lydian mode were suitable for feasts. Plato banned songs in the Lydian mode from his ideal republic because they made men "soft." Instead, he favored the Dorian mode, which was "warlike."

## The Understood *You* in Imperative Sentences

### Practice, p. 308

**A** 1. A. Q; B. I; C. D
2. A. D; B. Q; C. I
3. A. I; B. Q; C. D

**B** 1. Do not think about this problem anymore.
2. Close the door and lock it.
3. Use this brush to paint the trim.
4. Slice the apples while I roll out the dough.

### Assess, p. 309

**A** 1. I; 2. I; 3. Q; 4. I; 5. D; 6. I; 7. Q; 8. I
**B** 1. Do not look at me with those sad eyes.
2. Pay at the counter, and then come back with the receipt.
3. Do twenty laps every day if you want to stay in shape.
4. Memorize this poem, please, and recite it for the class.
5. Do not skate on that ice; it's not frozen through.

## Usage: *who* and *whom*

### Practice, p. 310

**A** 1. subject; 2. direct object; 3. object of the preposition; 4. direct object
**B** 1. Who; 2. whom; 3. Whom; 4. who; 5. who

© Pearson Education, Inc., publishing as Pearson Prentice Hall.

## Assess, p. 311

**A** 1. Clause: who will get the job

   Rewording of clause: he will get the job

   Function of pronoun: subject

2. Clause: who knows what she wants

   Rewording of clause: she knows what she wants

   Function of pronoun: subject

3. Clause: for whom the judges voted

   Rewording of clause: the judges voted for him

   Function of pronoun: object of the preposition

**B** 1. who; 2. whom; 3. who; 4. who; 5. Whom; 6. whom

### Using Dashes

## Practice, p. 312

1. That circus act the one with the aerialist
   ^

   walking on a wire high above the ground
                                          ^

   always makes me uneasy.

2. The meeting didn't you say it was at Tom's
                ^

   house? begins at 8:00.
        ^

3. The players, the coaches, and the grounds crew all were given a bonus.
                ^

4. The new corporate president he worked his
                             ^

   way up from stock boy, you know is sure to
                                    ^

   make some changes.

5. I hope that Ellen won't be oh, here she is now.
                           ^

## Assess, p. 313

1. Our team is winning the game—no, the other team just scored a touchdown.

2. *No dashes*

3. *No dashes*

4. This Sunday's game—it should be the best one this season—starts at 1:00.

5. Once the storm passes—if it ever does—the weather should be beautiful.

6. Morton—that very gentle old man who feeds the geese at the park—is friends with my grandmother.

7. I can't find my—ah, there they are!

8. Washington, Jefferson, Lincoln, and Teddy Roosevelt—these are the presidents whose faces are carved in the granite of Mount Rushmore.

9. Stephen Spielberg's new movie—have you seen it yet?—is sure to be a great success.

### Varying Sentences

## Practice, p. 314

**A** Sample answers:

1. When Tim consulted the Yellow Pages, he found the location of a nearby hardware store.

2. With a broad smile on her face, Lori replied enthusiastically.

3. After the assistant submitted his resignation, the president accepted it with regret.

4. Having analyzed the problem, Darren devised an ingenious solution.

**B** Sample answer:

A fire extinguisher is a device for putting out fires. Hardware stores stock several different types of extinguisher, but the customer's choice depends on the type of flammable material he or she wants to protect. Attached to the front of the device, the nameplate identifies the kind of fires an extinguisher will put out. Although home fire extinguishers are useful, they have a short discharge time. This lasts from 8 to 24 seconds. Most important, the user must direct the spray at the base of the fire.

## Assess, p. 315

**A** 1. Having outfitted ourselves carefully, we began to climb the mountain.

2. At the edge of the road stood a crumbling old house.

3. Swimming steadily, the lifeguard succeeded in reaching the child in distress.

4. Asking the witness question after question, the prosecutor probed relentlessly.

5. Because it was poorly designed, the project ran way over budget.

6. Since he was painfully shy, Tito did not attend the party.

7. Returning from baseball practice, we found that our food was cold.

**B** Sample answer:

On my own for about an hour, I walked along the beach. First, I began my walk near a rocky outcropping. I stopped every once in a while to examine unusual shells at the water's edge. Although at that time they seemed unique and intriguing, at other times they might be judged drab and dull. However, I soon lost interest in the shells. They were all along the beach, but I moved on. Farther on, the sand was almost pure white. On the beach, there was no litter or debris. Finally, I could not hold myself back. Taking a running start, I ran splashing into the water.

© Pearson Education, Inc., publishing as Pearson Prentice Hall.

# WRITING

## Autobiographical Narrative

### Practice, p. 316

Word webs will vary. In completing the last prompt, students should describe the scene in which the event took place by writing about the specific actions and feelings of the characters involved.

### Assess, p. 317

**A** 1. B; 2. A

**B** Word webs will vary. In completing the last prompt, students should describe the scene in which the event took place by writing about the specific actions and feeling of the characters involved.

## Comparison-and-Contrast Essay

### Practice, p. 318

**A** 1. Similarities: the goal of the game; the need for speed and stamina; teamwork
Differences: the amount of action; the ease in following the ball

2. **Sample answer:** In both sports, players frequently pass the ball back and forth to other players.

3. **Sample answer:** In football, the players carry and throw the ball, but in soccer, the players kick the ball.

**B** Sample categories:
strength, speed, ability to score

### Assess, p. 319

Sample answers for "dogs or cats as pets":

1. personal attention; exercise; grooming

2. Category: personal attention. Dogs: must be petted and played with often; Cats: do not require as much attention. **Category:** exercise. Dogs: must be walked or exercised daily; Cats: Do not need to have supervised exercise. **Category:** grooming. Dogs: must be bathed regularly; Cats: keep themselves clean.

3. Millions of people in the United States have pets. Two of the most popular types of pets are dogs and cats. There are many similarities in having dogs and cats as pets. Both need to be given food and water regularly. Both need to be taken to the veterinarian for checkups and shots. Both dogs and cats can be affectionate and can be good company. While there are many advantages to owning dogs, I prefer cats as pets.

   First of all, cats are much cleaner than dogs. Cats are constantly grooming themselves and never need a bath. Dogs have to be bathed regularly or they get very dirty and smelly. If dogs get into mud or dirt, they cannot clean themselves as cats do. Cats need only to be brushed regularly.

## Job Portfolio and Résumé

### Practice, p. 320

**A** 1. A; 2. B

**B** Students should list experiences that demonstrate their capacity to take on responsibility. They may also list useful skills they might have. Experiences include work experiences, volunteering, membership in a club, participation in a sports team, special training, mastery of a programming language, and so on. Students should include dates where relevant.

### Assess, p. 321

**A** 1. B; 2. A

**B** Students should accurately fill out the résumé template, including adequate contact information and relevant dates. In their descriptions, they should use active, formal language. The experiences they list should demonstrate their capacity to take on responsibility as well as identify any useful skills they might have. Work experiences should be listed under the "Work Experience" head. Other experiences, such as volunteer work or work for a school club, participation in a sports team, or special training, as well as awards or certificates, should be listed under the "Other Experience" head.

## Multimedia Report

### Practice, p. 322

Sample answers:

1. It is too broad. He cannot possibly cover all of the battles in the Civil War.

2. John could cover only the most important battles—the ones that decided the war's result.

3. He could videotape just one re-enacted battle; he could incorporate other relevant media.

4. Other audio and visual features that John could integrate into his multimedia report could be a slide show of Civil War photographs and documents, such as maps and correspondence. He could also play audio of Civil War songs.

### Assess, p. 323

Sample answers:

**A** 1. Kate's topic is too broad; I would concentrate on just a few artists or a smaller time period.

2. Kate could ask for help at the library, and she can use the Internet. She could also interview the local artist she knows.

3. Instead of just doing a slide show, Kate could videotape the local artist at work, while he explains his approach. Kate might also want to bring some of her grandmother's old paintings to class and describe the artists who created them.

**B** 1. Students should list a topic on some form of art, music, or film that is narrow enough to present well in a short time.

2. Students should give two relevant examples of media that can be used to support the topic.

3. Students should state that they plan to use the library and the Internet for research. Other additional options could be to conduct interviews, to take photographs, or to shoot their own video.

4. Students should briefly describe their multimedia report.

## Persuasive Essay

### Practice, p. 324

Sample answers:

1. homework limits

2. Homework should be limited to two hours per night.

3. Too much homework makes it difficult to participate in after-school activities. It also makes it difficult for students to have a job outside of school.

4. Each class is taught by a different teacher; he or she does not know what other teachers are assigning for homework. To solve this, teachers in each subject area could be given specific nights on which they can assign homework.

5. Some people might say that it would be impossible to limit homework because teachers do not know what other teachers are assigning. To solve this, I suggest that teachers in each subject be assigned specific nights on which they are allowed to assign homework.

### Assess, p. 325

Sample answers:

1. all schools should have uniforms; parents should not limit their children's time playing video games; schools should make it mandatory that students pass a swim test in order to graduate

2. (Topic: Parents should not limit video game time.) Students who play video games often have very good concentration skills. They are also usually very good at solving problems and puzzles. They have great fine motor skills and hand-eye coordination.

3. Argument: Video games cause young people to become violent. Response: This is very rare. For most young people, it lets them take out any bad feelings on the game and not in real life.
Argument: Video games keep young people from making friends. Response: Video game players make friends with other video game fans.

4. Parents should not limit their children's time playing video games. As long as kids finish their homework and chores, video games are a great way to spend their time. Video games help young people learn to concentrate for a very long time. Video game players also learn to solve problems. Finally, they have great hand-eye coordination.

## Problem-and-Solution Essay

### Practice, p. 326

**Chart: Students should complete the entire chart.**

1. The statement should clearly identify the problem.

2. Students should list the problem step by step, making sure to clearly describe each step.

3. Be sure students supply adequate examples for each of the solutions.

4. Concluding statements should provide a clear solution.

### Assess, p. 327

**A** 1. Students should target the statement of the problem to the audience. The statement should clearly identify the problem.

2. Students should list the problem step by step, making sure to clearly describe each step.

3. Be sure students supply adequate examples for each of the solutions.

4. Concluding statements should provide a clear solution.

**B** Students' essays should describe the problem, provide possible solutions to the problem, and contain a concluding statement.

## Reflective Essay

### Practice, p. 328

1. The writer is the focus of the essay.

2. She describes finding out that she will soon have a brother or sister.

3. The writer is afraid she will be ignored and neglected.

4. She learns that she enjoys being a big sister.

5. Students should choose events or experiences from their own lives.

6. Students should describe insights or lessons they learned as a direct result of the event.

© Pearson Education, Inc., publishing as Pearson Prentice Hall.

1. Students should choose events or experiences from their own lives.
2. Students should list descriptive details that relate to the event.
3. Students should describe their own thoughts and feelings.
4. Students should describe insights or lessons they learned as a direct result of the event.
5. Students' paragraphs should be written in the first person. Students should use specific details, thoughts, and feelings to describe an event and their own reaction to it.

### Research Paper

**Practice,** p. 330

**A** Narrowed topics will vary.

**B** Research questions will vary.

**Assess,** p. 331

Sample answers:

**A** 1. It is worth finding out why reality television shows are so popular.
2. Do you prefer shows that display people's special talents, such as singing or dancing? Do any of the people on reality shows seem like a good role model for young people?
3. If José includes information about the comedy shows of the 1950s and today, his topic will become too broad. He should cover only the popularity of today's reality shows to keep his topic narrow.

**B** Students should think of a time period in American history. They should describe their topic; state a thesis; explain where they would look for information about the topic; and describe their plan for organizing the information.

### Response to Literature

**Practice,** p. 332

**A** Sample answers:
1. The students could comment on how memorable the song is.
2. The focus could be on the feelings that the words and rhythm convey.

**B** 1. B; 2. A

**Assess,** p. 333

**A** Sample answers:
1. nameless mountain; thin layers of mist
2. In just a few words, this poem re-creates the mystery of the coming of spring.

3. Like all haikus, this is a beautiful and simple poem. It says a lot in just seventeen syllables, using simple words and images that everyone can appreciate.

**B** Students' essays should include a thesis statement with supporting evidence that interprets the poem according to the thesis.